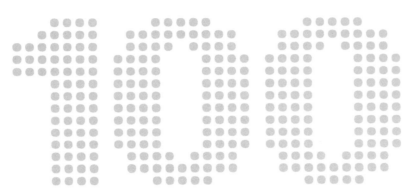

DISCOVERIES

Chief executive: Juliet Rogers
Publishing director: Kay Scarlett

Publisher: Diana Hill
Project manager: Emma Hutchinson
Editor: Desney Shoemark
Designer: Annette Fitzgerald
Photo researcher: Amanda McKittrick

Metro Books
122 Fifth Avenue
New York, NY 10011

ISBN-13: 978-1-4351-0434-1

Printed and bound in China

1 3 5 7 9 10 8 6 4 2

100
DISCOVERIES
THE GREATEST BREAKTHROUGHS IN HISTORY

PETER MACINNIS

contents

	Introduction	8
00	The law of large hammers	11
01	Discovering fire	14
02	Inventing agriculture	16
03	Discovering the art of preserving food	19
04	Discovering fertilizers	21
05	Discovering medicines from plants	24
06	Discovering ceramics	26
07	Discovering metals	29
08	Inventing writing	31
09	Inventing glass making	34
10	Pythagoras and "his" theorem	36
11	Finding the Earth's shape and size	39
12	Inventing the lever	41
13	Inventing gears	44
14	Inventing the water wheel	46
15	Developing the idea of atoms	49
16	Inventing rocket propulsion	51
17	Discovering magnetism	54
18	Inventing the lens	56
19	Beginning anatomy	59

Time-exposure image showing Polaris (the north star), VLA astronomy observatory, New Mexico, USA.

20	Inventing moveable type	61
21	Publishing an Atlantic trade route	64
22	Proving that the Earth moves	66
23	Discovering how the planets move	69
24	Inventing the telescope	71
25	Inventing the thermometer	74
26	Discovering blood circulation	76
27	Discovering photosynthesis	79
28	Inventing the barometer	81
29	Inventing the air pump	83
30	Discovering sexual reproduction	86
31	Inventing the microscope	89
32	Explaining gravity	91
33	Inventing the calculus	94
34	Discovering the color spectrum	96
35	Discovering the law of superposition	99
36	Discovering steam power	101
37	Inventing the telegraph	104
38	Showing that lightning is electrical	106
39	Inventing classification	109
40	Discovering vaccination	111
41	Measuring the universal gravitational constant	114
42	Inventing the electric cell	116
43	Inventing electric light	119
44	Understanding fossils	121
45	Discovering electrolysis	124
46	Detecting electromagnetism	126
47	Discovering the age of the Earth	129
48	The first electric motor	131
49	Discovering the inside of a cell	134
50	Discovering the principle of catalysis	136
51	Discovering the Ice Ages	139
52	Inventing immunology	141
53	Discovering gutta-percha	144
54	Understanding energy	146
55	Discovering anesthetics	149
56	Measuring the speed of light	151
57	Inventing photography	154
58	Developing the art of epidemiology	156
59	Inventing organic dyes	159
60	Inventing statistics	161
61	Inventing the spectroscope	164
62	Disproving spontaneous generation	166
63	Understanding evolution	169
64	Discovering petroleum	171
65	Inventing the internal combustion engine	174
66	Discovering genetics	176
67	Discovering antisepsis	179
68	Discovering the concept of ecology	181
69	Developing the periodic table	184
70	Inventing the telephone	186
71	Discovering germs	189

72 Harnessing alternating current 191

73 Discovering the thermionic effect 194

74 Discovering nutrition 196

75 Explaining the spectral lines 199

76 Discovering radio waves 201

77 Trying to find the ether 204

78 Discovering X-rays 206

79 Discovering radioactivity 209

80 Making liquid helium 211

81 Discovering quantum physics 214

82 Discovering hormones 216

83 Discovering relativity 219

84 Discovering plastics 221

85 Measuring the charge on the electron 224

86 Discovering what atoms are made of 226

87 Discovering X-ray diffraction 229

88 Uncovering human evolution 231

89 Discovering antibiotics 234

90 Discovering how fast the universe is expanding 236

91 Discovering atomic power 239

92 Inventing the digital computer 241

93 Discovering the transistor 244

94 Deducing the structure of DNA 246

95 Developing the integrated circuit 249

96 Discovering sea floor spreading 251

97 Measuring the cosmic background radiation 254

98 Finding the true cause of ulcers 257

99 Finding planets outside the solar system 259

100 Discovering the polymerase chain reaction 261

Discovery 101 264

The cutting room floor 268

References 271

A general reading list 277

Index 278

Image credits 286

Acknowledgements 287

INTRODUCTION

Science, technology, and the rise of modern humans

Contemplate the temerity, the hubris, of a writer intent upon reducing any scientist's life and works to a thousand words. I have gone beyond that, targeting great scientists, reducing entire branches of science to a thousand words or less, often tracing the descent of a brilliant idea through several later developments as well.

I am partly redeemed because the great discoveries of science tend to build on each other, so they form a story—a continuous narrative. I have arranged these discoveries into a rough chronological order, tweaked a little to reinforce the flow. The catch is that most discoveries took time to develop, so although I placed the discovery of the lens (18) near the first use of the burning glass, for example, I could have chosen to put it nearer to when telescopes (24) and microscopes (31) were invented.

I chose to take 1285, the date (give or take a few years) when spectacles were first used, because the lens seems to fit well there, just before the invention of printing, which led to more people reading and so needing glasses. In short, I have worked the dates, just slightly, to tell a more convincing tale. The spectacles were the application that made lenses and their optics common.

At the end of the book, I have listed some of the discoveries that I might have included if there had been more room. I started with a list of over 200 possibles, so if your favorite missed the cut, my apologies—but please accept that a few of mine missed out as well. Where I could, I slipped some of the absentees in as cameos among the stories I did end up telling.

As you read this book, some abiding themes will become apparent. The first human need was for a place to work (a village with hearths, storage and nearby fields), the second was for materials (food, glass, metals, ceramics), the third was for methods (smelting, writing, agriculture, measurement, engineering) that could be used, and the fourth was for a series of concepts like force, energy and interdependence. The glue that stuck it all together was communication.

You might notice the way scientists learned to question assumptions and think logically but, more importantly, observe the way they learned to measure everything, allowing the development of "rules of thumb" that later became laws. Very little of today's science would exist without measurement and statistics, although when measurement began, there were those (26) who felt knowledge was dishonored by people reducing it to mere numbers.

Humans have long been fascinated with the heavenly bodies. This image from *The Celestial Atlas*, published by Joannes Janssonios in 1660–61, includes detail of part of a celestial map.

Corona *Aufl.*

Christopher Columbus revealed previously unknown horizons just when people were ready and able to explore them. This portrait was painted by Sebastiano del Piombo in 1519.

One of the stronger threads follows the ways scientists deal (and dealt) with apparent contradictions, using methods that other scientists accept. Another lesser theme is the mythology of science: for example, the "just so" tales of James Watt (36) sitting by a fireside, seeing the lid of a kettle move, and being inspired to invent a steam engine. In most cases, the real story is more fascinating than the myth. But I leave it to the reader to work out what inspired a story that I omitted—the legend that James Joule took a thermometer on his honeymoon to measure the temperature at the top and bottom of a waterfall (the clues are all in the book). And by the way, Columbus (21) did not amaze anybody when he said the world was not flat. As you will see, people knew the planet was a globe long before then.

The other main theme I have consciously pursued is the effects of discoveries. For some time now, I have argued that a new discovery takes fifty years to show its full effects on society. The first twenty years are the realm of the dreamy enthusiasts, the next ten are for the early adopters, and by the end of fifty years, the idea or invention is part of everyday life. By then, we can begin to see its effects, whether it is printing, railroads, telephone, radio, computers, Internet or something else. Moreover, the effects are unpredictable: Who could have guessed that two World War II developments—jet engines and computers—would lead to us booking our overseas holidays online in the twenty-first century?

At the back of the book, for most of the chapters, I have provided references to help the reader explore further. Some of these are works that I relied on for information and, in particular, as the sources of the quotations I have used. I am a great believer in looking at what scientists think of their own work, and the work of others.

Most importantly for those wishing to undertake web searches, I have deliberately introduced place names and the appropriate technical terms, ready for use in search engines, and I have provided scientists' names, with dates, to help readers search out a particular key player. There has probably been only one Isaac Newton, but it may help to know that Harry Hess (96) is not a Canadian singer born in 1968, but a scientist who died in 1969, and so on.

Incidentally, when a number between 00 and 100 appears in parentheses, that is a shorthand reminder to see a particular chapter for more details. I have done this with as light a hand as possible, but in the best of all possible worlds, maybe this book would be created as hypertext of the sort that was envisaged by Vannevar Bush in 1945 (92).

THE LAW OF LARGE HAMMERS

How science and technology began

This "law" began as a joke. I invented it as a way of rhyming seppuku with orange ("they rhyme if you use a sufficiently large hammer"), but it brought back a memory of the ape in the film *2001: A Space Odyssey*—the one who learned to hit things with large bones.

That cinematic image probably owed something to Professor Raymond Dart (88), who proposed an osteodontokeratic culture: a hominid culture based on tools of bone (*osteo*), tooth (*donto*) and horn (*keratic*). According to Dart, tools made of these materials would have rotted away and this might explain why no tools were found with old fossils of pre-humans.

The first stone tools were made during or soon after the period Dart was studying. He may have been right about people using bones, teeth and horns first, or not: it remains an interesting supposition. Still, a couple of million years back, give or take a bit, somebody found that certain rocks, when banged together, broke to make sharp edges. That was their basic "Law of Large Hammers." Before long, somebody noticed that the shiny black rocks worked best. Somebody else discovered that glancing blows gave longer, thinner, sharper flakes, and technology began. Science—the art of explaining events and predicting effects—may have taken a little longer.

There is a school of thought which alleges that science always sets out to produce progress. But real scientists know that advances in science are not inevitable: science either remains static when findings lead nowhere, or it advances when a discovery offers an opportunity. While there are few setbacks in science, there are sometimes setbacks in the ways science is applied or used; many of the applications of science to warfare offer us examples of this. My aim is to plot the paths of progress.

A lot of everyday science is remarkably un-great. It involves nosing into dead ends and marking them as not much use, sometimes wrongly. Later, we will see how Thomas Edison missed seeing the practical value of the thermionic effect (73), and how Barry Marshall (98) printed a whole book of research papers by people who had his bright idea before him—and were ridiculed for it. Charles Darwin (63) found many who got there ahead of him in suggesting natural selection as the driving force of evolution.

When a discovery was ignored, science stayed where it was, but when people finally paid attention to it, science moved ahead. I have chosen to pursue those cases where an advance has been achieved, where a

Date: Several million years ago.

Location: Probably Africa's Rift Valley, where pre-humans originally lived.

Discovery: Given a sufficiently large hammer, any two items can be made to fit.

Discoverer: Unknown.

Impact: If you got in the way of the hammer, considerable. Large hammers offer a one-size-fits-all solution, and set the lower limit of science. All science since then has been about adding more forethought and polish to Large Hammer solutions.

Three-year-old lowland gorilla orphan Itibero breaks a palm nut with a stone, July 18, 2006, at the Diane Fossey gorilla center in Goma, in the eastern Democratic Republic of Congo, Africa.

discovery has been used as a foundation for further advances, or where a discovery has created a need for further advances. Science builds on advances and needs.

Nomadic humans have no use for ceramics or glass and need no paper mills, fertilizers, optical instruments, higher mathematics, relativity theories, electronics or genomics. In their cultures, those are not advances. In our western culture, such things have made our society what it is, but our society, our culture and our needs, have just as clearly shaped the way science has changed.

Modern humans are inventive, clever and inquisitive. For 30,000 years or more, they have been sharers of ideas and techniques. Ideas spread from valley to valley, as people visited their neighbors, or when traders came and carried new ideas away with them. War parties took prisoners, captives who might have ingratiated themselves (or saved their lives) by providing a new skill.

Many interesting inventions and innovations failed to lead anywhere. A new pepper grinder or razor does not change society in the way that a new method of steering a ship might do, and neither would provoke other scientists to think in new ways, to come up with new theories.

Some discoveries may seem more like technology, but science needed technology in order to advance. Then, once it had advanced, new sciences fed new technologies. The two go hand in hand, and I decided not to distinguish between types of great discovery. It seemed more useful to look at what makes a great discovery. The new technology of an MP3 player, for example, is unlikely to be rated as a great discovery. It is a boon and it has revolutionized the way we listen to music, but while digital storage and computer electronics are both great discoveries, the MP3 player is just a means to an end. For now, that is: who can say how this device may change education in the future?

The truly great discoveries are the enablers, the ideas that shape society, or which allow further discoveries that later change society. X-rays (78) were important, and they provoked Henri Becquerel to discover radioactivity (79). Later, Max von Laue (87) showed that X-rays could be diffracted, William and Lawrence Bragg used this diffraction to study how crystals are formed, and then Watson, Crick and Wilkins (94) used X-ray diffraction photos to deduce the structure of DNA. Look at all this from any direction, and X-rays were a great discovery.

I began with many more "possibles," and ruthlessly slashed to arrive at my final cut. My guess is that an unbiased judge would probably pick at least a few of those I culled as more important than my choices, but as the writer, I made the call. One thing is certain: our lives, without the discoveries I have chosen, would be far shorter, much more ugly and definitely more brutal than they are.

And that alone, surely, makes these discoveries great!

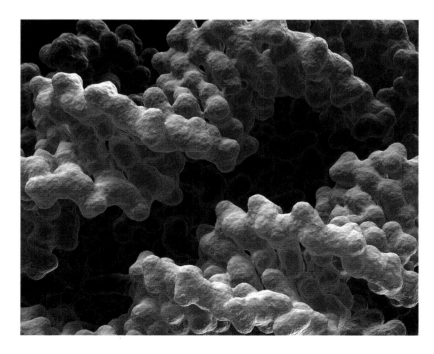

A close look at a DNA nucleosome.

DISCOVERING FIRE

The discovery that started pre-humans on the road to becoming human

Date: Some time between 1.5 and 0.5 million years ago (mya).

Location: Probably Africa's Rift Valley.

Discovery: Fire could be used to shape things and also to cook food.

Discoverer: Probably an unknown *Homo erectus*.

Impact: Fire allowed cooking of food, which delivered better nutrition. It led to a society where the elderly and/or women with small children stayed near the hearth to maintain the fire.

The two key things that define humans are using fire and using tools. In less developed parts of the world, a wood fire is often still the main source of energy for cooking, heating and light, and it is only a few hundred years since almost all humans relied entirely on wood fires. Even where coal was known, it was too hard to haul long distances, so people used local fuels, which usually meant wood.

Human pre-historians argue a lot. The evidence they seek is hard to collect, it has to be interpreted, and most people see what they expect to see. Some researchers are *lumpers*, who try to assign new finds to existing species, even if they are different. Others are *splitters*, who identify new finds as new species, even when they are very like an existing species. The truth probably lies in the middle, and if I leave out *Homo rudolfensis*, *Homo heidelbergensis*, *Homo ergaster* and a few others in this account, I am just keeping the story simple. I am neither a lumper nor a splitter.

For the sake of this discussion, we will consider *Homo habilis* (probably 2.4–1.6 million years ago), *Homo erectus* (probably 1.2–0.5 mya) and *Homo sapiens* (people who could think and talk as we do may have been here for 200,000 years, but at least for 50,000 years). All dates are open to challenge and revision as new material is found, or as existing material is tested in new ways. For example, *Homo erectus* may have survived until about 25,000 years ago, and might go back to 1.8 million years.

The first human-like beings were *Homo habilis*. They had small brains and ape-like bodies, but walked upright, and their remains are associated with tools in a style called Oldowan.

I once handed a good cast—a copy—of an ancient Oldowan chopper to a visitor to my workplace. I told her how well it fitted the hand. She was left-handed, and said the object felt all wrong. A quick survey of left-handers and right-handers convinced us the tool was in fact better for right-handers. At that point, we might have claimed that *Homo habilis* was right-handed, and made tools to fit, but we did not. Sometimes, interesting patterns happen by chance. Sometimes, whole theories are based on flimsier evidence than that, but you can't call them science.

Homo erectus made fancier tools in a style we call Acheulean, and sometimes their remains and tools seem to be associated with ashes, charcoal, or other signs of fire. Just as the right-handed tools might have been a chance thing, so might the traces of fire. Maybe dry leaves collected in a cave, and a wildfire set them alight; perhaps a burned bone came from an animal that was trapped in a fire.

Two dig sites at Koobi Fora in Africa have reddened sediments. This is a color change that happens between 400 and 750°F, and the sites are 1.5 million years old. The Cave of Hearths in South Africa has burned deposits that are 200,000 to 700,000 years old, while a site at Gesher Benot Ya'aqov in Israel *seems* to have been the home of fire-using humans 690,000 to 790,000 years ago.

Fire has been a major source of change for humans. It helps us dry foods to store them; to cook foods that would otherwise be inedible; and to make metals, pottery and glass. Fire drives steam and internal combustion engines and electricity generators, distills liquids, provides light and warmth, powers weapons and more.

In Australia, where the plants and animals were unsuitable for agriculture, the Aboriginal people adopted a practice that is sometimes called "firestick farming." Ecosystems were maintained by small, regular fires, which renewed vegetation, and ensured that standing fuel did not build up to levels that would sustain wildfires. In parts of the western United States, the Native Americans also used fire as a management tool.

Pre-industrial humans maintained fire by keeping a few coals or embers so they could restart a fire in the morning. Without embers, in the absence of matches, fires were started by friction, using a bow and drill system (or the hands) to spin a hard shaft in soft, dry wood and make it so hot it created an ember.

In parts of South-East Asia (Indochina, Burma, Malaysia, Indonesia), the fire piston is used. This is a bamboo (or hardwood or horn) cylinder with dry tinder in the bottom, greased with fat, which is rapidly compressed.

Olana camp villagers in Kenya starting a fire the traditional way.

The diesel engine works on the principle that when a cylinder is compressed, it gets very hot, and if there is fuel in the cylinder, the fuel ignites. In the same way, pushing a piston into the bamboo cylinder produces enough heat to set tinder alight.

In other parts of the world, a flint and steel can be used to make a spark to light tinder, just as electric sparks can light a gas jet.

Without fire, we would not be human.

INVENTING AGRICULTURE

How humans stopped being wandering hunter-gatherers and made permanent homes

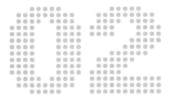

Date: About 12,000 years ago.

Location: New Guinea (sugar cane); Mesoamerica (potato, corn); Mesopotamia (modern Syria and Iraq) (wheat, barley, pea, lentil); China (rice, millet); Sahel region of Africa (sorghum, millet, rice); Andes, Amazonia (corn, lima bean, manioc, common bean).

Discovery: Seeds or cuttings could be planted to make more food, and animals could be kept and bred in captivity.

Discoverer: Many discoverers.

Impact: Settled people could own more than they could carry. Agriculture let some members of a population grow surplus food, while others developed specialist trades.

It isn't always easy putting a date on the earliest inventions, but sometimes there are clues. An archeological dig of an old village may reveal heavy items like mill wheels, or the skeletons of granary scavengers like rats. Each of these means people were staying in one place. And if you stayed put, you needed a local supply of food, so the people of the village were probably engaged in agriculture.

There are other clues as well, like pollen grains found in the middens where all waste from early villages was dumped. On the tough coat of its pollen grains, each plant has a distinctive outside pattern that lasts through the ages. Experts can examine these, sort and count the microscopic grains, and work out how common a species was thousands of years ago. Middens also contain bones that are easy to identify, telling us when particular animals began to appear on the menu in large numbers.

Then there are the stone tools such as sickles, used to cut stalks of grain; traces of the grains—distinctive fragments of silica called phytoliths; and particular wear patterns in skeletons that can be related to growing or processing food. Traces of a 9,000-year-old drainage ditch in Papua New Guinea, like remains of cultivated plants in a cave in Thailand, or the ruins of storage pits in the Middle East, are all evidence of agriculture.

One way or another, it is easy enough to find half a dozen indicators to show that a village was an agricultural hub. Even the very existence of the village might indicate past agriculture, though fishing villages probably came first, as long-term temporary camps. Perhaps agriculture was discovered in such a fishing village when seeds from food plants started unplanned gardens in places where kitchen scraps, hearth ashes, manure from domestic animals, and human wastes were dumped.

At the end of the last ice age (51), as the world was thawing out, there was a period called the "Younger Dryas," a cool, dry period that can be detected and dated in ice cores from Greenland. Humans had spread out during the good times, but the Younger Dryas set them back, and maybe this made people think. Those who got serious about agriculture would have flourished, and starving neighbors would probably have seen what they were doing and copied the idea—or died.

An Afghan farmer harvests wheat in a field on the outskirts of Kabul.

CLUES FROM ACROSS THE AGES

The obvious clues that a human society used agriculture include remnants of tools, hints of past crops, either in the form of fossil human feces, or coprolites, or other fossils. As well, information comes from bones left in midden heaps, but it even comes from the wear on human skeletons. Early grindstones were turned from a kneeling position, and archeologists say this left recognizable wear marks on leg bones and pelvises.

Perhaps things happened slowly, as wild berries, fruits or other seed parts were selected and brought home. The process of evolution means that plants are always adapting to the animals that feed on them. For example, mangoes are adapted to bats, acorns are adapted to squirrels, and many, many flowers provide nectar to the animals that pollinate them. We should not be surprised if potential crop plants adapted (or were adapted by selection) as people moved closer to domesticating those crops.

Whatever the cause, over the next few thousand years, many civilizations learned to grow their food in fields, to farm and to practice agriculture. They kept developing better tools, better plows, better harnesses for animals, and they found new crops or new variants that were better. It is still happening: the pecan nut was domesticated in 1846; the first Granny Smith apple appeared on a rubbish heap in Sydney, Australia in 1868; and the macadamia nut was cultivated first in the 1880s.

It is likely that many of the early food plants first emerged after spoiled food was thrown out and the seeds sprouted on a rubbish pile. If the gatherers had selected the biggest and the best fruits, this would have given the new crops a head start, but over time people must have started to see that there was some sort of inheritance, just as there was with people. They might have been a long way from discovering Mendelian genetics (66), but our Neolithic ancestors had the same brains as us.

Once they were growing plants and had vegetables to spare, it would have been only a matter of time before somebody had the bright idea of keeping a young animal, captured when its mother was hunted down, and fattening it up. Then somebody might have started breeding animals. Slowly, over time, where and when suitable animals and plants were found, hunters and gatherers became farmers.

With plenty of food, larger groups could stay together. The good farmers could use their extra food to pay specialists to weave cloth, to make pots or to make metal tools and weapons. Weapons were important, because people now had more possessions than they could carry, and other people might think it worth robbing them. That meant there was an opening for the evolution of royalty, the military and the makers and upholders of the law. This meant a need for taxes, which demanded new skills in measurement, counting and recording. And more guards.

In areas like Egypt, where flood waters poured slowly over the plain along the Nile valley each year, it did not take people long to discover irrigation. The land was flat, and the slow flow dropped an extra one-twentieth of an inch of silt each season, rather than washing the soil away. Large-scale irrigation meant the development of dams and canals, and that required a lot of co-operation in larger political units. And because you could not pack dams and canals up and carry them away, people had to settle where they were.

Civilization came riding in on the back of agriculture.

DISCOVERING THE ART OF PRESERVING FOOD

How people learned to store surplus food and stop it decaying until it was needed

In northern Australia, there is a small peak called Donkins Hill. It is named after Bryan Donkin who, with John Hall, made tinned meats in England, and commemorates a tin of Donkin's meat being eaten there in 1820. Tinned meat was still a novelty then, but preserved foods are very old in human history.

When food could not be preserved and stored, people had to live a nomadic life, moving after the food; if people lived in one place, they needed to be able to store food and stop it going bad. But even nomads smoked meat over a slow fire, or used the sun to make jerky or biltong. They would also have dried or smoked fish.

Even before people knew about germs, salting was a practical way to stop germs growing on meat. In *The Grapes of Wrath*, John Steinbeck described how Noah and Ma salted meat: Noah cut slabs of meat into small blocks which Ma put in barrels, with salt in between to stop the pieces touching, and extra salt in the gaps. The result was a keg of meat too salty for anything to live in it.

It works like this: water can escape from living cells and can also flow back in; high salt levels outside a cell stop water going back in, so the microbes in salted food soon dry up and die. When meat is dried, the salts in the meat are left behind and, once again, the salt levels stop bacteria and molds from growing. Bees have used this principle for millions of years, collecting nectar and then fanning it to evaporate most of the water, changing the nectar to honey. Spores that fall into honey cannot grow.

When the Egyptians preserved dead bodies, they used a chemical that acted like ordinary salt. This was natron, a mixture of sodium carbonate and sodium bicarbonate, which was also used in glass making. The mummies would have tasted better with salt, but since nobody was planning to eat them, natron was fine. It would be reasonable to suspect that the Egyptians knew about salting meat for as long as they made mummies, which means they must have started salting meat around 4,500 years ago.

Preservation either sets out to kill the food-spoiling microbes, or to slow them down, as refrigeration does. Geoffrey Chaucer was an English poet and scholar who died in 1400. In his *Canterbury Tales*, Chaucer has one character say of another character, a cook:

Date: Various dates, depending on the process, mainly after agriculture started.

Location: Anywhere that agriculture was practiced.

Discovery: The art of drying, smoking, salting, sealing, freezing and other treatments to stop food decaying.

Discoverer: Unknown: many people.

Impact: Food preservation saved food from the times of plenty for the lean periods.

Even today, fish are dried on racks to preserve them.

And many a Jakke of Dovere hastow soold,
That hath been twies hoot and twies coold.

In more modern (but similar) language, this says:

And many a Jack of Dover hast thou sold,
That had been twice hot and twice cold.

The Jack of Dover he refers to was almost certainly a pie. Refrigeration slows down the proliferation of microbes, but as Chaucer realised, more than 600 years ago, if food is warmed and cooled a couple of times, this makes it dangerous. Unlike Chaucer, we know that repeated warming of food can increase the number of bacteria to dangerous levels.

These days, we can see the science that lies behind food preservation methods, but each of the methods must have been discovered by chance, perhaps when an animal drowned in a brine pond or died in a snow drift, and was later found, free of rot. Food left too long over a low fire may have been dried or smoked, wheat and barley stored in pots in hot dry places stayed dry and undamaged, and so on.

Without knowing anything about spores, bacteria or fungi, humans found ways of keeping food from spoiling. The result was that they were able to live through bad seasons or times when there was no food to be had. They were able to store food such as turnips or hay to keep animals alive, and dried foods were light enough to carry on long journeys.

Unfortunately, some of the preservation methods also destroyed any vitamins that might have been in the foods. Sailors and other travelers who tried to live on salt meat and ship's biscuit (a very dry sort of bread) were at risk of developing "disease," as scurvy (74) used to be called. On short voyages, the passengers and crew had enough reserves to stay fairly healthy, but as voyages grew longer, people began to die, killed by the preserved food they thought was keeping them alive.

Eventually, people began to work out ways of getting around this dilemma. They found that pickling with salt and vinegar can stop vegetables spoiling, while not killing off the nutritional value. Pickled cabbage—sauerkraut—has most of the vitamin C found in the original cabbage, and vitamin C cures scurvy. (Salt meat had no vitamin C because the original meat had none.) Lime juice, an excellent source of vitamin C, was boiled to a concentrated germ-resistant syrup. This also retained some of its vitamin content—so long as it was not boiled in copper pots (copper surfaces are very good at destroying vitamin C).

With these refinements, preserved foods allowed westerners to discover the whole world. It was a mixed blessing!

DISCOVERING FERTILIZERS

How people realized that soil needs extra help to grow the best crops

Early farmers soon saw that the first crop from cleared land was always the best, and that production fell away as the soil became "tired." After a while, somebody may have noticed that crops grew best near ash deposits after cleared plants were burned.

This would have led to people using "slash and burn" agriculture—clearing a patch of jungle, planting a garden and, after a few years, moving on, leaving the jungle to reclaim the space. While jungle can recover from small clearings, moving the garden is harder on people, who need either to walk long distances each day, or move their village.

Once a society has towns and land ownership, "slash and burn" is no longer an option. That is why people have improved the soil for thousands of years, adding seaweed, human and animal waste, old bones, seashells, clay, anything they thought might improve the crop.

Most of these additives were probably discovered by chance. As a small boy, I saw a strange effect in a wheat crop. In one corner of the field, all the plants loomed two feet above those where I was standing. I asked the farmer why they were so much taller, and he told me the previous owner had always fed his horses in that corner, back in the 1920s, resulting in a rich supply of horse manure in the vicinity. The soil remained richer, a third of a century later. Seeing an effect like that, any farmer anywhere would be quick to wonder whether a whole crop might be improved in the same way, by spreading animal droppings.

Date: Uncertain, but quite a few thousand years ago.

Location: Most places where farming took place.

Discovery: Plants can be made to grow better by "feeding" them nutrients.

Discoverer: Farmers in many places.

Impact: Food production would have failed a long time ago without the use of fertilizers.

The use of fertilizers has turned countless rural landscapes into patchworks of vivid green crops.

In ancient Egypt, the Nile flooded every year, bringing muddy waers down and delivering rich new silt to the fields that supported an entire civilization. Because of this, Egyptians had less need to discover fertilizer or manure, but even they added the ashes from burned weeds to their soil as the waters went down.

There were many places where manure—organic fertilizer—was greatly prized. Folklore has it that when the Pilgrim fathers landed in America, the Native Americans showed them how to plant corn, encouraging them to "plant" a fish with each seed. This fish was probably menhaden; locally called "munnawhatteaug," which means "fertilizer." The colonists were soon using fish for fertilizer, applying 6,000 to 8,000 whole fish per acre, fed by seine fisheries that extended from New York to Maine.

In the early nineteenth century, Alexander von Humboldt (68) traveled from Prussia to the Americas, to observe, to collect specimens and to explore. In Peru, he learned about guano, the droppings of two seabirds, the guanay and the piquero, and how these could be used as a fertilizer. He took the idea back to Europe, but it was more than thirty years before anybody took any notice.

By the 1840s, chemistry had improved. People realized that the main nutrients needed in the soil were nitrogen, phosphorus and potassium, and guano was recognized as a good source of nitrogen. Within a few years, guano became big business: the people of Easter Island were taken as slaves to dig guano; wars were fought over guano islands; and in 1853, the US Congress passed a bill to allow guano islands to be annexed.

In 1849, a German chemist called Justus Liebig proposed what he called the limiting factor principle: you can increase all the other nutrients as much as you like, but productivity will still be limited by the biggest lack. For much of Europe, nitrogen was the limit. But although Chilean saltpeter and guano could be dug and hauled in ships, some traders learned to make a fat profit selling fake guano—and American magazines saw the need to publish methods of spotting it.

In 1909, another German chemist, Fritz Haber, came up with a way of making nitrogen compounds from atmospheric nitrogen, so when World War I started and Germany was blockaded, German factories could still produce the nitrogen compounds needed to make explosives: the Haber process may have fed people and saved lives, but it also prolonged a war and cost lives.

The original view was that fertilizer was a matter of "NPK"—nitrogen, phosphorus and potassium—and it is true that these need to be replaced in soils that are intensively farmed. But there is more to it, because most organisms also require tiny amounts of other chemical elements. These are usually referred to as trace elements or micronutrients. They include cobalt, copper, chromium, iodine, iron, manganese, selenium, and zinc. Citrus fruits also need tiny amounts of boron. If these trace elements are not in the soil, they must be added.

Plants use chlorophyll to capture energy from sunlight: a chlorophyll molecule contains hundreds of carbon, hydrogen and oxygen atoms, but right in the middle, there is a single magnesium atom. Without it, the chlorophyll is not made, plants get no energy, and they die. Chlorophyll also needs four nitrogen atoms, and proteins contain a lot of nitrogen. All the same, without a few sulfur atoms, proteins will not hold the right shape, and so will be useless inside cells.

Chemicals are not intrinsically evil. There is no magical advantage in using organic fertilizers, but sometimes, by chance, old seaweed or manure will just happen to contain some element a crop needs.

The problem with artificial fertilizers, when there is one, is not the "chemicals" they contain, but the chemicals they don't contain.

DISCOVERING MEDICINES FROM PLANTS

How people learned to borrow "biologically active" chemicals from plants to cure or prevent disease

Date: Thousands of years ago, or maybe 5 million years ago.

Location: Perhaps Africa, probably in a number of places.

Discovery: Plants can be used to treat various illnesses.

Discoverer: Unknown.

Impact: Agricultural humans, living in one fixed place, faced greater risks from parasites and other infections than nomads, but medicinal plants evened up the odds.

Animals can avoid predators by running or hiding, but plants need other ways to avoid being eaten. Spines and thorns will discourage larger browsing animals, but many plants make chemicals which taste bad or are poisonous. Over long periods of time, these molecules have evolved to have a maximum effect on the animal doing the eating.

Some of the arrangements are quite complex. In order to reproduce, apples need to be eaten by animals, which carry the apple seeds away and plop them on the ground in a fresh pile of fertilizer. To encourage the animals to eat the fruit, the apples taste sweet, but it would be a disaster if the animal chewed the seeds; it comes as no surprise, then, that apple seeds contain cyanide which is only released if the seeds are crunched. It is a small amount of poison, just enough to give a bitter taste, but that is enough to protect the seeds.

Other plants may produce chemicals that interfere with the breeding of the animal that eats them, but these molecules do not work the same way on all species. Humans enjoy chocolate which is poisonous to dogs, for example.

Just about all chemicals have some effect on living cells, so it's not surprising we can use some of them to treat illnesses. Chimpanzees also use medicinal plants, and a few scientists have speculated that the practice might go back five million years or more, to the time when the chimpanzee and human lines of evolution split. Possible, but unlikely, say most people; it is probably one of those questions science can never answer.

All the same, East African chimps use the same medicinal plants as humans in that region. When the chimps eat leaves as food, they usually stuff their mouths as fast as they can, eating leaves of 150 to 200 species in this way. But they behave differently on the rare occasions when they eat the leaves of *Aspilia*, a member of the sunflower family (there are five species of *Aspilia* in the area, but only three are eaten). The chimps test leaves by "mouthing" them, and either reject the leaf, or swallow it whole. The local Tongwe people use the leaves of the same three species to make a tea to treat burns, wounds and worm infections. Research has shown that the leaves contain a powerful antibiotic called thiarubrine-A, which kills worms and some bacteria. At this stage, nobody can say if the humans and apes discovered the cures independently, or if the humans copied the chimps. Chimps have been seen eating other medicinal plants that humans also use.

People have long been aware that certain plants cure certain illnesses, and many drugs traditionally came from kitchen gardens, which probably date back to the earliest days of agriculture. Herbs, many of them poisonous, were grown in kitchen gardens and used in small doses as medicine.

More formal medicinal use of plants probably started with the discovery that quinine could relieve a malarial fever. Actually, Europeans found that cinchona bark did this, somewhere around 1638: extracting quinine from the bark only came later, in 1820. Either way, it was a mixed benefit, because quinine made it easier for Europeans to survive in Africa, arguably making life harder for the Africans, who were largely resistant to malaria, thanks to slow evolutionary changes.

The scholar Alcuin asked his pupil Charlemagne (an eighth century French ruler) what he thought a herb was. "The friend of physicians and the praise of cooks," said the well-schooled king.

Hippocrates of Cos (the Greek physician who gave us the Hippocratic Oath) knew as far back as 400 BC that chewing willow leaves gave relief from headache. Today, we use a synthetic and improved form of the chemical found in willow leaves, and call it aspirin. In recent years, researchers have uncovered a number of other useful effects that come from taking aspirin—so we don't know everything yet, even about familiar drugs!

This worker selects ginseng roots harvested at a ginseng farm in Tonghua, China.

The problem with herbal remedies in the past remains a problem with herbal remedies today: the amount of the active chemical can vary with the time of day the herb is harvested (chimps seem to "know" this, and take *Aspilia* in the early morning). The dose also varies with the season, the age of the plant and between plant strains. Commercial preparations have much more carefully controlled dosages, and pharmaceutical companies now spend a lot of money identifying chemicals in plants, testing them, then trying to improve on nature.

Some of the modern drugs derived from living things include paclitaxel (from yew bark, used for cancer); penicillin (from a fungus, antibiotic); artemisinin (from Qinghao or wormwood, malaria); "Botox" (from a bacterium, used to control muscle spasm—or to reduce wrinkling); not forgetting cocaine, morphine and nicotine, all drugs of addiction, but with the potential to control illness or pain.

Keep that in mind, next time you pull a weed out by the roots!

DISCOVERING CERAMICS

How we learned to make waterproof storage containers

Date: About 10,000–11,000 BC.

Location: Japan.

Discovery: Baked clay can be turned into a container for food or water.

Discoverer: Jomon people of Japan.

Impact: Pottery containers allowed people to store food, safe from moisture, hungry rodents, insects and other pests.

Clay is easy to find, and interesting to play with, as every child knows. Clay hardens as it dries, and once humans knew how to use and manage fire, it would not have been much of a leap to think of drying a clay shape in a fire. Still, dried clay, even fire-dried clay, is not a ceramic. The temperature of a wood fire is limited to a few hundred degrees, and the proper firing of clay took a long while to discover. Even so, part of the method was known to early modern humans.

Somewhere between 29,000 and 25,000 BC, a figure known as the Venus of Dolní V stonice was made in Moravia, in what is now the Czech Republic. The figure was shaped from clay, animal fat, bone and bone ash, and it was fired in a dome-shaped kiln at 900–1,500°F, a very low temperature compared with those used to make pots today. Other figures found in the same area depict animals and the fired-clay heads of a lion and a rhinoceros, but no practical pots have been found there.

Small figurines like that could be stored in caves that were visited each year, or even carried by nomadic people, but fragile and heavy pots were of little use to people who were on the move. People who lived in one place needed pottery containers to store their food, while living in one place and storing food gave people the time to make pots in the first place. Until then, firing of clay shapes may have been known, but it wasn't important enough for people to study it or specialize in it. That did not come until the Jomon people.

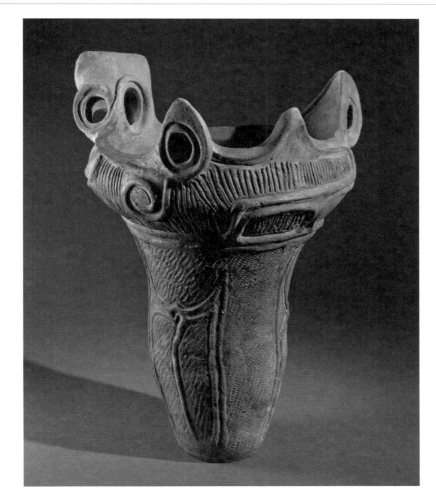

Jomon means "cord-mark" in Japanese, and refers to the cord-marked decoration seen in their pots. The Jomon people were traditional hunter-gatherers who lived in Japan from about 11,000 to 500 BC, at which time wet-rice agriculture reached Japan. All through those ten millennia or so, the Jomon people used ceramic pots and containers for cooking and storage.

By 8000 BC, ceramics were common on the Chinese mainland, and by 3000 BC, ceramic containers were common in both the Old World and the New World. American pottery was probably invented independently, but the diffusion of ideas would have spread the craft of pottery across Eurasia. It is just barely possible that the first humans in the Americas may have encountered ceramics as they passed out of Asia, but without writing, any potting tradition would have been lost along the way, since the migration from clay source to clay source probably took a number of generations. Before the development of writing, traditions only survived if they could be demonstrated regularly.

Our word "ceramic" comes from the Greek "keramos" which means pottery. If you go far enough back, the root word means something like "burnt stuff," but in reality, a ceramic is made by heating clay to a very high temperature to form a mass of tiny silicate crystals suspended in glassy cement. Nothing is actually burned.

Early pots were made by shaping a ball of clay, but then people got the idea that most children discover: making a long "snake" of clay and coiling it and squeezing the coils together. Coiled pots were made at Çatal Höyük (sometimes written Catal Huyuk) in Turkey, around 6500 BC. The coils were laid down in the desired shape before wet hands squeezed them together and smoothed them out. Then the pots would probably be fired in a bread oven or a primitive kiln, hardly more than a hole in the ground with a fire over it.

The coiling process worked, but it took too much time, and around 3000 BC, the slow wheel came into use. This was a bit like a turntable that allowed the potter to sit in one place and rotate the work; it was not the same as a modern potter's wheel, where the clay rotates continuously, letting the potter shape the clay, almost as a lathe shapes wood or metal. The modern potters wheel, called the fast wheel, came later.

Ceramics are important to archeologists, because pots break and are thrown away, but the bits do not rot, rust or decay. Greek and Roman pots with painted decorations can tell us a lot about daily life in an ancient world. They depict an interesting array of sports, clothes, dancing, and other activities.

The Lapita people take their name from a place in New Caledonia, where the first of the pots now called Lapita pottery were discovered. The Lapita people seem to have populated the Pacific islands of Micronesia, Melanesia and Polynesia from somewhere in New Guinea, taking pottery, breadfruit, language structures, and other clues with them. Of these, pottery is the best source of information, because it has been buried and left undisturbed over long periods.

Ceramics probably reached their highest point in the 19th and 20th centuries, when demand for porcelain insulators and sanitary ware drove a massive industry. The sanitary ware improved hygiene and extended lives, but the porcelain insulators allowed telegraph wires first, and electricity cables later, to be strung between poles over great distances, sometimes spanning continents and tying the world together (37).

And it all began with pots, or with a plump fired-clay doll, perhaps.

DISCOVERING METALS

How we learned to extract metals from their ores

There were seven metals known in ancient times: gold, mercury, tin, lead, silver, copper, and iron (on rare occasions, found as the metal in meteorites). Most of the time, people who wanted to get some metal had to treat an ore in some way, to smelt it to get the metal. A suitable ore had to be available, and then somebody needed to find or know a way to smelt the ore and use the metal.

Zinc has probably been smelted in India for at least 2,300 years, maybe 3,000, but the first European zinc was only prepared in 1736 (possibly using technology learned from India, as the method was identical). In the Middle East, the early Bronze Age coincided with the start of writing and the development of city states, but bronze was probably in use even earlier in what is now Thailand.

In some places, like sub-Saharan Africa, there was no Bronze Age at all. People jumped from the New Stone Age (Neolithic) directly to the Iron Age, probably because they had iron ore but no copper ore—although perhaps the iron technology was imported. Iron was probably being smelted and worked in the Middle East around 1100 BC, and it appeared 600 years later in West Africa.

Tin could have been smelted by accident if the right rocks were used to make a fireplace. People say copper and lead might have been discovered the same way, but this is unlikely, because copper smelting needs 2,000°F plus carbon monoxide to reduce the oxide. Lead could form by accident if the ore became buried in the ashes with limited oxygen, but both copper and lead were more likely to form in a potter's kiln. One attractive theory is that potters began decorating their pots with minerals to add color, noticed the metals that formed on the pots, and began experimenting.

Charcoal is dry and has 10 percent of the mass of the wood it came from, so charcoal fires burn hotter than wood fires—if they have enough (but not too much) oxygen. With good charcoal and the right amount of air, a temperature of 2,700°F is possible if the fire is surrounded to keep the heat in. (An open fireplace burning charcoal is unlikely to get higher than 1,100°F, even when a high wind blows through it; the same high wind that promotes burning also carries away much of the heat.) In other words, making metal required the heat of a kiln or an oven, not the heat of an open fire. It was an art, not luck.

Copper is a soft metal, good enough to make maces but not blades, so Çatal Höyük is generally referred to as a chalcolithic site, a place where

Date: 6500 BC, with further development over several thousand years.

Location: Çatal Höyük, Anatolia (in modern Turkey); probably other sites as well.

Discovery: The art of smelting lead, copper and other metals from their ores.

Discoverer: The lead beads found in the area must have been smelted from local lead ore, so there was clearly a discoverer who remains unknown. The copper, on the other hand, may have been from deposits of copper metal ("native copper"), which would not have needed smelting.

Impact: Stone tools such as knives, axes, spear- and arrow-heads were replaced by much more effective metal tools, while bronze weapons and later, iron weapons, overthrew kingdoms and empires.

Molten ferrosilicon is poured into molds from a furnace at a factory in Yanxiao village, China.

copper and stone were both used. Somewhere, somehow, somebody learned to make bronze, an alloy of copper with arsenic or tin. The earliest examples of copper/arsenic bronze come from Asia Minor in about 4200 BC, while the harder copper/tin bronze was used, in much the same area, from about 3200 BC.

We can come up with plausible "just so" stories to account for people making copper metal, but iron remains a bit of a mystery. It is strongly attracted to oxygen, which is why iron rusts so easily, and why iron oxide is a common iron ore. At around 1,650°F, the oxygen in the iron oxide is more strongly attracted to carbon, so if ore is collected and raised to this temperature in the presence of carbon, iron metal forms. It may be well below iron's melting point, but the metal forms readily at this temperature and it can be hammered and worked in a bloomery, and shaped into tools.

Smelting and refining did not always bring blessings—they also polluted the environment. Cores taken from lake beds in the Andes reveal that Peruvians were smelting copper 1,000 years ago, but around 1450 they switched to silver, which leaves a different pattern of pollution. They probably began smelting more silver because the Incas demanded that taxes be paid in silver. When the conquistadors took over in 1533, the silver-smelting pollution increased tenfold.

The ice of Greenland shows clear traces of pollution from copper production, dating back to about 500 BC. This probably came mainly from the use of copper and bronze around the Mediterranean, even as that area entered the Iron Age. The real advantage that came with the ready availability of iron was that it was cheap, and made it easy for people to maufacture iron weapons in large numbers. Even if gentlemen preferred bronze, a thousand poorly-trained peasants with shoddy iron stabbers can overwhelm 300 trained warriors with superb bronze swords.

Shipping may also have been a factor. Ships would certainly have been up to carrying Cypriot copper ore or metal by 2000 BC, possibly much earlier. But it is tempting to wonder whether tin or tin ore was being carried to the Mediterranean from Cornwall by then: it was certainly being mined and worked in Cornwall in about 2150 BC. All around, the general picture of early metal working is clear, but many of the finds leave us still wondering. Cast lead beads which date back to 6500 BC have been found at Çatal Höyük, but they must have been more of a novelty than anything useful.

From Weland to Ogoun to Cullann to Mpu Gandring, in many cultures, the smith is seen as having the powers of a magician—and no wonder!

INVENTING WRITING

How humans learned to keep records lasting longer than human memory

The Sumerians explained the invention of writing with a tale of a messenger who was so tired when he reached the court of a distant ruler that he could not deliver his message from the king of Uruk. Hearing this, the king took a piece of clay, flattened it, and wrote a message on it.

That story has a few gaps. Just for starters, how did the recipient know what the symbols meant? Still, what can we expect in a tale about events that happened so long ago, when it probably was not written down? The story of how Sequoyah developed a Cherokee script over twelve years, starting in about 1809, is a little closer to our time, but even that leaves us short of detail.

Sequoyah was the son of a Cherokee woman and a white fur trader, but he was raised as a Cherokee. He knew that other languages used alphabets, but he chose to have separate characters for each of the eighty-six (or eighty-five or eighty-four: there are variations) syllables that could be encountered in his language. That sort of "alphabet" is called a syllabary, which is easier to understand if we look at an example using the four syllables found in *enemy* and *Emma*. If we were inventing a syllabary for English, "enemy" and "Emma" might be written @$& and $%. That means "any" would be written @&, and "enema" would be @$%.

Date: Probably 3200 or 3300 BC.

Location: Sumeria, but later independently in Mesoamerica, China and possibly also in Egypt and the Indus valley.

Discovery: The art of making marks to represent sounds, syllables or words.

Discoverer: Unknown.

Impact: With writing came the transfer and expansion of knowledge, because now ideas could live on after a thinker died.

The Cherokees did not believe Sequoyah until his ten-year-old daughter wrote down what was said while her father was out of earshot and, when he returned, Sequoyah was able to read back a conversation he had never heard. After that, the new method was gleefully adopted.

Where Sequoyah used characters to represent syllables, some ancient writing systems used a symbol for each letter-sound (as we do in English), while others used a symbol to depict a word or idea, as happens in Chinese. These characters are called ideograms or logograms (meaning that each symbol stands for a complete idea or word)—and they can convey the same meaning in different languages, rather like the signs in airports or a numeral like 5 or 8, for example. Just to confuse things, some of those airport signs are also called pictograms, because they are actual pictures of what they represent.

Then again, Egyptian hieroglyphs are a mixture of alphabetic characters and ideograms, with a few extra symbols to clarify the meaning. Unlike Sequoyah's syllabary, most writing systems were not designed from scratch: they just grew, a bit like English spelling!

The Sumerians lived in what is now southern Iraq. Their writing probably started with marks on clay that Sumerian accountants used around 3300 or 3200 BC as tokens to record numbers of livestock and stores of grain—the sorts of records societies need, once they start farming. Over about 500 years, the symbols became more abstract, allowing ideas to be written down.

Egyptian hieroglyphs (literally "priestly writing") are unlike Sumerian cuneiform. They probably developed separately, but maybe like Sequoyah, they got the basic idea of marks to represent language from other people. The Harappan script from the Indus valley, in what is now Pakistan and western India, seems to be another independent growth, although nobody has yet learned to read it. The civilization which established it collapsed in about 1900 BC, so the script did not develop further.

As an inventor of writing, Sequoyah is in good company. The Egyptians say the god Thoth (the scribe and historian of the gods) invented hieroglyphs; the Sumerians credited either an anonymous king or the god Enlil; the Assyrians and Babylonians said the god Nabu was the inventor; while the Mayans owed their writing system to the supreme deity Itzamna, who was a shaman, a sorcerer, and the creator of the world. More sensibly, Chinese tradition attributes writing to a sage called Ts'ang Chieh, a minister to the legendary Huang Ti (the Yellow Emperor).

So which form of writing is best? That's a bit like asking what motor vehicle is best, without specifying if it is to be used on a highway or a goat track. Japanese uses two syllabaries (hiragana and katakana) as well as Chinese ideograms (kanji), and this works perfectly in Japanese. Chinese languages use one set of characters which can be read by speakers of different Chinese languages. But in languages like English, where words vary their form while sounding similar (paint, painter,

painting) or Indonesian, where a root word can be varied by prefixes and suffixes, an alphabet works best.

Bas-relief showing Egyptian scribes at work, c. 2494–2345 BC.

The oldest alphabets that we know about seem to have emerged in Egypt around 1800 BC. They were developed by people speaking a Semitic language, and only had consonants. They later gave rise to several other systems: a Proto-Canaanite alphabet at around 1400 BC and a South Arabian alphabet, some 200 years later. There were others, but you get the idea.

The Phoenicians adopted the Proto-Canaanite alphabet, which was later the basis for both Aramaic and Greek. Then, through Greek, it inspired other alphabets in Anatolia and Italy, eventually giving us the Latin alphabet, which became our modern alphabet. Aramaic may have inspired some Indian scripts, and certainly became the Hebrew and Arabic scripts. Greek and Latin inspired Norse runes and also the Gothic and Cyrillic alphabets.

The way was open for poetry, literature, history, philosophy, mathematics, recipes, technical information, tax, weather and astronomical records, religious teachings and more to be written down and passed from one generation to another.

INVENTING GLASS MAKING

Glass began as a shiny surface on pots, and ended up underpinning almost all of science

Date: 2500 BC.

Location: Mesopotamia.

Discovery: The art of making glass by heating clean sand and natron.

Discoverer: Unknown.

Impact: We use (or have used) glass for windows for houses and lanterns, to make light bulbs and tubes, lenses for spectacles, telescopes, microscopes and surveyors' theodolites, laboratory glassware from test tube to reagent bottle to Petri dish, thermometers, barometers, optic fibers, cathode ray tubes, and much more. Most modern science could not exist without glass.

Glass was known before humans knew how to make it under controlled conditions. Obsidian is a volcanic glass, formed when the right sort of lava cools very fast; and small lumps of glassy material called fulgurites are formed when lightning strikes sandy soil.

The stuff called nitrum, natrum or natron was a mixture mainly of sodium carbonate and sodium bicarbonate, harvested from dry lakebeds in Egypt, and traded all around the Mediterranean. Mixed with oil, it made soap, but it was also used in preparing mummies. Pliny the Elder believed some Phoenician sailors discovered how to make glass as they were sailing along the coast of modern Lebanon. He explained how traders landed at the mouth of a river and needed stones to prop their cooking pots on, over a fire on the sandy beach. Finding no suitable rocks, they used blocks of natrum from their cargo, and as the fire burned, they saw a clear liquid flowing out. Glass had been invented.

The discoverers of glass might not have been Phoenician, and they might not have been in Lebanon, but something like that must have happened somewhere, to somebody, although they would be unlikely to see a clear liquid flowing out. And obsidian was prized and traded by prehistoric people, because it gave such sharp edges. If somebody accidentally made something similar to obsidian, that would be a useful discovery to pass on, so it probably only had to happen once.

In reality, the first glass probably appeared in about 3500 BC, as glazes formed on pottery in Egypt and Mesopotamia. By 2500 BC, these two cultures both made glass beads. Archeologists say the art of glass-blowing was developed somewhere close to Syria in about the first century BC, but the glass was poor stuff. Soon afterward, writing about spiritual ignorance, St Paul wrote that we see "through a glass darkly," which is often taken now to mean "we see indistinctly, as in a mirror," because back then, glass was not much use for looking through. But glass technology was old by Paul's time.

In 1306 BC, a ship was wrecked off Uluburun near Kas in southern Turkey. Known as the Uluburun wreck, it lay in about 150 feet of water until it was discovered and studied between 1984 and 1994. The wreck's age was established by dating its supply of cut firewood, using tree rings, but the main interest was in the cargo of glass and copper ingots. The copper was probably from Cyprus, but the glass may have been made in crucibles found at Piramesses, near modern Qantir in Egypt. The ingots

Intricate stained glass windows such as this now grace places of worship, and even private homes, around the globe.

were deep blue (from cobalt), turquoise (from copper), and lavender. They were clearly on their way to be used by workers in other places.

The pharaoh Ramesses II (or Ramses the Great) ruled Egypt from 1279 to 1212 BC, making his capital at Piramesses (literally, "the home of Ramesses"). It was in the Nile delta, and recent excavations have shown that Piramesses covered some 10 square miles. Edgar Pusch has been excavating there since 1984, and in 2005 he reported finding a workshop which apparently produced faience, glass beads, and glass ingots for making glass vessels—but not any glass vessels.

The remains reveal that workers ground quartz-rich sand to powder, melted it at 1,650–1,750°F, solidified it, crushed and washed it to get rid of impurities, mixed it with coloring chemicals (or not: the ingot colors included clear as well as red, cobalt blue, and a transparent purple). Then the mix was heated to 1,800–2,000°F to make the ingots, which were sold or exported.

Most glass today is about 70 percent silicon dioxide (quartz or sand). In soda-lime glass, much of the rest is a mix of calcium and sodium oxides or carbonates. Pyrex® is borosilicate glass and contains about 10 percent boric oxide, while "crystal" contains at least 24 percent lead oxide, enough to make it show up on airport X-ray machines if you are carrying souvenirs in your hand luggage.

Which reminds us that while the role of laboratory glassware is an obvious use, glass caused some interesting chains of discovery. Glass was not only used to make cathode ray tubes, but also the vacuum pumps that exhausted those tubes. In time, this led to X-rays and much more.

More importantly, without glass to make prisms and other optical lab equipment, we would never have had any understanding of light, not to mention spectrometry, which allows us to see red shifts, chemicals in distant clouds and other curious things.

Legends are told about scientists answering the question, "What use is it?" in two ways. The first reply is, "What use is a baby?" while the second reply is, "One day, you may be able to tax it." As we will see, glass is just one example of a truly world-changing discovery or invention that is of limited apparent value at the time. The real significance and importance of a breakthrough can generally only be seen well after the politicians and bean counters who questioned its value are dead.

All good scientists consider bean counters to be evil, but our next scientist and his followers hated the beans as well.

PYTHAGORAS AND "HIS" THEOREM

A simple piece of geometry that made it easy to square up any job

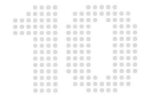

Date: Between 1900 and 1600 BC.

Location: Babylon.

Discovery: For any right-angled triangle, the area of a square drawn on the longest side—the one not touching the right-angle—is equal to the sum of the areas of the squares on the other two sides. As well, any triangle with sides of three, four and five units will have the shorter sides meeting at a right angle, making life easier for builders and masons.

Discoverer: Not Pythagoras. People in many cultures knew this principle before he was born.

Impact: Mainly in building and architecture, but also in geometry.

There is an old Greek tradition that Pythagoras (c. 580–c. 500 BC) sacrificed an ox to celebrate the discovery of what we now call his theorem. There are two problems in accepting this: Pythagoras knew he was not the discoverer; and he led a group ("the Pythagoreans") who were absolutely opposed to sacrificing animals.

The Pythagoreans had a number of amusing (to us) beliefs, like abstaining from beans, never eating from a whole loaf and not stirring a fire with iron. But as with the sacrifice, we have no way of knowing if these tales are true or legend, and we have no idea what they mean. The abstention from beans may have meant avoiding politics, since Greeks often voted by placing beans in jars, or it may have been more about the intestinal effects of beans.

Among other things, Pythagoras is credited with establishing the science of music. He studied the relationship between the length of a string and the pitch of the note in a musical instrument. He was also the first to say that the evening star, then called Hesperus, was also the morning star, called Aphrodite (the Greek version of Venus, the name by which we know it today).

There are Babylonian tablets that date back to about 1900 or 1600 BC which clearly refer to the theorem we attribute to Pythagoras; it was also known, before Pythagoras, to Indian and Chinese mathematicians, and probably in Egypt, where Pythagoras learned the basics of geometry. Perhaps he learned the right-angled triangle theorem there as well, and later found a neat proof. Just over 100 years ago, Elisha Scott Loomis published a book offering 256 different and valid proofs.

The Great Pyramid of Khufu at night.

Even a President of the United States of America found a proof once (it was James Garfield, in 1876). The 1940 edition of Loomis' book offered 367 proofs!

The Egyptians liked to align their pyramids, 4,500 years ago. The eastern and western sides of the Khufu (Cheops) pyramid are only an average of three arcminutes off a true north–south line. In fact, Kate Spence, a Cambridge Egyptologist, applied astronomy and logic to get dates for the pyramids, based on the tiny misalignments in the walls. The Egyptians lined up on the stars with amazing accuracy, not realizing that the stars precess (move) across the sky as the Earth wobbles on its axis like a top, once every 26,000 years. When the alignment "errors" are plotted against relative dates, a straight line appears, showing us how the Egyptian architects put their trust in the stars. There were, in fact, no errors: somebody just moved the goal posts!

Having their north–south lines, the builders still had to get the east–west lines sorted out, and that was where a Pythagorean triangle would have come in handy. It could be used to get accurate squares for the masons cutting the 2.5 million limestone blocks needed, and also for setting up a building alignment that would ensure the entombed Pharaoh would have a good afterlife.

Most western adults can recall and quote Pythagoras' theorem ("the square on the hypotenuse is equal to the sum of the squares on the other two sides"), even if very few of them would be able to present even one of the many proofs of the theorem. At the same time, very few adults have much of an idea about Euclid, who flourished about 300 BC, and who was rather more important in geometry. Euclid set out to work from a few basic ideas—five axioms and five postulates—to prove every other part of geometry.

The axioms were "self-evident truths," statements like, "Things equal to the same thing are equal to each other," and "If equals are added to equals, then the sums are equal." The postulates were a bit less self-evident, and included things like, "A straight line can be drawn joining any two points," and "Any straight line segment can be extended indefinitely in a straight line." From these building blocks, Euclid erected an amazing structure of deduction.

Proposition 47 in Euclid's first book is "Pythagoras' theorem," and it cites several earlier theorems which provide necessary sub-units. But those earlier theorems also depended on the theorems that went before them, and so on, right back to the axioms and postulates.

One curious impact of Euclid's own proof was the effect it had on philosopher Thomas Hobbes. Here is how Hobbes' eccentric friend, John Aubrey, described it. Notice the number of the item which so impressed Hobbes: it is Pythagoras' Theorem!

He was 40 yeares old before he looked on geometry; which happened accidentally. Being in a gentleman's library in ... Euclid's Elements lay open, and 'twas the 47 El. libri I [47th proposition, book I]. He read the proposition. "By G—," sayd he, "this is impossible!" So he reads the demonstration of it, which referred him back to such a proposition; which proposition he read. That referred him back to another, which he also read. Et sic deinceps [Latin—and so back to the beginning] that at last he was demonstratively convinced of that trueth. This made him in love with geometry.

Geometry had more uses. With the right information, you could even measure the whole planet.

FINDING THE EARTH'S SHAPE AND SIZE

How humans found out about their world

Science really began when people started making generalizations—rules of thumb that let them predict what would happen in a new situation, and why. Science uses careful observations to deduce things that could not otherwise be known or measured. Saying, "Sail west from Europe to reach China," was close to science, but when Columbus (21) said it, he was quoting 2,000-year-old Greek science.

Pythagoras was probably the first to talk about our planet being more or less spherical, but most Greek philosophers mentioned the shape at one time or another. Aristotle knew about it, and Archimedes clearly knew it, given his Proposition 2:

The surface of any fluid at rest is the surface of a sphere whose center is the same as that of the Earth.

Even Herodotus (c. 485–425 BC), the first historian, seems to have had a hint of the evidence. He described a circumnavigation of Africa by Phoenicians, and how they saw the Sun to their north when they passed around the southern tip of Africa.

These men made a statement which I myself do not believe, though others may, to the effect that as they sailed on a westerly course round the southern end of Libya [Africa], they had the sun on their right—to the northward of them. This is how Libya was first discovered to be surrounded by sea ...

In the second century AD, an astronomer called Ptolemy summed up the evidence: as you sail north, the Pole Star is higher in the sky; eclipses of the moon are seen at a later hour in the east than in the west, and the differences are proportional to the distances east or west; when you sail towards a mountain, you see the peak first; the Earth always casts a circular shadow on the Moon during a lunar eclipse.

When you put together all of these, the Earth just had to be a sphere, or close to it. Cylinders, flat and concave surfaces just did not measure up. Now, all the Greeks needed was a way of measuring the world. The problem was that they could not get a large enough tape measure, and even if they could, trees and mountains would get in the way!

Eratosthenes was a Greek astronomer, born in what is now Libya, and he died at Alexandria in Egypt. Being Greek back then was more of a cultural thing than a matter of living in Greece. If you spoke Greek, and especially if you were educated in the Greek way and lived among other Greeks, you were Greek, like Eratosthenes—or Archimedes.

Date: Around 500 BC to 200 BC, in several steps.

Location: Greece (in the broad sense, which includes Greek settlements).

Discovery: The world we live on is a globe, and we can measure its size.

Discoverers: Pythagoras (c. 582–c. 497 BC) or Parmenides of Elea (c. 540 BC–??) for the shape; Eratosthenes (c. 276–c. 196 BC) for the size.

Impact: Science often goes against our instinctive belief, and learning to accept a globular Earth prepared us for even bigger surprises. It also inspired us to explore our world.

Asian, northern Africa, and the Indian Ocean feature in this spectacular image of the Earth viewed from Space.

Eratosthenes learned about a vertical well at Syene (today's Aswan on the Nile). On a certain day of the year, the sun shone straight down the well at noon. And on the same day of the year, the noon sun was seven degrees and twelve minutes away from the vertical at Alexandria.

Divide 360° by fifty, and you will see that 7° 12' is one-fiftieth of a circle, so the two places are one-fiftieth of the way around the globe. Long before Eratosthenes, the Egyptians had noticed this difference in angle, but they thought the Earth was flat, so they used the angular difference to estimate distance of the Sun from the Earth as about 5,000 miles.

Eratosthenes knew the Sun was much further off, which meant the Sun's rays must all be parallel, so the difference just had to be a result of the curved surface of the Earth. Measure the distance from Syene to Alexandria, multiply by fifty, and there would be the circumference of the Earth.

The angles were fairly accurate: modern Aswan is at 24° 5' 23" north while Alexandria is at 31° 13' north, so the angle was only wrong by about 1 percent. But the distance estimate was far more questionable. Syene was not directly north of Alexandria, so they did not lie on the same meridian of longitude, meaning that if the measured distance was accurate, it would be too great. In any case, the estimated distance over land was always open to error.

The biggest snag is that Eratosthenes gave the distances in stadia. When units were not standardized, this was fine. But the length varied from city to city and we don't know how long Eratosthenes took a *stadion* to be. If we assume its most probable length, he was within a few percent of the correct measure of the planet—but he probably got close only because a few compensating errors evened out the rough bits.

In the end, Eratosthenes said: "If the extent of the Atlantic Ocean were not an obstacle, we might easily pass by sea from Iberia [Spain] to India, keeping in the same parallel."

All Columbus had to do was read. But as we will see later, there were a few other problems for Columbus.

INVENTING THE LEVER

The trick that made humans stronger

According to tradition, the Greek mathematician and scientist, Archimedes, once said something like, "Give me a lever long enough and a fulcrum on which to place it, and I shall move the world!" Perhaps he did say it. He certainly knew how to use a lever, and we have independent witnesses—the Romans—that he did it well.

Before Rome became a mighty power, Greeks established a number of colonies around the Mediterranean, some of them in places that the Romans later regarded as Roman territory. Archimedes lived in Syracuse, a Greek city on the island of Sicily. The island's ruler held him in high regard because each time the Romans came around, trying to attack Syracuse from the sea, Archimedes had a few clever surprises ready to upset the attackers, often literally. Some of these tricks relied on levers.

Many people in many cultures had used levers before Archimedes. The wheelbarrow is a form of lever, and so is the oar. So also is the *shaduf*, a basic bucket-on-a-pole that was used along the Nile to raise water from the river to the fields in the dry season; the screwdriver, the crowbar, the fishing rod, seesaws, scissors, pliers, and nut-crackers are all common levers.

So why do we associate Archimedes with levers? Mainly because he was the first to set down his ideas about using levers in a systematic way, ideas that he published in a book called *On Levers*. Then again, upsetting the Romans was a fairly good way to gain attention, but it came at a cost: he was killed by a Roman soldier when the Romans finally captured Syracuse.

Date: Unknown, but we will look at a famous application of it in 213 BC.

Location: Unknown, but quite possibly in Africa. Our case study happened at Syracuse on the island of Sicily.

Discovery: Using a long beam or bar can help lift a heavy weight.

Discoverer: Unknown, though the Syracuse case was the work of Archimedes.

Impact: For almost all of human existence, we have had to rely mainly on our own muscle power. Over time, we learned to harness animals, then steam, then other sources of energy, but at each stage, levers helped us maximize the gain.

There are three parts to a lever: the pivot point or fulcrum, the load and the effort. Scientists say there are also three types ("three orders") of levers. A wise old teacher once said to me, "I have a speech impediment: there are FLEa orders of lever: Fulcrum in the middle, Load in the middle, Effort in the middle." It always worked for me.

Archimedes' famous lever at Syracuse, often known as "the iron hand," was a first-order lever with a fulcrum in the middle and a grappling hook as the load at one end. As a Roman ship approached the port walls of Syracuse, the hook would grip the ship, raise the bows high and then drop the vessel. This would either throw the sailors around, make the ship fill with water, or even break it apart. Any of these results left a lot of discouraged, damp or drowned Romans, and the iron hand forced the Romans to abandon their attacks from the sea. They set up a slow siege from the landward side, using their ships to stop Greek vessels coming to the aid of Syracuse.

One snag is that we only have Roman accounts, some of them written almost 300 years later, but there is quite a lot we can work out. The Roman ships were quinqueremes, about 110 feet long and around 14 feet wide. Each had a crew of about thirty sailors and officers, plus 270 rowers and 120 marines. Each ship, with crew and arms, would have weighed around 100 tons.

That was quite a load, but the lever did not need to lift the whole ship, since most of the weight would have been supported by flotation. The earliest descriptions are from Polybius, who says the Greeks dropped rocks on the bows of the ships to make the marines retreat, lightening the bows (except for the rocks!). After that, everybody found out how well levers worked.

Levers still work well today, in many guises. Some train wheels, for example, are really levers in disguise. On a wagon, the wheels just roll, reducing the friction, and that is still so on most rail cars, but the driving wheels on a locomotive were, and are, different: they act as levers. Imagine yourself standing in a supermarket trolley, surrounded by ferocious animals (dogs, alligators, rabbits, your choice!), with nothing but a six-foot pole. Just as some people punt a boat with a pole, you can push your trolley along, helped by a lever. Now imagine you keep turning the pole, end over end. The driving wheels of a locomotive are continuous levers like your pole. They grip the track to push the locomotive along.

The driving wheels of an automobile are levers in exactly the same way. You need to think to see where the load, effort and fulcrum are (the fulcrum is where the wheel contacts the track or the road)—the driving wheel of any self-propelled vehicle is a form of lever. An automobile's steering wheel is also a lever, as is the tiller on a small boat or the jib of a crane.

Levers are all around us, but sometimes you need to open your mind to see the obvious. As you do, stop to think that the key in the lock, like

a door handle, is also a form of lever. Between them, the lever and the inclined plane in all its guises (ramp, screw, wedge, for example) power our world.

The science of levers began with Archimedes, but some of our fanciest lever systems come disguised as gears. That is another story—our next one, as it happens.

INVENTING GEARS

The invention that lets us control the speed, strength and direction of force

Date: Probably the first century BC.

Location: Antikythera, between Kythera and Crete.

Discovery: An unusual astrological "computer" which must have been made before 80 BC.

Discoverer: Elias Stadiatis, a Greek diver.

Impact: This revealed that there was far more technical sophistication in the ancient past than we thought.

The seas of the eastern Mediterranean can be treacherous or kind. Mostly, the storms in the shallow waters around the Greek islands bring bad luck, but just occasionally, they offer good fortune. Just before Easter in 1900, some sponge divers were working near Kythera when a storm forced them to take shelter near the island of Antikythera ("opposite Kythera," in Greek).

They had dived for sponges in this sheltered place before, but this time, they had a diving suit, and could go deeper than usual. That was how they found the wreck of a Roman ship in 140 feet of water. It had been there, undisturbed, since about 80 BC, but over the next year and a half, the wreck was largely stripped, with the finds going to Greek museums.

In 1901, one lump of "rock" from the wreck was found to contain gears, and slow cleaning began. Derek Price started studying the bits in 1951, and in 1959, he astounded the scientific world by claiming that the device was designed to crank out astronomical or astrological detail on a series of dials. People knew the Greeks had used wooden gears, but this mechanism was (and is) a puzzle. It contains fine metal gears, more like intricate clockwork from the eighteenth or nineteenth century.

Gears were used in ancient times to transfer power to where it was needed. In 330 BC, Aristotle described a geared windlass, and mentioned using smooth wheels to transfer motion by friction. Somewhere around that time, give or take a century, crude wooden gears must have been used to change the rotation of a vertical water wheel into the movement of a horizontal mill wheel.

The first gears probably did not involve any ratio other than 1:1, so gears were not used for speed change at first—that came with the introduction of the odometer. Literally a "street measurer," the odometer used a tooth on a cart wheel to turn a gear wheel one step each time the tooth reached the gear wheel. In more advanced designs, the first gear turned another gear, but in some versions, a full turn of the first gear wheel dropped a metal ball, or registered the count in some other way.

We know about odometers because they were large enough to be noticed and described, but immortality for a machine depends on more than just being described: at least one copy of the description needs to survive through to today. Books are printed now, and copies are widely distributed, but that wasn't always the case; in past times, a book might

FASHION GEARS UP

In the 1850s, when fashionable ladies started wearing crinolines, the only thing that allowed the seamstresses to keep ahead was the sewing machine, generally operated by a foot treadle which turned a flywheel which drove a set of gears to produce the speed that was needed. When the workers stopped for a well-earned cup of tea, some of them would have added sugar that had been crushed in a set of rollers that were linked by gears.

be just half a dozen handwritten copies, stored in wooden buildings where lamps were used for light and fires were used for warmth. Perhaps there were lots of clever little devices like the Antikythera device, but their descriptions were destroyed. Still, the idea of gears was out there.

The astronomical clock on the Old Town Hall in Prague, Czech Republic.

Maybe water clocks once drove systems of gears to operate displays that showed the time. People say so, but it sounds like a "just so" story to account for the way people started building clocks with gears in the 1300s. However it happened, the late 1300s were good for people who knew how to make gears. Clock-making began early in the century, but most of the oldest clocks have long since been scrapped. However, there is a clock still running in Rouen in France that existed in 1389, while a clock in Salisbury in the south of England has been there since 1386. It has no face and only strikes the hours, but it most definitely has gears—and they were all being used to change speed.

If you look at it the right way, a gear wheel is another form of lever, and a gear train—a set of gears—is just a compound lever. By the time of the Industrial Revolution, force-shifting gears were well understood, and geared winches were used to allow a single person to lift huge weights. When steam engines came into the picture, they made everything faster, and gears multiplied the speed.

Before steam, power came either from slow water wheels, or from equally slow wheels turned by an animal or a team of animals. Then came the slow steam engines of Boulton and Watt, which gave about four powerful revolutions of their giant flywheels in a minute. The only ways to get factory machines turning at a reasonable speed were to use gears or to use a belt system that was equivalent to gearing up. Belts often slipped, so where a lot of power was involved, gears were preferred.

Bicycles had gears, linked by a chain; clocks and watches all ran on gears; and moving toys had clockwork motors. Later, when battery-powered toys became common, there were usually gears involved somewhere.

Because there is always a risk of fingers, pets or other delicate things being trapped between the gears, they are usually hidden away out of sight. We are generally unaware that electric drills, food blenders and mixers, tape recorders, microwaves, washing machines, windscreen wipers and many other everyday objects contain gears, and would not work without them.

Between the gears of heavy machines and the fine gears of chronometers, the toothed wheels changed our world.

INVENTING THE WATER WHEEL

The first source of power that did not involve humans or animals

Date: Before 80 BC.

Location: Probably somewhere in Greece.

Discovery: Water can be used to make a mill (or mill wheel) turn.

Discoverer: Unknown.

Impact: The first labor-saving device, the water wheel provided free energy, whereas animal-powered mills and machinery required feed for the animals and treadmills required food for the humans.

Unless the water supply dries up, water wheels provide highly reliable energy from a source that, unlike animals, does not need feeding. But water wheels probably started out as devices used to raise water from a river to fields high above the river bank. If a moored paddle steamer sits in a current and the paddle wheel is disconnected from the engine, it will turn; something similar would happen to a water-raising wheel when it sits in the current of a river.

The earliest surviving reference to water wheels comes from about 80 BC, when a Greek poet called Antipater of Thessalonika mentioned young women being relieved of the work of operating a handmill, since water had taken over the hard work. Soon, water wheels were being used in areas where there was plenty of rainfall all year round—places where slaves were hard to get.

There are three types of water wheel. The simplest to link to a mill stone is a horizontal wheel, where water flowing past vanes or paddles makes the wheel turn a vertical axle that drives the mill. Then there are wheels where the axle is horizontal and the wheel is vertical, and these come in two forms: *overshot*, where water drops (or falls) onto the front side of the wheel and carries the front of the wheel down; and *undershot*, where water passes under the wheel, making it turn. The simplest undershot

wheel just sits with its base in a water current. Vertical wheels all need at least two gear wheels.

Water wheels were not particularly good at gathering energy, compared with the efficient turbines in modern hydroelectric stations. Still, when there were no animals to feed, all you had to do was have a big enough mill, and a sufficiently long fall of water to get enough energy from it.

Particularly with overshot wheels, mill owners needed to divert water out of the river, somewhere upstream, and run it through a channel that wound around the contours on a gentler gradient than the river bed. Sometimes this process would involve a weir or a dam that raised the water level, but if there were several mills along a river, they would sooner or later start to interfere with each other.

The Domesday Book was completed in 1086. This inventory of what the Normans had taken when they invaded England reported that there were 5,624 water wheels, about one for every fifty households. Bread was a staple food, and so mills were needed, all over the country. The Domesday Book also records two mills in Somerset which paid their rent, before 1086, with blooms of iron, which makes it fairly clear that those mills were being used to forge iron.

Beauty meets function in these fine examples of overshot water wheels.

Cistercian abbeys in twelfth century France commonly used water wheel power to grind grain, to sieve flour, to full (treat) cloth and to tan leather. At other times, water power crushed olives and operated bellows for forges, and for the fires used to brew beer. A paper mill powered by water existed in Spain in 1238, and seven such mills were to be found in Italy by 1268. Paper was made by pounding linen, either by hand, or by foot, or by water power. Water power was easier, when you could get it.

In France, a tributary of the Seine River, the Robec, had two mills in the tenth century, four in the eleventh, ten in the thirteenth and twelve at the start of the fourteenth century. Before long, the medieval world was running out of space for mills, and disputes began to break out as dams and weirs grew higher, backing water up to the next dam upstream, reducing the fall at the upper dam.

At peak times, the Garonne River at Toulouse in France has a flow of up to 9,000 tons of water a second, about a fifth of a cubic mile of water a day. Damming something like that meant driving thousands of 20-foot oak logs into the river bed in two rows and then filling the gap between with rocks, gravel, oil and wood to make a watertight wall.

There were three Garonne dams: Château-Narbonnais, La Daurade and Le Bazacle, and between 1278 and 1408, various acts of dam-raising led to lawsuits and orders to demolish dam extensions and pay damages that were mostly ignored. By 1408, the La Daurade company had ceased to exist, its last shares snapped up by the shareholders of Le Bazacle, ending the dispute.

In later times, windmills took over part of the task, simply because they could be located where there was no reliable flow of water—but windmills were not as powerful as water wheels. The early Industrial Revolution grew up near rivers, but over time, the water wheels were replaced by steam engines.

Now, as long as the mills could get fuel and enough water for the boilers, industry could move away from the rivers. The problem was that with all those steam engines, with all that fuel being burned, the mills became, as William Blake put it, dark and Satanic. Smoke and soot enveloped industrial England, and the methods, engines and technology spread around the world.

With power and technology in place, science could begin to grow faster. There had been developments for more than 2,000 years, developments which laid the foundations.

So it is probably time we looked at the chief foundation of our understanding of science: atoms.

DEVELOPING THE IDEA OF ATOMS

How the secret behind modern chemistry was discovered

How do you decide if there are such things as atoms? Ancient Greek mathematicians deduced everything from established facts, using careful logic, and Greek philosophers preferred to think they did the same. Yet the idea of atoms was only there because people like Leucippus and Democritus were alarmed by the idea that you could keep slicing matter into smaller portions forever. There had to be a limit, they said, an 'a' (not) 'tomos' (splittable) particle—but they had no evidence that atoms were real.

The nearest they ever came to a proof was when Lucretius (c. 99–55 BC) wrongly identified atmospheric dust, dancing in the sunlight, as atoms. It was a nice try, but no cigar. René Descartes (1596–1650) liked the idea of matter being a sort of continuous gloop, but he had no evidence either.

Robert Boyle (1627–1691) looked at the effects of pressure on gases, and wrote of "the spring of the air," because compressed gas pushed back, like a compressed spring. Isaac Newton (1643–1727) thought this proved that a gas was made of bits, which was right, but he imagined them staying still and repelling each other, which was wrong. Evidence is sometimes only as good as the interpretation you put on it.

These days, we use a model which was first proposed in 1738 by Daniel Bernoulli (1700–1782), who argued that the elastic behavior of gases meant they had to be whizzing around and bouncing off things, that this was how the pressure was achieved. But once again, there was no proof. It was a good model, but nobody took much notice for another hundred years.

Johann Kepler (1571–1630) (23) was on the right track when he looked at crystals in the early 1600s. He realized that you get nice, neat arrays only when you pack a whole lot of identical units together—just as oranges can be stacked in a display, but grapes won't stack neatly, because the bunches are different shapes.

Then, in 1781, René Haüy (1743–1822) dropped a friend's calcite specimen, a group of crystals, and broke it in two. Rather than getting upset, his friend gave him the smaller piece, which Haüy examined later. He saw that the outside faces of a crystal could be explained by regular stacking of the basic units. He went on to show that you could also create other faces by regularly omitting rows of units, so an octahedron or a dodecahedron could be created by the appropriate stacking of units.

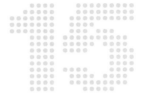

Date: 470 BC to 1808 AD.

Location: Greece and England.

Discovery: Matter is made up of small, very tough particles called atoms.

Discoverers: Leucippus (fifth century BC); Democritus (c. 460–370 BC); Daniel Bernoulli (1700–1782); John Dalton (1766–1844).

Impact: Once we knew matter was made of atoms, it became much easier to understand or to predict how chemicals behaved, and in the end, it led to most of modern medicine and genomics.

These days, models of atoms are accepted without question, even though the models are completely unlike our modern understanding of atoms.

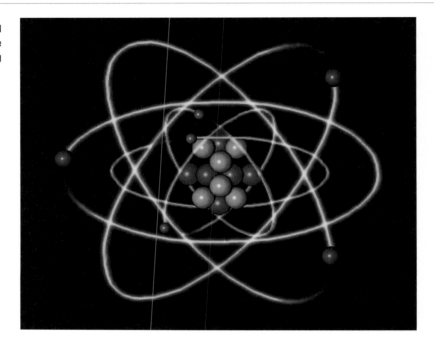

Here was clear evidence for atoms, but still people ignored it. Then, in 1808, John Dalton (1766–1844) introduced atoms to chemistry, asserting that matter is composed of atoms of different weights. That was the only explanation he could see for the way chemicals seemed to have standard compositions. Dalton viewed chemistry as a changing of partners with small groups linking together. It would take a while, but after Dalton, we could write H_2O—though the letter symbols we use today were invented by Dalton's early supporter, Jöns Berzelius (1779–1848), much to the annoyance of the Englishman, who wanted to use picture symbols instead.

Still, there were people who refused to believe in atoms. They might be a convenient fiction, but there was no proof that they were real. Nobody had seen an atom, after all! Even leading chemists like Wilhelm Ostwald (1853–1932) doubted atoms, saying he could do useful work without accepting atoms.

But the evidence had been available since 1827, when a Scots botanist called Robert Brown (1773–1858) was looking at some pollen grains under the microscope. Many plant species have pollen grains that are easy to recognize, but as he looked at a suspension of pollen in water, he saw some of the grains moving. They were not swirling around in a current but moving randomly, so that sometimes the whole pollen grain turned over, or the side would move inwards, like a punching-bag being thumped hard.

It was a mystery. Brown could see pollen of all ages moving, but he wondered if the pollen might be swimming like sperm cells. (This is not as silly as it sounds, as some plants like ferns and mosses have male cells that can move.) He ruled out this possibility by grinding up a bit of rock that had been taken from the Sphinx in Egypt. The movement was still there. The mystery was marveled at, and called "Brownian motion," but it went unexplained until 1905, when Albert Einstein (83) suggested that the movement was caused by energetic molecules making a direct hit. In 1911, Jean Perrin used Brownian motion to estimate the size of an atom, and even Ostwald agreed: atoms are real.

A standard teaspoon holds about 5 milliliters of liquid. A teaspoon of gas contains about 100 million million million molecules of gas. A teaspoon of water contains more than a thousand times that many molecules of water. When water is boiled to steam, it fills a great deal more space, which is why steam engines work, and the operation of steam engines is easily explained if we assume that atoms exist.

You can also explain rockets if you assume that atoms exist.

INVENTING ROCKET PROPULSION

How we found a way of flying that would even work in space

Gunpowder may have existed as far back as 700 BC, when something like gunpowder was used to fumigate Chinese houses at "the changing of the year." Rockets probably developed from fireworks that whizzed across the ground. Called *ti lao shu*, or "ground rats," they were meant to amuse or alarm, and we know that in 1264, the empress Kung Sheng, the emperor's mother, was offended when a ground rat came straight at her during a courtyard display of fireworks.

By then, somebody had already had the idea of attaching ground rats to arrows and firing them at cavalry. There is even a possible reference to rockets from 969 AD, but they were definitely used against the Mongols in 1232. Given that, 1180 seems a fair guess if we need a date for the invention of gunpowder rockets. The Mongols were very good at picking up on new tricks, especially anything they could use in warfare, and by 1241, they were using rockets against the Magyars at Buda, one half of modern Budapest.

On July 17, 1969, the *New York Times* apologized for an attack (published in its issue of January 13, 1920) on Robert H. Goddard (1882–1945). Among other things, the attack had asserted that rockets could not fly in a vacuum, as they had nothing to react against, adding that Goddard "seems to lack the knowledge handed out daily in high schools." As the first Apollo team approached the first landing on the Moon, the newspaper conceded that:

Date: About 1180 AD.

Location: China.

Discovery: Gunpowder in a closed tube could make a flying fiery object.

Discoverer: Original discoverer unknown. The modern liquid fuel rocket was first flown by Robert Hutchings Goddard of Worcester, Massachusetts in 1926.

Impact: As weapons, rockets were mainly used as incendiaries until World War II, when they became ballistic missiles, and soon after, carried humans into space.

Further investigation and experimentation have confirmed the findings of Isaac Newton in the seventeenth century and it is now definitely established that a rocket can function in a vacuum as well as in an atmosphere. The Times *regrets the error.*

There is a great deal left out in that jump from Buda to New York—or Massachusetts, where Goddard worked. In the 1700s, the Mongols, now known as the Mughals, introduced gunpowder rockets into India as war weapons. Some of their rockets were captured by British forces and taken back to England, where William Congreve improved the design. These became the Congreve rockets that were used as incendiaries in a naval attack on Copenhagen in 1807. They contained two types of powder: propellant and incendiary. The incendiary powder was in a canister with large cloth-covered holes—when the rocket landed, the powder ignited, the cloth burned, and the flames poured out.

Because rockets were lighter than guns, they were used as artillery in a few land battles during the Napoleonic wars, and as incendiaries, along with mortar bombs, in the British attack on Fort McHenry near Baltimore, Maryland in 1814. After that, rockets were mainly used as signals, or to get rescue lines to wrecked ships. It seemed that the rocket era had ended. A few stories were being written about travel into space, but nobody was talking about rockets.

In Russia, however, Konstantin Tsiolkovskii (1857–1935) was thinking about rockets in space, and in 1903, he had the bright idea of using liquid hydrogen to fuel a rocket. As liquid hydrogen had only been known for eight years, and had only been available in quantity for two years, Tsiolkovskii was quick off the mark!

The beauty of liquid fuels is that they can be turned on and off, whereas a solid fuel like gunpowder just keeps burning until it is all used up. There is no real control with a rocket using solid fuel: you just have to point and hope. Although Tsiolkovskii had the idea of using liquid fuels, he never followed through.

But Goddard had the same idea soon after, and by 1914, he had a patent for a liquid-fueled rocket. Teaching and war work got in the way of early development; then he had to arrange funding. He started serious work in 1922, and his first model flew in 1926. At ignition, his wife Esther started a primitive movie camera, but the film ran out after seven seconds. Too heavy at first to lift off, the rocket burned for another thirteen seconds before the thrust was greater than the mass, and it flew, unfilmed. Using liquid oxygen and gasoline, the rocket was only off the ground for 2.5 seconds, climbing 41 feet, and landing 184 feet away in a cabbage patch.

During the 1930s, German scientists began investigating liquid fuel rockets, and succeeded in flying the V2 during World War II. This was the first human-made object to reach space, but the V2 was a poor sort of weapon. It caused some alarm, but was too inaccurate to do real harm—though it showed that liquid fuel rockets could reach space.

Soyuz TMA-8, the twenty-ninth manned flight to the International Space Station (ISS), carried thirteen crew members from several different nations including Russia, the USA and Brazil.

After the war, the USA and the USSR gathered up many of the German rocket scientists, and put them to work on their space programs. The liquid fuel rockets became bigger and more complex, but there was still a need for serious power to raise the spacecraft off the ground, so solid fuel boosters are used as well. These are basically tubes, 50 feet long and 5 feet wide, filled with high explosive, mixed with a sort of glue that keeps it all together.

Each time you watch a space craft take off, you can see the solid-fuel boosters blazing, in the tradition that reaches back to China, the Mughals, Copenhagen, Fort McHenry and the rockets' red glare. But the rest of the rocket's flight uses liquid fuels and owes more to Robert Goddard's 2.5 second initial flight and Germany's V2 rockets.

DISCOVERING MAGNETISM

How we found that certain pieces of stone and magnetized iron would point in one direction only

Date: 0 AD ± 200.

Location: Probably China.

Discovery: Magnetized items line up north and south, and attract or repel each other.

Discoverer: Probably an unknown Chinese scholar.

Impact: The compass allowed longer voyages. Ships could navigate the Mediterranean all year around, instead of ceasing operations during poor visibility times (for six or seven months each winter). Ships were also able to cross oceans, knowing they were going in the right direction.

The attraction between iron and lodestone (magnetite) was known in China as far back as the fourth century AD, but it seems that the compass existed even earlier than that. A spoon known as a "south-pointer" is described in Han dynasty (second century BC to second century AD) records. This was not used for navigation, but as part of a system of determining burial times and places—and later for Feng Shui purposes.

During the T'ang dynasty (seventh to eighth century AD), Chinese scholars found a way to magnetize iron needles. At first, they rubbed them with magnetite, but they later discovered that needles became magnetic if they were cooled from red heat and held in a north–south direction. Soon, they were balancing these needles on points or hanging them from silken threads—Sung dynasty ships regularly made it all the way to Arabia, and found their way home again, around 1000 AD.

In 1975, an American astronomer called John Carlson described an Olmec artifact found at San Lorenzo in southern Veracruz, Mexico. The object, known as M-160, is made of hematite which *may* have been used as a compass. It certainly *could* have been used as a compass, and Carlson noted that a number of Olmec buildings were aligned 8° west of north.

As magnetic north and true north vary with time, it seemed plausible that the buildings had been aligned with a compass. Carlson knew this was not evidence—just an intriguing indication that some of the Mayans might have known about the lodestone compass as far back as 1000 BC. He called for further evidence, but none has yet been found.

We know much more about the use of the compass in Asia and Europe. The mariner's compass with its "compass rose" was invented in Europe, somewhere around 1300, although Europeans probably knew about the compass in 1190, when Alexander Neckham mentioned it.

But knowing about it and using it are two different things. Before the compass came into general use, mariners had to rely on the stars, the sun and glimpses of the coast, helped out by soundings, where a lead weight was lowered to the sea floor. The lead weight had a hollowed-out piece at the end which was filled with tallow, so that bits of the sea floor would stick. Where the water is shallow enough, a bottom of sand, grit, mud or other materials can be quite informative, and on a clear day or night, the sun, the stars and the coast help navigators. In deep water with fog or cloud, however, a compass makes life a whole lot easier.

A ship's compass can make life a lot easier for mariners, especially in grim weather.

In 1269, Pierre de Maricourt (Peter Peregrinus, or Peter the Pilgrim) was fighting in a war in Italy, but he found time between battles to write out *Epistola de Magnete* ("A Letter about Magnetism"). He described magnetic poles, and explained how to make a compass by magnetizing iron wire with lodestone and floating it on a piece of wood on water. It must have been a slow war.

The magnet and the compass remained popular with the ignorant and the confused. By 1600, when William Gilbert began to be well regarded by other scholars, the compass and magnet were well known, but so were the effects of static electricity. Gilbert had practiced medicine in London from 1573, but in 1599, he was elected President of the College of Physicians, and appointed court physician to Queen Elizabeth.

He survived just long enough to be (very briefly) physician to King James VI of Scotland after James took over the English throne as James I. Gilbert died in 1603, the same year as the queen, but he had a glorious few years, publishing *De Magnete* ("About Magnetism") in 1600. This book, written in Latin, explained in detail how amber and lodestone (that is, static electricity and magnetism) differed. He showed how the Earth has a magnetic field, and even used a dip circle to conclude that the Earth is a giant magnet with magnetic poles near the geographical poles.

One of Gilbert's comments shows how science had improved since the time of Aristotle. Hearing that sailors believed the smell of garlic would destroy the effectiveness of a compass, Gilbert put this to the test, covering compass needles in garlic, and finding that it had no effect whatsoever. The spelling is the standard English of that period.

But when I tried all these things, I found them to be false: for not onely breathing and belching upon the Loadstone after eating of Garlick, did not stop its vertues: but when it was all anoynted over with the juice of the Garlick, it did perform its office as well as if it had never been touched with it.

Gilbert asked mariners for their views, and discovered that they would "sooner lose their lives than abstain from eating Onyons and Garlick," indicating that the tale was false. It would be a while before Hans Oersted (46) brought electricity and magnetism back together, but magnetism had emerged from the shadowy world of magic and superstition.

Slowly, scientists were learning to be skeptical—to question everything—and learning to identify and classify their knowledge.

INVENTING THE LENS

How we learned to bend light in a controlled way to make fire and see the unseen

Date: Around 1285 AD.

Location: Pisa or Florence, Italy.

Discovery: Using spectacles to assist vision—the first known application of lenses for viewing something.

Discoverer: Alexandro della Spina or Salvino d'Armati.

Impact: Spectacles, cameras, projectors, lighthouses, CD players, binoculars, telescopes and microscopes all use lenses.

In 424 BC, a Greek playwright named Aristophanes made a reference in his comedy, *The Clouds*, to "that pretty transparent stone with which they light fires." In the play, a character called Strepsiades proposes using a burning glass to melt the wax on the tablets where his debts are written down, thereby erasing any record of his problem. (Until the Middle Ages, a writing tablet was a waxed board, and notes were scratched into the wax with a sharp-pointed stylus. A similar tablet is mentioned in the *Summoner's Tale* of Geoffrey Chaucer, written 1,800 years later.)

Clearly, a lens of some sort was available in ancient Greece, but it would have been useless for vision, because the ancients did not make good enough glass, or have lens-grinding technology. Still, a hand-blown sphere, filled with water, could concentrate the Sun's heat and set fire to dry material.

The earliest lens shapes date back to around 2000 BC. These are made of rock crystal and appear to have been ground, but we can only guess at what they were used for. One possibility is that they might have been used to focus the light of a lamp or candle: as far back as the late nineteenth century, Belgian lace-makers labored late into the night, holding their work in the spot of bright light thrown by a lens in front of a candle or lamp.

A magnifying glass like that is called a converging lens, and the use of a lens like Aristophanes' burning glass was mentioned by a Roman called Seneca (4 BC–65 AD), who said it could be used to read "letters however small and dim." This suggests using a lens like spectacles, but it could also refer to light being focused on the page.

There is another sort of lens, the diverging lens, which spreads light out. This diverging lens is useful for people who are near-sighted (like Piggy in William Golding's brilliant novel *Lord of the Flies*), but useless for starting a fire, because the lens will never create a hot spot. We can deduce that Golding was weak on physics, and we can guess that the use of a burning-glass to improve vision was the accidental discovery of somebody who was far-sighted.

An optical lens can only work if it gathers all the light from one part of the source, and bends it to the same point. We need a sharp focus, but we also need material that is clear and free of bubbles that might scatter the light passing through.

Lenses have come a long way ... This image shows the interior of a Fresnel lens at Grays Harbor Lighthouse, USA.

By the late 1200s, good quality glass was available in Venice, and some of it even traveled as far as Oxford, where an English scholar called Roger Bacon (1210–1294) experimented with gunpowder, flight, and viewing things through "a lesser segment of a sphere of glass or crystal" (a lens, in other words). Bacon was a scholar and wrote in Latin, but his surviving accounts are confusing. It seems likely that he used his lenses as hand magnifiers, in order to see more clearly.

In the 1200s, most people stayed within a few miles of their homes for their entire lives. A minority of people—merchants, pilgrims, soldiers and scholars, for example—traveled widely. So it was quite possible for people in Italy to hear about Bacon's experiments and vice versa. This Latin phrase means "the same, the other way around," and in Bacon's world it needed no explaining; just as English is the language of international communication today, until the 1600s all European scholars knew, spoke and wrote in Latin.

So it is possible that two Italian friends, Spina and Armati, learned of Bacon's work and extended it to make a pair of spectacles that could be worn. On the other hand, Bacon may have heard what Spina and Armati were doing, and decided to investigate further. The surviving records only tell scraps of the story, but we know that better glass was becoming available, the idea was being discussed, and Armati's tombstone described him as "inventor of spectacles," while a manuscript in Pisa gives Spina the credit. It matters little: the time was right, and spectacles emerged, making it easier for people to read.

In a time when lighting was poor, this would have been a boon. As photographers know, getting a clear focus or a good depth of field is easier with a small aperture. Our eyes have an iris which opens out in dim light, allowing more light into the eye, but the larger aperture makes it harder to focus. This is why it is easier, for example, to thread a needle in a strong light which makes our iris smaller, reducing the aperture. We have largely forgotten what it was like to read by the light of one or two candles, but it was normal in the past. People either needed assistance to focus their eyes (spectacles) or to focus the light on what they were examining.

So, knowing how to grind lenses was also a license to make money, and all over those parts of the world where reading was important, people got busy, grinding and polishing lenses so that those with poor vision, especially rich older men, could continue to read.

Once printing spread out across Europe, just about everybody with money would need spectacles, so there were more lens grinders, and the likelihood of discovering applications like the telescope became greater. It might have come sooner, if the Black Death had not set Europe back in the middle of the 1300s.

Still, look on the bright side: the Black Death made people care more about medicine.

BEGINNING ANATOMY

How we began to understand the human body by dissecting the dead

Around 330 BC, Aristotle wrote that the human brain was used to cool the blood, because it was cool when you touched it. The playwright Aristophanes, who discussed burning-glasses in *The Clouds*, has Strepsiades say, elsewhere in the same play, that Amynias was not in his senses, and appeared to have had his brain shaken. Obviously the Greeks had at least *some* ideas about anatomy.

Move forward 500 years, and ancient Rome was a barbaric place where death was common, especially if you were a gladiator. More often, gladiators were slashed and wounded, then they would be stitched up, and if they survived, they could fight again. The doctors who patched them up got to see a certain amount of living human anatomy. Cutting up cadavers was still not allowed.

Galen (129–199 AD) worked in Pergamum (modern Turkey, then a Roman town) as a surgeon to gladiators. He went to Rome in 161, left during a year of plague in 165 but returned in 166, and landed an easy job looking after Commodus, the son of emperor Marcus Aurelius. Galen wrote anatomical works in his spare time, but most of his investigations were on animals, because he studied what happened when the spine was cut at different places, something we would call vivisection today. Commodus is known to us best as the slightly fictional evil emperor in the film *Gladiator*.

Galen certainly worked with human bones, but the liver he described as a human liver was actually a dog's liver, his description of muscles around the eye and the larynx came from an ox, and his tongue description was based on the tongue of a Barbary ape. Still, Galen recognized that the testes and the ovaries were equivalent to each other. Pliny the Elder's explanation is probably more typical of Roman anatomical understanding:

Many skilful masters of surgery, and the best learned anatomists, are of the opinion that the nerves of the eyes reach to the brain. I think they pass into the stomach. This much is certain, I never knew a man's eye plucked out of his head, but he fell to vomiting upon it, and the stomach cast up all within it.

After Galen, work on anatomy stopped. All the detail people needed had been written down by Galen—there was no more to say, for the "Prince of Physicians" had said it all. When Avicenna (the European name of a Persian physician who was really Abu-Ali al-Husain ibn Abdullah ibn Sina) published his great medical work in about 1010, the anatomy came straight out of Galen.

Date: About 1300.

Location: Bologna, Italy.

Discovery: The art of opening and examining a human cadaver, to see how it works.

Discoverer: Possibly Mondino de Luzzi (1275–1326).

Impact: Dissection gave physicians some idea of what was happening inside the human body.

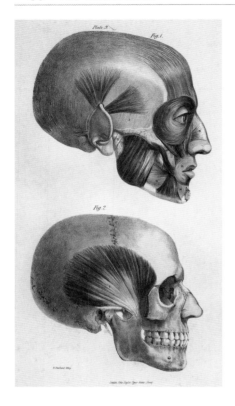

Detailed studies of anatomy allowed artists to render accurate (and useful) representations of the body's structures.

Avicenna's work was translated from Arabic, and copies spread across Europe, becoming the new medical standard—but it contained little that was new where anatomy was concerned. Avicenna did make a few advances. He found, for example, that the urine of diabetics tastes sweet, after noticing that ants were attracted to the urine of a diabetic man.

Then somewhere around 1300, something changed and public dissections of cadavers began in Italy. It wasn't much at first: Mondino de Luzzi sat on a high chair and read from Avicenna while a barber-surgeon did the actual cutting. This was only done to confirm what Galen and Avicenna had said, but once the principle of dissection was accepted, real anatomy could follow.

When one Azzolino of Bologna died in 1302, there were hints that he had been poisoned, so a court order was given to have his body opened and inspected . Reading between the lines, this was not unusual in that period. When Pope Alexander V died suddenly in 1410, his successor, Cossa, was suspected of poisoning him, so Pietro d'Argellata carried out a post mortem examination and cleared Cossa.

There was clearly no problem with post mortem examination, but there is a persistent myth that Pope Boniface VIII banned dissection in 1300. What he actually banned was the old Crusader custom of boiling down the bodies of dead comrades, so as to take their bones home for burial. Somehow, this was confused with boiling bones to clean them for anatomical study. In any case, the real ban had little effect: both Henry V of England and Philip IV of France had their bones boiled after they died.

The artists Leonardo da Vinci (1452–1519), Albrecht Dürer (1471–1528), Michelangelo (1475–1564) and Raphael (1483–1521) all dissected bodies to improve their art, but medical dissection was still limited to confirming Avicenna. As a young man of twenty-three, Vesalius (1514–1564) published a drawing of a human with a pig's sternum, a dog's liver, and an ape's coccyx, but he made amends in 1543 with an exquisite set of drawings of the human body that came out under the title *De Humani Corporis Fabricae*, meaning "Of the Structure of the Human Body."

Now, even those with no access to cadavers had realistic and accurate illustrations to examine and study, and nobody was likely to suggest that the nerves of the eye connected to the stomach. It wasn't a perfect solution, because medical students needed to experience cadavers. Supplies were obtained from executioners but also from the so-called "resurrection men" or "body snatchers," grave robbers who would steal corpses from fresh graves. One pair of villains became a little too proactive in obtaining supplies: in 1827 and 1828, William Burke and William Hare sold their seventeen murder victims to the University of Edinburgh's Medical School. When they were caught, Hare gained an indemnity by testifying against Burke, who was convicted, hanged, and himself dissected at the same Edinburgh Medical School.

INVENTING MOVEABLE TYPE

How a single idea made it possible for everybody to own books

Two or three generations after writing was introduced in Greece, the first attempts at logic, mathematics and science appeared there. In Europe, two or three generations after the introduction of printing using moveable type, science emerged. There may, or may not, be a link between the two sequences of events.

Printing from woodcuts was common, but imagine the work involved in carving a whole page of text, backwards, on wood! It was done occasionally, but it was easier to have a scriptorium—a writing room where monks wrote multiple copies of books by hand. This meant, of course, that the output was heavily biased towards religious works. Worse, even with monks, the labor costs were so high that most people could not afford to own even one book; as a result, few people bothered learning to read.

Still, a few books were printed by xylography, where whole pages were transferred from inked, engraved wood to paper in a press. Johannes Gutenberg switched printing over to typography, where individual letters, all cast in molds, were grouped together to make words, sentences, paragraphs, pages and books. It would not have been easy: he needed to develop methods for casting the letters, a way of holding them together, and a suitable form of oil-based ink. He needed to combine these with a press, like the screw presses used to squeeze the oil from olives or the juice from grapes.

It needed the goldsmith Gutenberg, a man who understood metal, to revolutionize the world with a method of making many copies of the same letter, ready to be put into frames, to make up a page of print. Gutenberg's ingenious method for making all the letters the same height guaranteed that when paper was pressed onto the ink-covered type, every letter would print on the page.

Many technologies take two generations to fully mature, and the products of the first fifty years of printing are generally referred to as the *incunabula*, a Latin phrase meaning "swaddling clothes"—the wraps placed around a baby. But the basics were there.

We tend to think of the time before printing as time of scrolls, but books came before printing. The pages had to be written in a neat hand, all nicely lined up on unlined paper, and every copy carried the risk of mistakes slipping in, or even of deliberate changes being made. Printing was just a better way to make many identical copies page after page, ready to be bound into a book. The change Gutenberg made was not

Date: Maybe 1448; the first confirmed Gutenberg book still in existence dates from 1454.

Location: Mainz, Germany.

Discovery: The art of assembling type to make and print whole pages.

Discoverer: Johannes Gensfleisch Gutenberg (1400–1468).

Impact: Gutenberg's idea may well have triggered (or ensured) the Renaissance. Printing made it possible for people to own copies of the Bible, triggering the Reformation. In the longer term, it led to more people reading, and the faster spread of ideas and methods.

An early printing press, c. 1550, portrayed by Philip Galle.

inventing the book, but inventing a way to deliver books faster, more reliably, and cheaper.

The typeface used in Venice by Aldus Manutius (c. 1450–1515) was based on the handwriting of a scholar called Alcuin (737–804), in the style used by the Italian poet Petrarch (1304–1374). Around 1500, it was called Aldine type; today, we call it italics.

Even after printing began, some books were still made by hand. There are, for example, fifty-eight pre-1500 copies of Geoffrey Chaucer's *Wife of Bath's Prologue* still in libraries today. A 1998 study of these allowed scholars to work out the "family relationships," just as biologists do with plant or animal species, and now they know which manuscript is closest to the "ancestor," Chaucer's original.

After serious printing took over, there were many fewer "mutations." More importantly, any work of scholarly interest could be reproduced hundreds of times over, so that books could escape and spread, carrying ideas away, faster than they could be banned. And the idea of printing was also free to travel, so people elsewhere could print works, either in Latin or in the local language.

The change was not immediate. Even in 1460, some years after his first publication, when Gutenberg presented a popular encyclopedia, the *Catholicon*, he described it like this:

... this noble book "Catholicon" has been printed and accomplished without the help of reed, stylus or pen but by the wondrous agreement, proportion and harmony of punches and types, in the year of the Lord's incarnation 1460 in the noble city of Mainz of the renowned German nation, which God's grace has deigned to prefer and distinguish above all other nations of the earth with so lofty a genius and liberal gifts.

If the *incunabula* ended in 1500, the real impact of printing did not come until the 1540s, when Paracelsus published his *De Rerum Naturae* ("Concerning the Nature of Things") in about 1541. Next, Leonhard Fuchs published his *Natural History of Plants* in 1542, in which he described, as well as 400 German plants, about 100 foreign plants, including peppers, pumpkins and maize from the New World.

Vesalius (19) published his amazing anatomy book, *De Humani Corporis Fabricae* ("Of the Structure of the Human Body") in 1543, a book with drawings and descriptions which are an excellent guide, even today. That was also the year Copernicus (22) published *De Revolutionibus Orbium Caelestium* to describe his model of the solar system.

These were all in-depth works, written by specialists, in the languages of their disciplines. Scientists were writing for people who shared the same interest, and to grab attention, they needed to provide new facts: it was no longer as easy to make a book by cobbling together the words of ancient authorities. New facts meant new experiments, and in 1544, Sebastian Münster published the first major world compendium of geography, his *Cosmographia universalis*. The process continued when Agricola (44) published *De Natura Fossilium* ("On the Nature of Fossils") in 1546.

Ideas had been let loose in the world, and the world was about to expand. It is worth wondering what effects the Internet will have by 2069, when it is 100 years old.

PUBLISHING AN ATLANTIC TRADE ROUTE

How a well-reported voyage across the ocean made Europe aware of America

Date: 1492.

Location: Between Europe and North America.

Discovery: There were lands across the Atlantic Ocean, west of Europe.

Discoverer: Christopher Columbus (1451–1506).

Impact: The creation of empires, the funding of economic and industrial development, new causes of European wars and, in the twentieth century, a new world order.

The careful reader might note that I have given Columbus' discovery an unorthodox title. This lets me avoid weighing the merits of hypothetical Phoenicians, legendary Irish monks, proven Norsemen or definite Basques—or anybody else who had sailed across the Atlantic for one reason or another. Many people had sailed across to the more northern parts of North America before 1480, some to visit, some to fish, and a few to settle, but only Christopher Columbus gets the credit for "discovering America." Why?

Columbus was an Italian navigator who set out to find India (or the Indies) for Spain, and found the New World instead. He was wildly wrong when he claimed that the Caribbean islands were the Indies, though it wasn't all his fault. Columbus based his calculations and assumptions on confused travelers' tales about the Indies from Muslim traders; when he found brown-skinned people in what he thought was roughly the right place, he declared he was in the Indies. So how did Columbus get the distance wrong?

Basically, he had relied on Eratosthenes (11) at second-hand for an estimate of the circumference of the planet. The Greek word *stadion* reminds us of the Latin word *stadium*, and there is indeed a link. The *stade* was a foot-race over a distance of about 200 yards held in a special place called a stadion, where a course was marked out, one stadion long. In Greece, this varied from 172.2 yards to 210.3 yards, but in Egypt, the stadion could be as long as 242.8 yards.

One of the shorter standard values was adopted by scholars and so the Earth's circumference was generally taken in Columbus' time to be around 18,000 miles, when in fact it is about 25,000 miles.

So Columbus could estimate the distance from Spain to India traveling west over the Atlantic, but his estimation was based on faulty data. And there was another snag: people had traveled east, overland to China (which was regarded by Europeans as the same thing as India), and they had over-estimated the distance.

With only a rough (and too large) estimate of the distance east to China, and working on a world globe which was too small, Columbus was justified in expecting to find "India" about where America is, when he sailed west. Still, if it was all that easy and that clear, why had nobody set sail for "India" before?

The answer, in a nutshell, is "better shipbuilding." Ships were becoming larger and easier to steer, and navigational instruments—the astrolabe and the compass—were getting better. The Irish monk, St Brendan, may have crossed the Atlantic in a coracle, and the Vikings certainly crossed the ocean in open boats which relied mainly on rowing (unless the wind was behind them). But the new ships could sail across the wind, and were even able to crawl sluggishly against the wind.

During the 1400s, ships from Spain and Portugal began venturing out into the Atlantic and down the coast of Africa, slowly extending their way into areas that had previously been blank on the map. The Canary Islands were known to the Romans in 40 BC, but they stayed free of Europeans until a French ship was blown there in 1334 before returning home to France. Soon, other ships were headed there, and a couple of decades later, Spain was ruling the Canaries.

The Portuguese arrived on uninhabited Madeira in 1421. Well before he set sail for "India," Christopher Columbus had sailed to Madeira with sugar cane for his mother-in-law's plantation there. So sailing further out into the Atlantic was not a big thing: the Canaries or Madeira were only 10 percent of the way to America, but even going that far involved a lot of sailing out of the sight of land.

There is an old story about six blind men investigating an elephant. One feels the leg, one the animal's side, one the tusk, another feels the trunk, one touches the ear, and the last encounters the tail. Each, of course,

Replicas of the ships—the *Santa Maria*, the *Nina* and the *Pinta*—in which Columbus and his crew set sail for the New World.

offered a different account of what "the elephant" was like. In the same way, the Vikings, the Basques and Columbus came back with varying accounts of the new western lands. Only one of these stories got people interested enough to follow up on it. Columbus was in the right place at the right time.

When Columbus returned and reported finding "the Indies," the time was ripe: shipping was capable of making the voyage, navigation was good enough to get there and back, and it was possible to publish books about these new places. A flood of Europeans poured into the Americas. New animals and plants were discovered, as well as new medicines and new products.

Previously unknown horizons had opened up, and people were that much more open to new ideas.

PROVING THAT THE EARTH MOVES

Looking for perfection in the universe, Copernicus changed our understanding of it

Date: 1514–1543.

Location: Frombork, East Prussia (now Poland).

Discovery: The Sun rather than the Earth is the center of the solar system.

Discoverer: Nicolaus Copernicus (1473–1543).

Impact: Scholars refined an inaccurate calendar and understood the solar system better. This knowledge also prepared the way for Kepler's clarification of planetary movement and Newton's laws of gravity.

Around the year 1500, scholars across Europe and the Middle East knew the calendar was wrong. It no longer coincided with the movements of the stars, and astronomical events such as equinoxes did not occur on the same date each year.

The Julian Calendar was created for Julius Caesar in 45 BC, based on a year of 365.25 days, which was not quite accurate enough. A year is really 11 minutes and 14 seconds shorter than that, and those little differences added up over time. By the 1500s, the spring equinox in Europe arrived ten days early, and deciding the correct dates of religious feasts and important festivals was becoming more and more difficult.

In 1512, the Fifth Lateran Council in Rome set out (among other things) to rectify the calendar, and learned men were invited to suggest improvements. One of these was a Pole, known to his friends as Mikołaj Koppernigk; to scholars who used Latin, he was Nicolaus Copernicus. He replied that the length of the year, and of the months, and the motions of the Sun and Moon, were not yet well enough known to permit the creation of a more accurate calendar. And then he got on with his life.

Copernicus was born and educated in Poland. He went to Bologna in 1496 to study canon law, but became interested in astronomy. He took leave from his position as a canon at Frombork Cathedral, in what was then East Prussia and is now Poland, and when his leave ran out, he got

The complexities of the Copernican system for explaining planetary movements. Each of the planets from Mercury to Saturn is shown. Notice the four moons of Jupiter (24).

an extension to study medicine at Padua for two years, returning home with a degree in canon law from Ferrara. He reassumed his position as canon, but continued his studies of astronomy.

People knew the world's shape, but they still thought the entire universe revolved around the Earth. This standard model of the universe annoyed scholars like Copernicus who believed in ideas of mathematical perfection and in nature showing regular, symmetrical patterns. The existing model had too many irregularities and inconsistencies.

The planets seemed to follow their own paths, disagreeing with the steady turning of the stars. Sometimes, planets even seemed to move backwards. The ancient Greeks knew about this. The word "planet" comes from a Greek word that means "wanderer." But in 150 AD, a

Greek astronomer called Claudius Ptolemy "explained" this by saying that the planets moved in a different manner from the stars, occasionally looping the loop, so to speak. He called these loops "epicycles."

Ptolemy's model gave the right answers, but Copernicus thought the universe should be more regular; he felt that circular paths were much more likely. When he tried a model that put the Sun in the middle, and assumed that everything else moved in neat circles around it, he found he could explain, more or less, all the back-and-forth movements of the planets. Adopting this model made it clear that the planets closer to the Sun would have shorter orbits or "years."

This, in turn, helped explain the occasional apparent backward movements of the planets. Inner planets go once around the Sun faster, so they catch up with and pass outer planets. Now, imagine a fast car on a road, passing a slower car. If a passenger in the fast car looks across, past the slower car, to a distant hill, it will look as though the slower car is moving backwards. In the same way, when we look at the other planets from our moving planet, they may seem to go backwards when viewed against the stars.

His model was passed around, and discussed. In 1533, the papal secretary told the then pope, Clement VII, about the Copernican model. In 1536, Cardinal Nicolaus Schoenberg of Capua urged Copernicus to publish his ideas. He finally did so, just before he died in 1543, in a book called *De Revolutionibus Orbium Caelestium* ("On the Revolutions of the Heavenly Spheres"). Copernicus' model was interesting as an idea, and nobody had any problem with it, because it worked mathematically, and because it was suggested by a church scholar.

Copernicus' ideas met with church acceptance, but a hundred years later, Galileo (1564–1642) would attract the Inquisition's attentions for saying much the same thing. Then again, even if the Reformation had begun, religious concerns had not started to grow when Copernicus was alive, while Galileo's troubles happened during the Thirty Years' War, when questioning authority was "not done."

Copernicus really did not discover anything new, because one or two ancient Greeks had already had the same idea. But he played an interesting "what if?" game, and he was too important, well known, well connected and well regarded for people not to pay attention. His lasting effect was to encourage people after him to think that there could be another model, and that this model made things much simpler.

Legend has it that Copernicus was given a copy of his book as he lay dying in his bed. He had suffered a stroke and would probably have been unaware of it being placed in his hands. He would also have been unaware that his Lutheran editor, Osiander, fearing the wrath of the church, had added an anonymous "letter to the reader"—which people assumed was from Copernicus—saying that the ideas in the book were just a model and were not to be taken as truth. Soon, however, the Copernican model would be taken far more seriously.

DISCOVERING HOW THE PLANETS MOVE

How the Solar System went from being a mystery to a validated system

Evidence can sometimes lead us badly astray. The Greeks knew the Earth was a sphere; they also knew that wherever you went, things always fell straight down, which meant that everywhere, things headed for the center of the Earth. That was slightly wrong, but their next conclusion was *badly* wrong: *if everything fell to the planet's center, it had to be the center of the Universe.*

Somebody once told the philosopher Ludwig Wittgenstein that the ancients must have been rather foolish to have believed in the geocentric system, with everything revolving around the Earth. Wittgenstein supposedly replied, "I agree. But I wonder what it would have looked like if the Sun had been circling the Earth?" It might be just a yarn, but his question is a valid one.

Things would have looked much the same, if we were just looking up at the sky from time to time, but it became harder as people's observations became more accurate. Copernicus had shown that he could work the calendar fairly well if the Earth orbited the Sun, but he assumed circular orbits, and those just did not work, not when you had accurate measurements.

Kepler started his adult life studying to be a Lutheran minister, but he became a teacher of mathematics and produced a book which showed off his mathematical skills. Impressed, Tycho Brahe (1546–1601) invited Kepler to come and work as his assistant in Prague. When Tycho died, Kepler acquired all of Tycho's incredibly accurate measurements, added to them and started analyzing the data.

Kepler was lucky to start with Mars, which has the most eccentric orbit, since this made it easier for him to realize that the orbits of the planets are ellipses, not circles. This was his first big breakthrough. The first two laws fell out easily:

Each planet travels in an elliptical orbit with the Sun at one focus.
For a given planet orbit, the vector to the Sun sweeps equal areas in equal times.

The telescope appeared at about the time Kepler proposed these two laws in 1609, and the instrument was certainly around before he proposed his third law in 1619. At that stage, however, it was a mere toy, nowhere near as accurate as the giant sighting instruments that he and Tycho had used to map the stars, and the movements of the planets across the field of the stars. These were basically angle-measurers, but a clever number cruncher could do a lot, given enough angles to work on.

Date: 1609–1619.

Location: Praha (Prague, modern Czech Republic); Linz (Austria); and Württemburg (Germany).

Discovery: The three laws of planetary motion.

Discoverer: Johann Kepler (1571–1630).

Impact: The Copernican model could be dismissed as "just a model," Galileo's ideas could be challenged and threatened, but Kepler's laws spoke for themselves. The geocentric universe was dead.

Kepler's illustration of his first cosmological model, as published in his book, *The Cosmographic Mystery*.

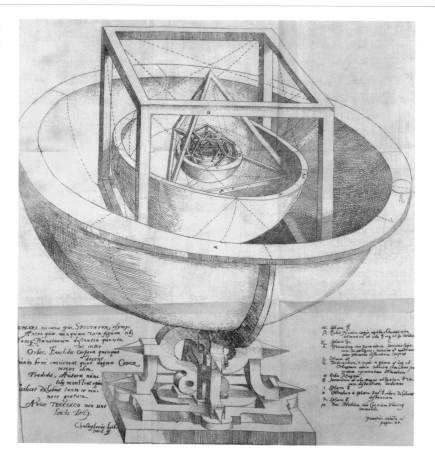

The ellipse was a shock, because ever since the Greeks, circles had been seen as special and perfect. The second law was something of a relief, because it was fairly apparent that the planets sometimes moved faster across the sky than at other times: like somebody on a swing, slowing at the top end of each swoop, a planet moves more slowly when it is further away. This meant that when the planet was furthest from the Sun, the area swept out each day by a line joining the planet and the Sun stayed the same, because the planet slowed down.

The third law took rather longer, and Kepler only published it in 1619. It was a time of unrest and the Thirty Years' War had started in 1618: it was mainly but not entirely about religion and, most of the time, it was fought between Catholic and Protestant nations.

Because the war was mostly about religion, outspoken people were at risk, and as armies advanced and retreated across Europe, independent thinkers needed to move to safe areas. Kepler was sometimes quite outspoken, and he had been forced to move twice (and defend his mother against a charge of witchcraft!)—perhaps we can excuse him for slowing down just a bit.

The third law read:

For any two planets, the squares of the periods are proportional to the cubes of the distances from the Sun.

This was excellent stuff, because the periods could all be worked out from observations taken on Earth, and this meant that all of the relative distances could be worked out. If we ever managed to work out how far it was from the Earth to the Sun, then the distances of all of the other planets would be simple arithmetic.

Kepler wasn't idle between laws. In 1611, he published a small book on the subject of "hexagonal snow." He deduced, from the shapes of snow crystals, that snow must be made up of densely packed spheres— particles of the same size and shape (15). In reality, water molecules are not spheres at all, but he was on the right track. We can only imagine what Kepler would have been able to achieve if he'd had a decent telescope.

INVENTING THE TELESCOPE

A device that lets us see distant things that were previously invisible

I enjoy geeky things, so I like being one of the few people alive today who has seen a bit of Galileo. In 1986, armed with the necessary knowledge, I climbed the stairs of an elderly building beside the Arno River in Florence. On the very top level, I found the cluttered case I was looking for.

It used to be hidden away, but now you can even find it on the Internet—one of Galileo's fingers, preserved in a reliquary in the Museum of the History of Science (Museo di Storia del Scienza) in Florence. The finger was crammed in with many other items. As I looked, I wondered if this was the same finger he held aloft when he murmured, sotto voce, "But it still moves." Not that he spoke English, of course, but he may have said *"Eppur si muove,"* the Italian equivalent.

More than likely he said nothing of the sort, but Galileo is important. He is commemorated in Florence because of his importance, and he was admired in his own time because everybody knew he was important— including Galileo. The trouble with Galileo, complained his contemporaries, was that he kept rubbing their noses in his cleverness. And importance.

Somebody in the Netherlands, probably Hans Lippershey (1570–1619), may have made the first telescope, but Galileo made it widely known.

Date: 1610.

Location: Firenze (Florence), Italy; or, possibly, the Netherlands.

Discovery: Lenses can be combined to view distant objects.

Discoverer: Galileo Galilei (or Hans Lippershey).

Impact: A vast broadening of perspectives and possibilities, stemming from the realization that there was more to the universe than the ancients had seen.

And Galileo pointed it at Jupiter, to see the four largest satellites of Jupiter, the ones we now call the Galilean satellites:

On the 7th day of January in the present year, 1610, the first hour of the following night, when I was viewing the constellations of the heavens through a telescope, the planet Jupiter presented itself to my view, and ... I noticed ... that three little stars, small but very bright, were near the planet, and although I believed them to belong to the number of the fixed stars, yet they made me somewhat wonder, because they seemed to be arranged exactly in a straight line, parallel to the ecliptic, and to be brighter than the rest of the stars.

Galileo called them the "Medicean stars," after the powerful Medici family of Florence. He also revealed their true importance: they were moons of another planet. No longer could people say the whole Universe revolved around the Earth: the evidence was there for all to see. Galileo clearly knew that Jupiter, just like the Earth, was a planet, and even considered that there might be people living there, able to see the moons he had seen, but from Jupiter's surface.

... since only that hemisphere of theirs is illuminated which faces the Sun, the moons always look entirely illuminated to us who are outside their orbit and closer to the Sun, but to anyone on Jupiter they would look completely lighted only when they were at the highest points of their circles. In the lowest part that is, when between Jupiter and the Sun they would appear horned from Jupiter. In a word, they would make for Jovians the same changes of shape that the Moon makes for us terrestrials.

Unlike Galileo, Francesco Sizi was an Aristotelian, and he had a wonderful time proving that Galileo's Jovian moons could not possibly exist. There are seven days in the week, he said, seven windows in the head (eyes, nostrils, ears, and mouth), seven metals named in the Bible, and seven planets, all with assigned roles in astrology. These "moons" clearly had no effect on humans, so therefore, in Sizi's opinion, they did not exist!

While Galileo was a modern scientist in many ways, a stern opponent of the Aristotelians, he refused for some time to believe in Johann Kepler's elliptical orbits for the planets. Galileo had been brought up to believe that circular orbits were perfect, and that was all there was to it. In the end, he accepted the elliptical orbits, but it reminds us that old mind-sets cling tenaciously.

If the early history of the telescope is uncertain, we have a good record of the name "telescope." There was a banquet in Rome to honor Galileo on April 14, 1611, at which a Kefalonian poet called Johann Demisiani suggested the name. This started the scientific tradition of naming new instruments by combining suitable Greek roots.

Over the years, different telescopes have been designed. Isaac Newton developed a reflector which avoided most of the problems with colored fringes caused by the spectrum, which Newton also discovered. Telescopes grew: lenses and mirrors got larger, to a point where the

Jupiter and four of its moons, as viewed by the Voyager I space probe.

weight of the glass is enough to make it flex and warp the image; 200 inches, the size of the famous Mt. Palomar telescope, is close to the limit for optical telescopes.

It is a long while since astronomers peering at the sky gave way to cameras. Now, we put telescopes in space (like Hubble) or at the South Pole (the PLATO telescope at Dome A), or we use radio telescopes and interferometers to create images based on other wavelengths. We have come a long way since Galileo, but everything has to start somewhere.

Mainly, we needed to learn how to measure things.

INVENTING THE THERMOMETER

How we acquired the art of measuring temperatures

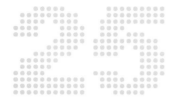

Date: 1612.

Location: Padova (Padua), Italy.

Discovery: That temperatures could be measured and compared.

Discoverer: Sanctorius Sanctorius (Santorio Santorio) (1561–1636); Gabriel Fahrenheit (1686–1736).

Impact: In general, the thermometer allowed the study of heat, and let experiments be repeated. Modern medicine is quantitative, relying on measuring temperatures, pulses, hormone levels, blood pressure, blood sugar and more. It had its start with Sanctorius.

In 1592, Galileo Galilei (24) built a crude thermometer using air in a tube with a drop of water as the marker, but this was of little value, since changes in the atmospheric pressure would change the apparent temperature reading. Like Galileo, Sanctorius used an air thermometer.

Santorio (to his Italian friends) was Sanctorius to people speaking or writing Latin—his friend Galileo Galilei wrote mostly in Italian, and so we call him by his Italian name. The two of them exchanged a lot of ideas, and it is sometimes hard to tell who discovered what.

A popular myth has Galileo discovering the pendulum principle while watching a church candelabra, which he supposedly timed, using his pulse as a time keeper. But it was Sanctorius who invented the pulsilogium, a neat little gadget where the physician altered the length of a pendulum until it swung at the same rate as a patient's pulse. Then all the physician had to do was read off the length setting to get a relative pulse rate.

Before Gabriel Fahrenheit, there were only air thermometers, but after Fahrenheit, mercury thermometers had scales with two fixed points. Clearly, there was a need for some standard form of temperature measurement, so why was Fahrenheit the first to use mercury in a thermometer? After all, ancient Rome had both mercury and glass, and Evangelista Torricelli, the inventor of the barometer (28), died almost forty years before Fahrenheit was born. If people could use mercury in barometers, why not in thermometers?

The answer lies in the way a thermometer is made. Mercury only expands a very small amount with a rise of 1°, so we have a very large reservoir (the bulb), feeding into a very thin tube. In this way, a tiny expansion is magnified, and can be measured.

Mercury easily gets dirty from dust and oxidation, and dirty mercury "wets" the glass it touches, so the mercury sticks to the glass. With a barometer, the attractive force of the wetting effect is much less than the force of gravity on the whole mass of mercury, and you can ignore it.

This is not the case with the ultrathin tube of a thermometer. The random wetting from dirty mercury gives random, unscientific results, so for quite a while, mercury was no use as a thermometric fluid. Then along came Fahrenheit, who knew that barometer readings could be affected by temperature, and who also knew how to get mercury clean. With clean mercury, you could have a reliable mercury thermometer.

THOSE LATIN NAMES

Why do people need to have a separate Latin name? Nouns and names change their endings in Latin to indicate different meanings or senses, just as we use *we*, *us* and *our*, an old hangover from Anglo-Saxon. This sort of change is called inflection, and it uses a few standard forms with standard endings, which is why so many famous Roman men have names ending in -us while women's names often end in -a. It gets complicated, but if you want to learn more, the key terms to pursue are declension, case and gender.

Fahrenheit knew he wasn't the first, and happily admitted it in a friendly way when he described his achievement:

About ten years ago I read in the "History of Sciences" issued by the Royal Academy of Paris, that the celebrated Amontons, using a thermometer of his own invention, had discovered that water boils at a fixed degree of heat. I was at once inflamed with a great desire to make for myself a thermometer of the same sort, so that I might with my own eyes perceive this beautiful phenomenon of nature and be convinced of the truth of the experiment.

He set one fixed point—the boiling point of water—then set the freezing point of water at 32°, so as to avoid negative numbers, because he thought negative values were too hard altogether for ordinary folk. In fact, Michel Stifel (1487–1567) had introduced the public to negative numbers in his *Arithmetica Integra* in the previous century. Stifel called them *numeri ficti*, or fictitious numbers.

Fahrenheit's attempt to avoid negative values failed, but the curious range hides the fact that his was technically a centigrade thermometer, because it had a scale of 100 degrees. It ran from "… the most intense cold obtained artificially in a mixture of water, of ice and of sal-ammoniac or even of sea-salt …" or 0°F, to his own human body temperature, which he nominated as 100°F. Later, when the boiling point of water was set at 212°F, body temperature was taken as 98.4°F, and eventually changed to 98.6°F to allow a simple conversion to 37°C.

The important thing about Fahrenheit's method for making a thermometer was that once people could measure temperature, the way was open for somebody to recognize the difference between temperature and heat, although that would have to wait for Joseph Black (1729–1799). All the same, Fahrenheit, with his established scale, could now report that rainwater always boiled at 212°F, and that oil of vitriol (sulfuric acid) boiled at 546°F according to his thermometer. The scientific measurement habit was beginning to catch on.

The development of reliable thermometers made scientific measuring more viable.

DISCOVERING BLOOD CIRCULATION

How we learned that blood goes around and around the body

Date: 1628 (published then—the discovery was probably earlier).

Location: London, England.

Discovery: Blood flows around the body and returns to the heart, to be pumped around again.

Discoverer: William Harvey (1578–1657).

Impact: Building on the anatomy of Vesalius and developing a new physiology, Harvey's revolutionary work convinced later investigators that medical science had to be put on a new footing.

William Harvey began his medical studies at the age of fifteen, and in 1599, went to Padua in Italy where he had no problem following the lectures, as they were all in Latin. He studied with the anatomist Fabricius (1537–1619), and even stayed at his house outside Padua, returning to England in 1602.

Realdo Colombo (1510–1559), who succeeded Vesalius (19) at Padua, had shown that blood moved from the right side of the heart to the left side by passing through the lungs, in what we now call the pulmonary circulation. Colombo had also shown how the heart was acting like a pump; that when the heart contracted, the arteries expanded, and vice versa. With this hint, Harvey was well set to explain what was actually happening.

Fabricius had seen and described the valves in veins in 1603. This must have influenced Harvey; if any pump builders had been around at that time, the function of the valves would have been immediately obvious. Harvey's notebooks still exist, and they reveal that he had the main ideas of blood circulation by 1615 yet, seeking more proof, he held back from publishing until 1628.

Harvey offered as proof a woodcut, showing how the operation of the valves in a visible vein on somebody's forearm could be demonstrated by a simple experiment. Place one finger on a vein near the wrist, to stop blood flowing toward the heart, then slide a second finger up the arm, pushing blood up and out of the vein. While the first finger stays in place, no blood enters the vein, because the valves stop it flowing back, but as soon as the first finger is taken off the vein, it immediately refills from below.

One feature of Harvey's work horrified the followers of Galen. Like Sanctorius, he measured things, and they said Harvey had "doffed the habit of the anatomist" in order to play the mathematician. This was a reference to his measurements on the heart output of living animals, which suggested that the blood could not be continually formed from the food we eat, as there simply wasn't enough food.

Let us assume, he said, that the ventricle holds only 2 ounces of blood, and that it beats seventy-two times a minute. In the course of an hour, the heart will pump 8,640 ounces—540 pounds—three times the weight of a heavy man. Where, he asked, did all that blood go? Here was a scientific proof of a rather different kind, based on a question, not an answer.

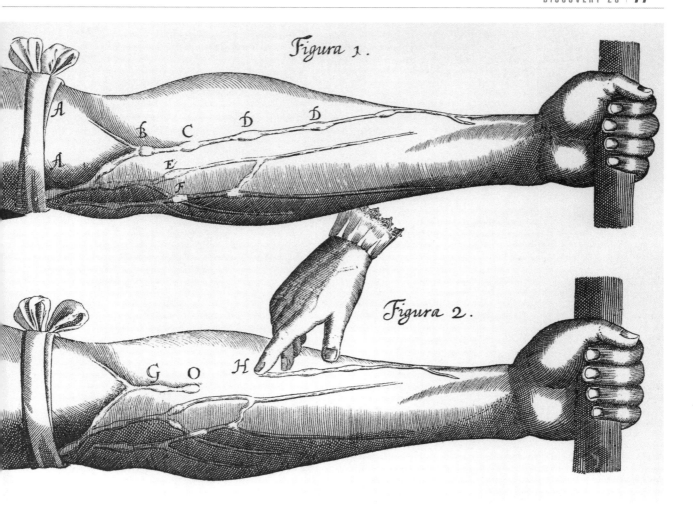

He argued that the blood had to be recirculated in some way, and if we could not see how, that did not matter, because the measurements showed it happened. To traditionalists, that was unacceptable behavior. The proper way to go about an investigation was to read Avicenna, Galen and Aristotle, and apply what they said.

In the end, the mathematical approach would become the standard one, but for now, mysticism was popular because it could be used to conceal a multitude of errors; in the absence of any clear model or theory, the errors would continue. It was a bit of a stand-off.

Harvey argued from logic because he lacked one key fact. He could not see the capillaries—tiny blood vessels that transfer the blood from the arteries and back to the veins. Today, we can see them under a low power microscope in the tail of a fish or a tadpole, but while he used a magnifying glass, he had no microscope, and could not make his case in

Harvey's woodcut illustration clearly showed how valves function in veins.

a fully scientific way. Eventually, he was forced to use a mix of evidence. Here, we see him arguing by analogy; the Sun, in the second paragraph, was the Sun of Copernicus, Kepler and Galileo.

We have as much right to call this movement of the blood circular as Aristotle had to say that the air and rain emulate the circular movement of the heavenly bodies. The moist earth, he wrote, is warmed by the Sun and gives off vapors which condense as they are carried up aloft and in their condensed form fall again as rain and remoisten the earth, so producing successions of fresh life from it. In similar fashion, the circular movement of the Sun, that is to say, its approach and recession, give rise to storms and atmospheric phenomena ...

This organ deserves to be called the starting point of life and the Sun of our microcosm just as much as the Sun deserves to be styled the heart of the world.

There had been an attempt at giving a blood transfusion to Pope Innocent VIII in Rome in 1492, and Andreas Libavius had suggested transfusions in 1615. Then, thirty-seven years after Harvey published, Richard Lower carried out serious experiments at Oxford in 1665, transfusing blood between animals. He began with dog-to-dog transfusions, and progressed to transfusing sheep blood into humans in 1666. In 1667 in France, Jean-Baptiste Denis transfused calf blood into dogs, then lamb or sheep blood into humans, losing two human patients, while two others survived.

Blood transfusions from different species will normally kill the patient, because clots form. As some of the patients did not die in these early attempts, we must assume that the tubes clogged very quickly, before any blood reached the recipient, and little blood was passed over—or that they were remarkably lucky. By 1678 though, there had been enough deaths to cause the Paris Society of Physicians to outlaw transfusion without permission from the Paris Faculty of Medicine. The understanding we had was just an unsafe glimmer.

But the light was growing.

DISCOVERING PHOTOSYNTHESIS

How we learned where plants get their solid material

The Aristotelians, the pre-scientists, had fixed ideas, and nothing would sway them from their preconceptions. Johann van Helmont's famous willow tree experiment gave important and valid results, but he interpreted them in a way that reflected the orthodox thinking of his time. Each time there is a change in a mind-set or paradigm in science, we find people who follow the old ideas, trying desperately to explain the data under the old system.

Van Helmont exhibited a mix of different styles: he was a physician and alchemist who was quite a neat and careful experimenter; his problem was that he thought there was just one element—water—and that everything else was made from it. A Greek philosopher called Thales (c. 624–c. 545 BC) had proposed the idea, and early in the 1600s van Helmont set out to find evidence to support this view.

I took a vessel of earthenware and put into it, 200 pounds of dried earth. I watered this with rain water and planted into it a young willow, which had a weight of 5 pounds. Five years later the same plant had a weight of 169 pounds and three ounces ... I dried the earth in the vessel and determined its weight at the end of the experiment as 200 pounds minus two ounces. The total weight difference between the old and the young plant was thus clearly derived from the water.

It was meticulously done: he had a tin cover to stop dust getting into the pot, the water was as free of salts as it could be—but he failed to consider gases. This is odd, because it was van Helmont himself who gave us the word "gas." He intended to call it "chaos," but because of the way the Greek word for chaos is pronounced in Flemish, we ended up with "gas" instead.

Ironically, he even identified a particular gas which was produced in two different ways: carbon dioxide, which was the source of the extra mass gained by the willow. He showed that burning charcoal gives off a gas identical to that given off during alcoholic fermentation, a gas which he called *gas sylvestre*, or "forest gas." Today, we know it as carbon dioxide.

He also believed in spontaneous generation and reported that mice grow if a shirt, soaked in human sweat, is left in contact with wheat for twenty-one days. You can almost imagine the way in which this "recipe" came about, with a sweaty shirt being discarded in a cupboard where there was some wheat, with mice sneaking in to nest or eat the wheat, and three weeks later being found.

Date: Early in the 1600s; published posthumously in 1648.

Location: Vilvoorde near Brussels, Belgium.

Discovery: A plant gains weight which does not come from the soil it grows in.

Discoverer: Johann Baptista van Helmont (1579–1644).

Impact: Little at first, though it flagged an unusual situation for others to investigate.

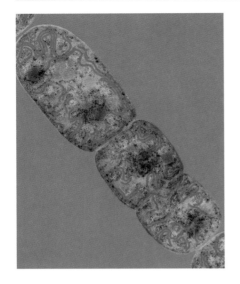

A thread of several cyanobacteria cells. Cyanobacteria (also called cyanophyta) fix atmospheric nitrogen and enrich the soil and the seas with useful nitrogen compounds.

By the 1770s, chemical thinking and methods were getting closer to those of modern times, and so were some parts of biology. Stephen Hales (1677–1761) had shown in 1727 that water is pumped through plants, rather as blood is pumped through animals, people thought. The results were there, even if the reasoning was a bit imperfect.

Oxygen was still unknown, but in 1772 Joseph Priestley (1733–1804) detected it when he put a burning candle in a sealed container with a sprig of mint. Before long, the candle went out, because there was not enough oxygen left. Ten days later, Priestley lit the candle again, using a concave mirror to focus the Sun's heat on the wick. By then, the mint had converted most of the carbon dioxide back to oxygen, and the candle burned brightly in the "restored air." He came close, but not close enough, to finding oxygen.

In 1779, oxygen was formally discovered when Jan Ingen-Housz (1730–1799), court physician to the Empress of Austria, took leave and went to England to carry out a set of experiments. He was able to show that plants absorb carbon dioxide during the day, and emit the same gas at night. Whatever was going on, light was a part of it. He then put a small green waterplant in a sealed container and exposed it to bright light. Bubbles of gas formed, but when a similar plant in a similar container was kept in the dark, there were no bubbles. Now he knew that light caused plants to form a gas.

By 1796, Ingen-Housz went further. Plants needed soil to give them a grip, he said, adding that many plants gained water from the soil through their roots, but that some unusual plants (like cactuses and agaves) did not take root in the soil, so they must gain some sort of food from other sources.

Then comes the amazing key comment: Ingen-Housz had found why the "vegetables are so inconstant in their effects on the air." He had distinguished between photosynthesis which produces "food," and respiration which converts that food.

I was fortunate enough to discover the true reason, why plants did sometimes correct bad air, and sometimes made it worse ...

In 1782, Jean Senebier (1742–1809) showed that carbon dioxide was taken up in photosynthesis, and in 1804, Nicholas de Saussure (1767–1845) showed that water played a part in photosynthesis as well. When Julius Robert Mayer (1814–1878) explained in 1845 that solar energy was being converted to chemical energy, the basic facts were all there. Discovering the biochemical pathways would take longer, but people knew roughly what was happening, thanks largely to the way our understanding of chemistry (first) and energy (later) had developed.

As the nineteenth century got under way, science began to run much faster, but before we get to that, there are a few other milestones we need to visit.

INVENTING THE BAROMETER

How we learned to weigh the air and make a vacuum

Aristotle was certain that Nature would not tolerate a vacuum. Nature abhors (detests) a vacuum, he said. For most people, if Aristotle said so, that was it, at least for a while. After 1600, however, people began questioning things, especially the pronouncements of Aristotle. A lot of the questions came from one man, Galileo Galilei, who kept offering difficult facts and observations that challenged Aristotle's ideas.

In his 1638 book, *Two New Sciences*, Galileo mentioned that pumps could not raise water above a certain level by suction. To make this sound more like an everyday fact, he claimed that a workman who came to repair a pump had told him this—but he actually learned about the problem from a letter written to him by Giovanni Batista Baliani, another scientist. (Galileo may have felt the Inquisition would hesitate to challenge facts known to ordinary people.)

This discovery is sometimes credited to Robert Boyle (1627–1691), although Boyle was only eleven when Galileo's book was published! Each discovery has its legend, and the legend is often readily debunkable, yet the discovery itself remains unassailable. Such discoveries were unlikely in England in the 1630s, but Italy was alive with experimentation, with the experimenters passing ideas and findings to each other, to the benefit of all, and to the benefit of science.

In 1641, Gasparo Berti and other researchers in Rome took a very long tube, sealed it at one end, filled it with water and tilted it after the open end was placed in a container of water. They saw that a space formed at the top of the tube, and noted that the height of the water column was 34 feet or 18 cubits—the exact limit to which pumps and siphons could raise water. The Aristotelians scrambled to find a reason why this space was not a true vacuum, suggesting that the gap contained "spirits," because light passed through it.

Evangelista Torricelli predicted that a similar result would be achieved more easily using mercury, which is 13.6 times as dense as water, meaning that a tube 2 cubits long would be more than enough. When his student Vincenzo Viviani set up the first barometer, he used such a tube, with the same setup, and got the equivalent result: mercury drained from the tube, leaving a column of mercury 1.3 cubits (about 30 inches) high and a vacuum (except for some mercury vapor) at the top of the tube.

Torricelli took it further, though. He deduced that the Earth's atmosphere extended up 50 miles, and argued that this caused the twilight we see at morning and night, because the atmosphere scattered the light. If the air

Date: 1644.

Location: Firenze (Florence), Italy.

Discovery: That it was possible to form a vacuum; and that the pressure of the atmosphere at sea level supports a column of mercury about 30 inches high at sea level.

Discoverer: Evangelista Torricelli (1608–1647), assisted by Vincenzo Viviani (1622–1703).

Impact: The first barometers showed that a vacuum was possible, but in a short time, also showed us a great deal more about the atmosphere.

GALILEO'S PUMP WORKMAN

Galileo noticed that pumps could not raise water above a certain level by suction. He quoted a "workman" as telling him:

... that it was not possible, either by a pump or by any other machine working on the principle of attraction, to lift water a hair's breadth above eighteen cubits ...

Early researchers trying to find ways of creating a vacuum used glass tubes filled with different liquids. In the process, they stumbled upon the idea of air pressure. Here, the experimenter risks mercury poisoning while making a simple barometer. The tube on the right contains a vacuum at the top.

went on forever, all of space would be lit up, but if the air did not go that far, the twilight effect would be less. The barometer was created as a way of generating a vacuum, and investigations into atmospheric pressure only came later: once again, pure research had delivered a surprise.

The important thing to remember is that there are no moving parts in a barometer. This means that all the forces in the barometer are balanced. The downward push of the mercury in the barometer is exactly the same as the downward push of the air outside the barometer. If the air pressure is greater than the mercury pressure, the mercury level will rise until there is a balance; and if the mercury pressure is greater, its level will fall until there is a balance. The barometer takes no more than a couple of seconds to balance when you first set it up. After that, as the air pressure slowly changes, the mercury level stays in balance with it, giving us a direct measure of the pressure which the air is placing on the open dish of mercury.

Soon people all over Europe were playing with mercury barometers, but in 1646, Blaise Pascal (1623–1662) made a barometer using a mixture of water and wine. At this time, there were still people who thought Aristotle was right—that there was no vacuum at the top of the barometer, just "spirits." They were correct in a sense: what we call vapor is not that far from their spirits. But Pascal challenged the Aristotelians to predict the height of the water-and-wine column.

This was cunning: Pascal knew that the mixture was less dense than water, so the column ought to be higher. The Aristotelians, however, said that wine was more "spirituous" (whatever that means), so the column would be shorter than a water barometer's column. A public test revealed that the column was 20 cubits high—clearly greater than the 18 cubit column of water. I suspect that Pascal had already tested it, and so was laying a trap. Whatever the truth, it worked.

Next, he wrote to his brother-in-law, Florin Perier, and asked him to take a mercury barometer up a nearby mountain, Puy de Dome, and measure the pressure at a greater altitude, to see if it fell. Perier must have been a very patient brother-in-law, because carrying one of those barometers would not have been easy. The bits were heavy and fragile, a bad combination for carrying up mountains. Still, Perier was up to the task and made the experiment in September 1648, confirming that the barometer level fell as he climbed upwards.

Air pressure began to make sense.

INVENTING THE AIR PUMP

How we learned to make a device that could compress air

Once Torricelli had shown that you could achieve a good vacuum inside a barometer, the Aristotelian line that Nature detests a vacuum was finished. But knowing vacuums could be created was not the same as knowing how to make one. That needed an air pump, and there are two of them in this story. Each could either increase or decrease pressure, so we will deal with them in the order of their construction.

The Thirty Years' War ended with the Peace of Westphalia in 1648. Now, Otto von Guericke, the former burgomaster of Magdeburg, was finally free to pursue some interesting science which had emerged with the barometer earlier in the 1640s. His plan was to use a pump to take the water from a water-filled barrel, and he started by adapting a fire-fighting pump design.

When he first tested his system, air leaked in, so he put a small barrel of water inside a large barrel full of water, and again pumped the small one out. Air still leaked in. Eventually, he realised that the pressure drove both water and air through the wood and into the smaller barrel, so he switched to metal containers.

Once he had a successful pump, von Guericke made two items known as the Magdeburg hemispheres. These were two hemispherical metal cups which were put together and pumped free of air. Until air was let back

Date: 1650 and 1656.

Location: Magdeburg, Germany; and London, England.

Discovery: A way of removing most of the air from a container.

Discoverer: Otto von Guericke (1602–1686); and Robert Hooke (1635–1703).

Impact: This led directly to many discoveries about gases, and then to an understanding of atoms.

into the hemispheres, they could not be separated, even by two teams of eight horses or by heavy weights hanging from them.

Robert Boyle (1627–1691) was an unusual scientist for his time, because he measured things, and drew up tables to see how two lots of numbers varied around each other. This odd (for its time) habit gave us Boyle's Law, which states that doubling the pressure on a gas halves its volume.

When von Guericke studied the effect of low pressure on his hemispheres, he was happy just to describe it, without measuring anything. Boyle described what happened inside the vacuum: without air, fires went out, sound died away and animals died. That was normal, but he was one of these new scientists who measured things as well as describing them.

It was Boyle's good luck to have Robert Hooke as his assistant. Hooke attached himself to Boyle while he was at Oxford, and repaid Boyle's kindness by making an air pump for him. Boyle in turn had Hooke made Curator of Experiments at the Royal Society.

Boyle did well out of their partnership: Hooke developed Hooke's Law, which describes how springs behave under load and, significantly, Boyle referred to air under pressure using the term "the spring of the air," describing it in similar terms. When he reported his own law, Hooke mentioned that it applied to all manner of things: wood, glass, horn, suspended wires, hair, sinews, stones and even compressed air. Clearly, the two of them collaborated well, but Boyle's Law did not come from the pump. It was, however, inspired by it.

In that experiment, Boyle poured mercury ("quicksilver") into a "siphon" (a J-tube) with the short end sealed off. He measured the size of the trapped air column, comparing this with the height of the mercury column pressing down.

Here is how Boyle explained it. The language is hard for us to understand today, but it is worth the effort:

… we began to pour quicksilver into the longer leg of the siphon, which by its weight pressing up … that in the shorter leg, did by degrees streighten [shorten] the included air: and continuing this pouring in of quicksilver till the air in the shorter leg was by condensation reduced to take up by half the space it possessed (I say possessed, not filled) before; we cast our eyes upon the longer leg of the glass … and we observed, not without delight and satisfaction, that the quicksilver in the longer part of the tube was 29 inches higher than the other. Now that this observation does both very well agree with and confirm our hypothesis, will be easily discerned by him that takes notice what we teach … air … able to counter-balance and resist the pressure of a mercurial cylinder of about 29 inches, as we are taught by the Torricellian experiment … being brought to a degree of density about twice as great as that it had before, obtains a spring twice as strong as formerly. As may appear by its being able to sustain or resist a cylinder of 29 inches in the longer tube, together with the weight of the atmospherical cylinder, that … as we just now inferred from the Torricellian experiment, was equivalent to them.

Ottonis *de* Guericke
EXPERIMENTA
Nova (*ut vocantur*) Magdeburgica
De
VACUO SPATIO.

Later, when people began to apply the pressure of steam to do work, Boyle's investigations must have been very useful indeed.

In the nineteenth century, mercury vacuum pumps took over. Whatever needed to be emptied was first filled with mercury and attached to a long tube, also filled with mercury. When this was set in place, upside down, all the mercury dropped down, emptying the container and delivering a vacuum as good as the one at the top of a barometer—perfect but for a trace of mercury vapor. Later, chemicals called "getters" were used to absorb the mercury vapor as well.

Everything has to start somewhere, whether it is ideas, pumps, or even plants and animals.

DISCOVERING SEXUAL REPRODUCTION

How we came to understand the way new animals and plants are formed

Date: 1651.

Location: England.

Discovery: All animals develop from fertilized eggs.

Discoverer: William Harvey (1578–1657).

Impact: We needed this insight to make sense of classification, evolution and genetics.

The steps to understanding sexual reproduction feature many scientists. Their main interest, of course, was in how humans reproduced, but every biologist understood that animals were easier to dissect and study—and that they probably reproduced in a similar way.

Aristotle offered two competing theories. In *preformation*, each parent contained the seeds of the next generation, which contained the seeds of the next and so on, like a set of Russian dolls. In *epigenesis*, a fetus was formed from some part of the mother or father, perhaps the semen—although Aristotle thought the fetus more probably formed from a clot of menstrual blood.

The problem was that until microscopes were available, sperm cells and egg cells were very hard to see, but William Harvey (26) found a way to bypass the problem. He was personal physician to King James I and to King Charles I from 1625 to 1647, and this gave him the chance to dissect deer from royal parks. In one dissection, he found a fetus "about the bignesse of a pigeon's egge." The parallel was clear, and the embryos of birds are easy to observe by opening eggs at various time intervals after incubation begins.

Even though he had never seen a mammalian egg, Harvey's 1651 work, *De Generatione Animalium* ("On Animal Reproduction"), carried a frontispiece illustration showing the Greek god Zeus opening an egg-shaped container, labeled *ex ovo omnia* ("everything comes from eggs"), as reptiles, birds, a fish, insects and mammals (including a human) emerge from the container. His friend Martin Llewellyn translated Harvey's Latin into English, and captured Harvey's key idea in verse:

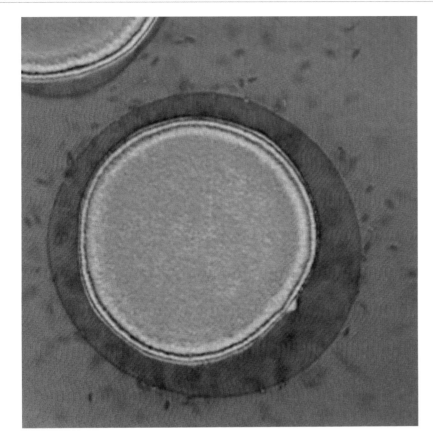

With today's high-powered microscopes, it is easy to see a single fertilized ovum.

That both the hen and housewife are so matcht,
That her son born, is only her son hatcht,
That when her teeming hopes have prosp'rous been,
Yet to conceive, is but to lay within.

Aristotle's teachings had stayed popular because there were some good observations buried among the ratty ideas. It is possible the oddities were inserted into Aristotle by later copyists because, up to Medieval times, it was common to support cherished ideas by attributing them to older scholars. Llewellyn's version of Harvey, equating a pregnancy to internal egg-laying, would not have surprised Aristotle, who had looked at the curious gestation that happens with the dogfish, a small member of the shark family that gives birth to live young.

Still nobody had seen a mammalian egg, but in 1668, a Dutch physician named Regnier de Graaf saw follicles in a mammalian ovary, and took them to be the same thing as a developing egg in a bird's ovary. Sadly, even though he was a member of Britain's Royal Society, and drew the Society's attention to the work of Anton van Leeuwenhoek, de Graaf did not use a microscope. If he had, he might have seen the tiny egg inside the follicle. He was on the right track, but never quite got there.

William Harvey had no way of understanding the part played by semen, because van Leeuwenhoek's letter describing spermatozoa was not written until 1676, nineteen years after Harvey died. The word "semen" means seed, and one model of human reproduction had a man planting his seed in a fertile woman, as he might plant a wheat seed in a field. The idea was that the seed then grew into a child, but children often resemble the mother as well. That was explained by saying the mother's nurture had somehow imprinted on the offspring.

Some people thought the sperm cells were parasites, after it was reported in 1699 that each sperm cell contained a *homunculus* (literally "a little human"). Almost fifty years later, this was revealed as a hoax, but until that revelation, many philosophers made grave announcements based on the claim.

So, in the 1700s, the problem was identifying the roles of the alleged egg and the alleged small animals found in semen, which is made up of swimming sperm cells and fluid. In the end, some time in the 1770s, Lazzaro Spallanzani (1729–1799) took semen and eggs from frogs, and showed that without the semen, tadpoles would not develop. He then filtered dog semen and used what we would now call artificial insemination methods to show that when sperm were absent, no young were produced.

There was just one catch: Spallanzani dismissed the sperm as parasites, *and* concluded that while semen was needed, the filter had removed both the parasites and whatever was needed to fertilize the egg.

Meanwhile, the botanists had joined the hunt. In 1694, Rudolf Camerarius (1665–1721) published details of some experiments where he had removed the male organs of plants, preventing seeds from forming, but when he dusted the pistils (the female parts) with pollen, seeds formed.

Things proceeded slowly in the 1700s, though Joseph Koelreuter (1733–1806) hybridized two species of *Nicotiana* (relatives of tobacco) by cross-pollination between 1760 and 1766, and showed that the offspring had traits of both parents.

Then, in 1797, a quiet German called Konrad Sprengel, dismissed from his post as rector of Spandau for neglecting his church duties to do research, wrote a book on sex in plants. He detailed how some flowers cannot self-fertilize because the male and female parts mature at different times. He was mostly ignored until Charles Darwin used Sprengel's work on the mutual interdependence of insect and flower as a powerful argument that evolution is driven by natural selection.

Sex was officially on the biology agenda.

INVENTING THE MICROSCOPE

How we developed the art of seeing very small things

Like the telescope, the microscope's origins are hidden. It was invented in the Netherlands, around 1590, probably by Zacharias Janssen (c. 1580–1638), although he may have inherited the idea from his father. Hans Lippershey, who claimed credit for the telescope, might also have invented the microscope, although Janssen and his brother claimed later that Lippershey stole their father's design.

These early microscopes were more than a magnifying glass, because they contained several lenses, but they were little better than magnifying glasses, and it took about seventy-five years for designs to improve to the point where they made the invisible become visible.

As we move our eye closer to something, the image on our retina becomes larger, until eventually the image blurs. A microscope brings our eye incredibly close to an object, while keeping the object in sharp focus. When you look into the eyepiece of a modern microscope, it is as though your eye is level with the bottom of the objective lens, hovering just above the slide on the microscope stage.

Each lens has to form a clear image for the next lens to operate on, and each lens has to be perfect. By 1665, the methods for grinding lenses and combining them allowed Robert Hooke to look closely at a range of small things, and then draw them for engraving and printing. The most popular were a flea and a louse (reflecting the state of hygiene in those days), but he also showed vinegar worms, the edge of a razor, the point of a needle, the stinging hairs on a nettle, and something, seen in a slice of cork, which he called "cells." This was the first time that cells had been observed.

... there were usually about three-score of these small Cells placed end-ways in the eighteenth part of an inch in length, whence I concluded that there must be near eleven hundred of them, or more than a thousand of them in length of an inch and therefore in a square inch above a Million, or 1,166,400, and in a Cubick Inch, above twelve hundred Millions, or 1,259,712,000, a thing most incredible, did not our Microscope assure us of it by ocular demonstration.

Hooke published *Micrographia* in 1665, complete with large fold-out sections. Copies were sold to many places beyond London; considering the fire which destroyed large parts of London the next year, this was a good thing. It was even more of a good thing because a Dutch draper, variously called Anton or Antonie van Leeuwenhoek, saw a copy and, you might say, was hooked.

Date: 1665.

Location: London, England.

Discovery: With the aid of a microscope, very small objects can be observed and drawn.

Discoverer: Robert Hooke (1635–1703).

Impact: While most people lacked the money and skill to own and use a microscope, Hooke's *Micrographia* let everybody see what tiny things really look like.

Some of the early microscopes were remarkably powerful despite being relatively simple. This is the instrument that Robert Hooke used.

Van Leeuwenhoek made microscopes with single but very powerful lenses. One surviving lens has a magnification of x275, but some may have delivered as much as x500. With these, he examined all sorts of things, from human spermatozoa (he emphasized that he obtained his sample blamelessly as "residue from conjugal coitus"), and even bacteria. He wrote his accounts in Dutch and sent them to the Royal Society in London, where all 190 of them were translated into English and published.

Van Leeuwenhoek did not grind his lenses. He made them by heating glass and drawing it out into a fine thread, breaking it and melting one end to make a small globule. This may sound easy enough, but it is almost impossible in the flame of a Bunsen burner. Readers wishing to try this might have more success with a spirit burner.

The amazing thing is that people took so long to link van Leeuwenhoek's tiny animalcules to disease. Then again, perhaps some people did make the link: around the time of Hooke's *Micrographia* and the Great Fire of London, London was also suffering from plague.

In 1722, Daniel Defoe, better known for writing *Robinson Crusoe*, produced *A Journal of the Plague Year*, which was probably based on the diaries of his uncle, Henry Foe, who had witnessed the plague. In this work Defoe makes an odd comment which only makes sense if you think "germs":

[I am amazed to find that some people] ... talk of infection being carried on by the air only, by carrying with it vast numbers of insects and invisible creatures, who enter into the body with the breath, or even at the pores with the air, and there generate or emit most acute poisons, or poisonous ovae or eggs, which mingle themselves with the blood, and so infect the body ...

Later developments included adopting the newly-invented organic dyes (59) which were effective stains for certain types of cells or parts of cells, making them show up more clearly. The development of achromatic lenses counted for even more. These were designed to avoid *chromatic aberrations*, where fringes of the colors of the spectrum blur the image. Then there were oil immersion lenses, where a drop of oil links the objective lens to the microscope slide, allowing magnifications of x1000.

At that magnification, however, we begin to lose resolution. Because light behaves like a wave, there is a limit, and in simple terms we are unable to see as separate any two points (the technical expression is "resolve any two points") which are less than a wavelength apart. Jumping way ahead of our leisurely stroll through time, things improved in the 1930s. Once quantum theory revealed that electrons could be regarded in some ways as waves with *very* short wavelengths, people were able to make electron microscopes of amazing resolution.

But that's a later story.

EXPLAINING GRAVITY

What Isaac Newton really thought when (if) he saw the apple fall

Nobody knows if Isaac Newton ever saw that apple fall. If he did, his key thought was probably not "Hmmm—things fall to the ground!" People had known and talked about things falling for more than 2,000 years. French poet Paul Valéry, however, knew how Newton was different:

One had to be a Newton to notice that the Moon is falling, when everyone sees that it doesn't fall.

The apple story was made popular by Voltaire. William Stukeley, Newton's biographer and friend, claimed Newton told him the story, so maybe the apple fell, and made Newton wonder why it should be so. What counted was that Newton wondered why an apple fell from a tree when the Moon did not fall from the sky. Then he realized the Moon was falling in such a way as to keep its position!

During the summer of 1665, plague reached Cambridge from London, and the university was closed. Newton took refuge in nearby Lincolnshire until April 1667, with one short trip back to Cambridge in 1666. This gave him a long period for thought and calculation, and many or all of his later great ideas seem to have developed then.

He explained the Moon problem later by asking readers to imagine a cannon on a high mountain that fires a cannonball very fast. As the ball flies away, it drops, but as it drops, the ground falls away below it, because the Earth is a sphere. If the ball went fast enough, he said, it would never reach the ground, but keep going until it ran into the back of the cannon. This was an early thought-experiment, and it left out things like air resistance on the ball and the impossibility of launching a cannonball at such great speed. But it didn't matter, because people caught his drift.

Another way of looking at it is to imagine whirling a stone around on a string. We feel a pull on the string but the important thing is that the stone is also pulled, by a force that keeps it moving in a circle. Whenever it was that he came to this problem, Newton applied some of Kepler's ideas and some of his own to find an answer.

By 1666, he more or less understood the way forces are involved in movement. In particular, he had worked out his first law of motion:

1: Every body continues in its state of rest, or of uniform motion in a right [straight] line, unless it is compelled to change that state by forces impressed upon it …

Date: 1666.

Location: England.

Discovery: A theory that explained gravitation.

Discoverer: Isaac Newton (later Sir Isaac Newton) (1643–1727).

Impact: Like taking the cover off a clock, this revealed the inner workings of the universe.

So a force was acting on the Moon. Kepler had shown that orbiting bodies move in ellipses. This was all Newton needed to work out that the force of gravity varied with distance according to an inverse square law. If you double your distance from the center of the Earth, the tug of gravity will be just a quarter ($1/distance^2$) of what it originally was. The trick is to remember that you are almost 4,000 miles away from the center of the planet when you stand on the ground at sea level.

An eighteenth century portrait of Sir Isaac Newton, by Sir Godfrey Kneller.

In mathematical terms, the force F between two masses, m_1 and m_2, is proportional to the product of the masses, divided by the square of their distance R: $F \propto m_1 m_2 / R^2$.

That might have been enough for most people, but Newton had two more laws of motion up his sleeve, along with a neat corollary:

2: The change of motion is proportional to the motive force impressed; and is made in the direction of the right [straight] line in which the force is impressed ...

3: To every action there is always opposed an equal reaction; or, the mutual actions of two bodies upon each other are always equal, and directed to contrary parts ...

Corollary: A body, acted upon by two forces simultaneously, will describe the diagonal of a parallelogram in the same time as it would describe the sides by those forces separately ...

Between them, the laws of motion, the law of gravitation and the corollary gave people all they needed to fire cannonballs or rockets at each other, to launch satellites and space craft to other planets, and to build bridges and buildings that would stand up. This would have been enough for most people, but Newton went on and on—he is the subject of the next two stories.

Aside from the work described there, Newton was a member of parliament, and he invented the reflecting telescope. He feuded with all sorts of people (including Leibniz, Hooke, Flamsteed, and Stephen Gray); he dabbled in alchemy; he was first Warden and then Master of the Royal Mint; and President of the Royal Society for twenty-four years (which helped him in his feuds).

Now, about Newton's dates: you can pretty well take your pick. He was born in 1642 by the old Julian calendar (on Christmas Day), which is January 4, 1643 on the Gregorian calendar that we now use—although it was introduced into England only in 1752. The date of death on Newton's tombstone is given as 1726, because in those days, New Year's Day was March 25. So his death on March 20 in what we call 1727 was recorded as a date in 1726, and his January 4 birthday was in 1642! By the Gregorian calendar, he died on March 30, which was 1727 anyhow.

Whatever dates you take, Newton's life was a glorious time for science.

INVENTING THE CALCULUS

How mathematicians learned to calculate about things that are always changing

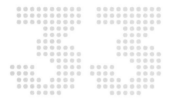

Date: Somewhere between 1666 and 1684.

Location: London or Cambridge or Lincolnshire, England; or perhaps Hanover (Germany), or France.

Discovery: A mathematical way of dealing with rates of change as presented in complex equations.

Discoverer: Either Isaac Newton (1643–1727), Gottfried Wilhelm Leibniz (1646–1716), or, most probably, both of them, independently.

Impact: The calculus made it easy to solve a wide range of mathematical problems, providing exact answers where no answer at all seemed possible.

Imagine a ball, thrown into the air, just as it reaches the highest point. One moment it is going up, the next moment it is coming down. If you take smaller and smaller fractions of time, there must be a point where it is neither going up nor coming down. Yet if you measure accurately enough, there is no such moment; all the time the ball is rising and falling, its speed is changing. So, how can we ever calculate how fast it is going, or how long it will take to get from A to B?

Infinitely small things worried the Greek philosophers, which is why they invented atoms, just to do away with the notion of particles that could be cut in half, again and again, forever. There had to be a limit, they said. Newton solved the problem by looking at limits.

The Greeks toyed with the paradox known as *Achilles and the tortoise*. Achilles runs ten times as fast as the tortoise, but gives the tortoise a 10 yard lead. The race begins, and Achilles sprints 10 yards, but does not catch the tortoise, which has traveled another yard, and when Achilles travels that, the tortoise has gone a tenth of a yard, and so on. So Achilles can never catch the tortoise, argued the Greeks.

In real life, they knew the tortoise was toast. A few of them might even have felt that the tortoise would be passed at 11.111111 … yards. Then again, they had no system of mathematics to deal with this kind of scenario, so maybe they didn't. The realm of fairytale mathematics, and treacherous tiny segments of time, attracted the interest of scientists in the seventeenth century. They felt compelled to deal with these ideas.

At the end of the 1600s, Newton claimed that he, rather than Wilhelm Leibniz, had invented the calculus as a way of dealing with the pesky curves that pop up in life. He swore he started work on it in 1666, and that Leibniz saw a manuscript of his in 1676 that might have given him a start. Newton certainly had no trouble working out in 1680 that if gravity obeyed an inverse square law, orbiting planets would describe ellipses.

Leibniz started work on calculus in 1674, and published his first paper on it in 1684, while Newton did not publish his version until 1693. With no clear evidence, it seems fair to assume that the two geniuses had the same idea independently, because the time for calculus had arrived.

They say Leibniz taught himself Latin when he was eight, and by fourteen, he could read Greek as well. We may as well believe this as not:

Find the derivative

$\text{slope}(S) = \dfrac{y_1 - y_0}{x_1 - x_0} = \dfrac{g(x+h) - g(x)}{(x+h) - x} = \dfrac{g(x+h) - g(x)}{h}$

$f'(x) = \lim_{h \to 0} \dfrac{f(x+h) - f(x)}{h}$

$f'(x) = \lim_{h \to 0} \dfrac{(x+h)^2 - x^2}{h}$

$= \lim_{h \to 0} \dfrac{x^2 + 2xh + h^2 - x^2}{h}$

$= \lim_{h \to 0} \dfrac{2xh + h^2}{h}$

$= \lim_{h \to 0} \dfrac{h(2x + h)}{h}$

$= \lim_{h \to 0} (2x + h)$

$\text{Slope}(T) = \lim_{h \to 0} \dfrac{g(x+h) - g(x)}{h}$

$\dfrac{df}{dx}$

$\dfrac{d}{dx}(x^n) = nx^{n-1}$

$= \lim_{h \to 0} \dfrac{\sqrt{x+h} - \sqrt{x}}{h}$

$= \lim_{h \to 0} \dfrac{x + h - x}{h(\sqrt{x+h} + \sqrt{x})}$

$= \lim_{h \to 0} \dfrac{h}{h(\sqrt{x+h} + \sqrt{x})}$

$= \lim_{h \to 0} \dfrac{1}{\sqrt{x+h} + \sqrt{x}}$

$= \dfrac{1}{2\sqrt{x}}$

$f'(x) = \lim_{\Delta x \to 0} \dfrac{f(x + \Delta x)}{\Delta x}$

$f'(a) = \lim_{h \to 0} \dfrac{f(a + h)}{}$

$f'(a) = \lim_{h \to a} \dfrac{f(x) - f(a)}{}$

$(x, f(x))$ $y = g(x)$ Secant Lines $(x, g(x))$ Tangent Line x $x+h$

these legends of precocity in the scientific greats are as tenacious as any urban myth. It matters little: what really counts is what he did later on.

The son of a professor of moral philosophy, his interest was more in the mathematical side of philosophy. In his lifetime, Leibniz introduced the use of the dot to indicate multiplication, popularized the decimal point, the equals sign, the colon for division and ratio, and the use of numerical superscripts for exponents (x^2 and x^3) in algebra. The elongated sigma for summation in calculus, and the way we use the letter "d" in differential calculus (as in dy/dx) are his also.

And whatever else Newton did, he never designed a calculating machine as Leibniz did. Only Blaise Pascal had done so before him, and Charles Babbage did so later. Yet while others followed Leibniz, his design was used in building the first totalizator (also called a tote or pari-mutuel—a machine used to manage betting on horse races), because it could multiply and divide.

Leibniz wanted to influence society. He hoped to create a united Europe, before even Germany was united, and long before anybody dreamed of the European Union. In the end, he was librarian to the court of Hanover, although when the Elector of Hanover went off from there to England to take up his new throne as King George I in 1714, Leibniz was left in Germany, presumably because of his disputes with Newton.

The complex equations of calculus make it relatively simple for mathematicians to solve problems.

Whatever the reason, he remained in Hanover, and died a couple of years later. But his inspirational influence extended beyond the grave: he left behind a "sleeper" in the form of a letter written to the French Academy of Sciences in 1701, in which he outlined the binary system used by all modern computers.

I enclose an attempt to devise a numerical system that may prove to be entirely new. Briefly, here is what it is ... By using a binary system based on the number 2 instead of the decimal system based on the number 10, I am able to write all of the numbers in terms of 0 and 1. I have done this not for mere practical reasons, but rather to allow new discoveries to be made ... This system can lead to new information that would be difficult to obtain in any other way ...

How right he was—but it is time to look at one of Newton's other amazing discoveries, the spectrum of colors hidden within ordinary white light.

DISCOVERING THE COLOR SPECTRUM

How we came to understand the way color lurks in white light

Date: Between 1666 and 1672 (probably closer to 1672).

Location: Southern England, probably Cambridge.

Discovery: How white light was divided into a number of colors by a glass prism.

Discoverer: Isaac Newton (1643–1727).

Impact: This led to our understanding the electromagnetic spectrum and the nature of light.

In 1672, Isaac Newton told how he had studied the "celebrated phenomenon of colors." He was not the first to see white light enter a prism and emerge as colors on the other side, but he was the first to explain why it happened. At the time, most people assumed that color was a mix of light and dark—that the prism somehow added the color. Robert Hooke was one of the strongest supporters of this view.

With two neat experiments, Newton demolished Hooke's ideas, and began one of the great feuds of science. In one experiment, he used a second prism to pull the colors back together again, and showed that the result was white light. In the other, he used a second prism and a slit to show that when a band of colored light passed into the second prism, it was passed on unchanged. Hooke's theory was in tatters, and Newton had an enemy for life. He published nothing else on optics until after Hooke died in 1703.

Poor Newton—he simply could not help bursting out with the truth, even though it got up people's noses! Novelist Aldous Huxley assessed him like this:

If we evolved a race of Isaac Newtons, that would not be progress. For the price Newton had to pay for being a supreme intellect was that he was incapable of friendship, love, fatherhood, and many other desirable things. As a man he was a failure; as a monster he was superb.

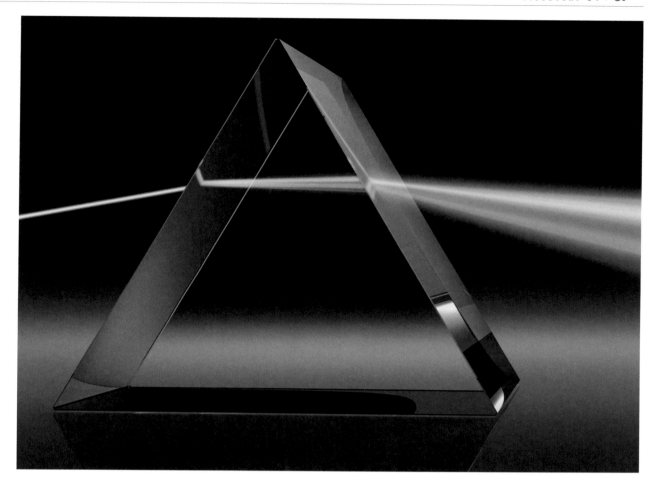

The Newton experiment is often shown with a triangular prism sitting on its base, with light coming from below, bending as it passes through the apex and being directed down on the other side. He actually used sunlight shining down through a window, and being bent through the apex of an upside-down prism to shine upwards onto a wall, about 20 feet away. The room must have been darkened in some way, with just one beam of light entering it and throwing a pale spectrum onto the wall, red at the bottom, violet at the top.

Newton gave the colors the name "spectrum," a Latin word meaning specter or apparition. The actual colors were by no means new—they were just the colors of the rainbow. But how many of those were there? Aristotle said three; others saw four to match the four Greek elements; Roger Bacon chose five, because there were five "bodies" in the eye— three humors and two coatings. There were others who also favored three, seeing links with the Holy Trinity. In the early 1300s, however, a clever Dominican friar called Theodoric of Freiberg dismissed the Trinity argument. After all, he said, men do not have three teeth or three eyes!

The vivid colors of the spectrum are reflected in many aspects of nature. Think of rainbows, and sunlight glinting on a dewdrop.

In fact, the spectrum contains an infinite number of colors, and the number we "see" is subjective. Newton took the number Ptolemy had favored—seven—and gave them the names we use today: red, orange, yellow, green, blue, indigo, and violet.

Newton said he could not separate out any further colors from any narrow band of light selected from the spectrum. But his experimental setup would not have given monochromatic light in any selected band, because the rays from the Sun are not completely parallel. He should have been able to see some further separation, but perhaps he intended his "result" to be taken only as an idealized case. If not, then he fudged his experiment.

Newton stated correctly that different colors are refracted (bent) through different angles, both in prisms and in lenses. If an astronomer focuses a telescope on the green light from a star, the colors on either side will be fuzzy. We call it "chromatic aberration," and we can now make lens combinations that correct for this, but Newton thought it would be impossible and designed a new kind of telescope using reflecting mirrors. All modern large telescopes are based on this design.

Visible light is just a small part of a much larger electromagnetic spectrum, but this took time to find. We will visit some parts of it later, but the names infrared and ultraviolet are worthy of note: infrared means "below red," and ultraviolet means "above violet," referring to the positions in which Newton would have seen his first spectrum on the wall, with violet at the top (the most refracted), and red at the bottom. But how do you "see" something that cannot be seen?

Around 1800, an astronomer named Sir William Herschel was measuring the temperatures associated with different colors. He had been using filters to view the Sun, but found that some filters let more heat through than others did. This led him to wonder if different colors had different amounts of heat.

Sampling along the spectrum from violet to red, he found the temperature rising, so he tested just beyond the visible range, measured an even higher temperature, and named the radiation "calorific rays." He then showed that the rays behaved like visible light—that they were reflected, refracted and transmitted like light—the same tests Heinrich Hertz (76) later applied to his radio waves.

A year after that, Johann Ritter tested the other end of the spectrum, using silver chloride to detect radiation beyond violet. Photographers would later make use of the way light makes silver chloride go black, but Ritter tested the spectrum with it, and found that there was a band of radiation, even better at blackening the silver chloride, which we now call ultraviolet.

I think Newton would have enjoyed that.

DISCOVERING THE LAW OF SUPERPOSITION

How we first became aware of the way rocks are laid down and formed

Niels Stensen (Nicolas Steno) was a Dane who left home in 1660 to study medicine at Leyden in the Netherlands, also spending some time in Paris and Montpelier before moving to Florence in 1665. He became fascinated with anatomy, and gained the attention of the Grand Duke of Tuscany, Ferdinand II, who liked to encourage both scientists and the sciences.

Steno had discovered the pores of the skin that sweat passes through, and he was becoming interested in the way muscles contract. The Duke gave him a hospital post that left Steno time to carry out his research, and he was also elected to the Accademia del Cimento (Experimental Academy), a body inspired by Galileo's approach to experimentation.

In 1666, two fishermen caught a large shark off Livorno (Leghorn), and Duke Ferdinand had the shark's head sent to Steno. He dissected it, drew it, and published his findings. It was a straightforward anatomical drawing, but if it was a Great White Shark (as some say), then the drawing was rather less than accurate. In fairness to Steno, the head was in poor condition by the time he received it.

Steno noticed that the teeth of the shark resembled unusual stones called *glossopetrae* which came from the island of Malta. Pliny the Elder believed these had fallen from the sky during lunar eclipses. Others said they were the tongues of serpents turned to stone by Saint Paul when he was shipwrecked on Malta in AD 59, thus providing the origin of their name, which literally means "tongue stone."

Steno identified the tongue stones as shark teeth, which was a reasonable thing for an anatomist to do. His next step was to wonder how the tongue stones got to where they were found, deep inside rocks, especially if the world was only a few thousand years old, as most people then believed. We will return to the age of the Earth later, but it is possible Steno realized he was on dangerous ground here—as a Protestant in a Catholic country—not long after the religion-based Thirty Years' War.

Like Galileo (24), he wanted to challenge orthodox thinking. He wanted to argue that the shark teeth had been solid in the first place (rather than being gifts from the heavens, or tongues of snakes), because when they were found, the surrounding rock showed an impression of the teeth. He also wanted to argue that if marine fossils like shark teeth are found high on mountains, those mountains must once have been under the sea.

Whatever his motivation, Steno converted to Catholicism in 1667 and two years later published what is usually called "his *Prodromus*," in

Date: 1669.

Location: Firenze (Florence), Italy.

Discovery: Rocks are generally laid down in horizontal layers, with the oldest rocks on the bottom, and the youngest on top.

Discoverer: Nicolas Steno (Niels Stensen) (1638–1686).

Impact: This was an essential step before anybody tried to work out a geological history of the world.

The 3,000 foot escarpment of the Vermilion Cliffs in Arizona, USA, reveals seven major geologic formations in layer-cake fashion.

which he put forward his ideas. A prodromus is an introduction, a prologue, but he never went further. In 1675, he was ordained as a priest; in 1677, he was appointed a bishop, and left geology behind.

In England, Robert Hooke and botanist John Ray had also said fossils were the remnants of living organisms. As a bishop, Steno was well placed to act behind the scenes to make this sort of challenging science more acceptable in a changing Church, but his major visible contribution to science came in the *Prodomus* when he spelled out a set of basic principles of geology which spread fast, even before he was ordained: by 1671, there was an English translation available.

This translation is less than helpful, because it was entangled in some of Steno's thinking which was valid at the time, but is far from valid today. Here is a modern version that conveys two laws and two principles that Steno left for us.

The Law of Superposition: in a sequence of strata, any stratum is younger than the sequence of strata on which it rests, and is older than the strata that rest upon it.

The Law of Original Horizontality: strata are deposited horizontally and then deformed to various attitudes later. That is, undisturbed true bedding planes are nearly horizontal, though we need to note here that cross-bedding is possible where sandhills or sandbanks are being formed.

The Principle of Lateral Continuity: strata initially extend sideways in all directions. That is, every outcrop in which the edges of strata are exposed demands an explanation, and strata on two sides of a valley represent erosion of the rock between.

The Principle of Cross-cutting Relationships: *anything that cuts across layers probably post-dates them. This applies particularly to igneous intrusions such as dykes.*

Steno also noted that there are two major rock types in the Apennine Ranges near Florence. The lower rocks have no fossils, while the upper layer is rich in fossils. In keeping with the thinking of his day, he took the lower layer to be rock laid down before the creation of life, while explaining the fossils in the upper layer as relics of Noah's flood. He was wrong, of course, but for the first time somebody had tried to point to geological evidence of different periods of the Earth's history. It was a good start. It would be a while before we understood fossils (44), but now people recognized what they meant.

DISCOVERING STEAM POWER

How we found an energy source that could be used anywhere

When water is boiled to make steam, it keeps the same temperature as it expands to 1,517 times the volume occupied by water at that temperature. When the steam condenses back to water, it leaves an almost perfect (99.93 percent) vacuum. In modern steam engines, the power comes from the *push* of steam under pressure, but Thomas Savery thought the *pull* of the vacuum (that is, the *push* of the atmosphere against the vacuum) was more effective. In early steam engines, the real work was done by atmospheric pressure pushing against the vacuum left by the condensed steam, so we call the early engines atmospheric engines.

Savery's patent was for "Raising Water By Fire," because nobody had any idea of the power of steam. There is a popular legend that James Watt was the first to see this power while watching a kettle boil, but he would have been about eighty years too late—or 1,700 years too late, if you count some inventions of Hero of Alexandria, who had used steam in the first century AD.

The truth is even more satisfying.

Savery collaborated with Thomas Newcomen to make steam engines that worked. The cylinders would be filled with steam at local atmospheric pressure, then the steam was made to condense, creating a vacuum. The air pressure then pushed the piston down, doing work on whatever the piston was attached to.

Date: 1698.

Location: London, England.

Discovery: A steam-powered pump.

Discoverer: Thomas Savery (c. 1650–1715), James Watt (1736–1819) and others.

Impact: It was slow, but in time, the water wheel, animal power, wind power, and human power would become less important in factories, in sea and land transport, and in farming. The world would go faster, and distant places would be more closely linked.

Some of the Newcomen engines pumped water out of mines, some raised water to the higher floors in grand London houses—but they were all inefficient. The engine required several times as much steam as was needed to fill the cylinder, because most of the steam condensed as it entered the cool cylinder.

Clearly, then, Watt did not invent steam power: he invented *efficient* steam power and, most importantly, he did so after repairing a model of Newcomen's engine.

In the Newcomen engine, steam pressure pushed a piston up to the neutral position, raising one side of a pivoted beam. At the same time, the pump shaft on the other side of the beam went down. Then cold water was sprayed into the cylinder under the piston, condensing the steam, and making a near-vacuum in the cylinder. Air pressure pushed the piston down from the outside, and this moved the beam, which in turn raised the pump shaft on the other side of the beam, moving water out of the mine.

In other words, the so-called atmospheric engines had a power stroke that saw the piston being pushed down into the cylinder, but modern engines have a power stroke that pushes the piston out. The atmospheric method offered a slow, cumbersome and inefficient engine. Then again, if there were riches to be won from a mine, and the mine had water in it, even the cumbersome was worth trying.

Efficiency mattered only a little bit when the Newcomen engines were pumping out coal mines because there was plenty of coal to be had, right there in the mine. If you were using one of Cornwall's 600 steam engines to pump out a tin mine, the efficiency of coal use was very important indeed, because the nearest coal was a long way off—but we are getting ahead of our story.

Many years later, Watt told the story of a walk he took one May Sunday in 1765, and how he solved the problem.

The idea came into my mind, that as steam was an elastic body it would rush into a vacuum, and if a communication was made between the cylinder and an exhausted vessel, it would rush into it, and might be there condensed without cooling the cylinder.

Steam would rush from the cylinder into a separate condenser, cool to water and leave space for more steam, and so on, while the cylinder stayed hot. As a good Scottish Sabbath-observer, Watt could think quietly about the problem as he walked, but it would never have done for him to work on it on a Sunday, so his first model was made the following day. This timetable may well be the origin of the kettle yarn in which he watched the kettle one evening, and built a steam engine the very next day.

Watt had help from Matthew Boulton, a businessman who saw the problem clearly. As early as 1776, Boulton told a visitor, "I sell here, sir,

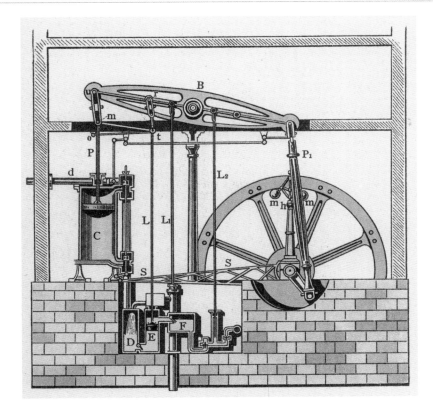

This diagram from around 1765 clearly demonstrates the workings of James Watt's steam engine.

what all the world desires—power." He also had help from John Wilkinson, an ironmaster who bored the accurate cylinders Watt needed. Wilkinson also installed a Watt engine in 1776 as a blowing machine, the first time a steam engine had been used for anything except pumping water.

But if Boulton sold power, Watt sold efficiency and reliability. He invented another new device, the centrifugal governor you can see on most of the steam engines still running today. This was Watt's greatest invention, though he also invented the "horsepower," now replaced in most parts of the world by the watt as a unit of work done.

The horsepower gave practical engineers a way to talk about work done, and a way to think about energy, but the governor was far more important. Two heavy balls hung from a vertical shaft which was turned by the engine. As the shaft rotated faster, the balls moved away from the shaft, moving a set of levers that reduced the steam supply. If the engine slowed for any reason, the balls dropped and the steam valve was opened. In each case, the speed would be maintained.

Watt had come up with the idea of feedback, which led to cybernetics, and so to one branch of modern computing—and all this more than 200 years ago!

INVENTING THE TELEGRAPH

How we learned to send messages over long distances

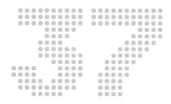

Date: 1729.

Location: Charterhouse, London, England.

Discovery: An electric charge can travel and be used to convey a message.

Discoverer: Stephen Gray (1666–1736).

Impact: By the 1870s, telegraphs linked and changed the world.

Science can happen anywhere, but an alms house in London—a refuge for "merchants decayed by piracy or shipwreck," distressed gentlemen, old soldiers, and former royal servants—is an odd setting for a scientific discovery. Yet that is where Stephen Gray had found a home, and it was in the former Carthusian monastery that he sent an electrostatic signal along 293 feet of "packing string." It was a step, but ahead of its time, and not really in the right direction.

Gray had no source of current such as a cell, no real understanding of insulators and conductors, and no scheme like Morse code to facilitate the sending of complex messages. There was also no such thing as an electrical relay—but we will come to that later.

Until the 1800s, telegraphs were semaphores, using levers on a tower to make signals to another tower which could repeat the signals and so on. In the early 1800s, Napoleon's France had semaphore towers around the coastline, and England's main ports were linked to the Admiralty in London, allowing signals to be sent by day in clear weather. A few of the towers are left in Brittany in France, and places called "Telegraph Hill" are still dotted around England, the USA, Australia and New Zealand.

In other places, lights, flags and bells could be used to send pre-arranged messages. As early as 1775, Paul Revere's colleagues used a prearranged "one, if by land, and two, if by sea" lamp signal to indicate which way British troops were moving on Lexington. Well into the nineteenth century, flags and lights were used to signal the arrival of mail, ships and trains to the townspeople.

In 1746, the Abbé Nollet led a Carthusian monastery, part of the same order that once owned London's Charterhouse. Nollet wanted to find out if an electric charge traveled instantaneously, so he arranged a 1 mile circle of monks, each pair linked by long iron rods. He then connected the two end monks to a charged Leyden jar, a primitive but effective capacitor or charge storage device.

When the circuit was closed, the monks all shrieked and dropped their iron rods at the same time. Nollet had proven that, given a less than infinite number of monks, you could send the works of Shakespeare around the world. It would be slow and might have trouble crossing open water, but these were mere details: the potential was there. Others were also experimenting: a Dr. Watson sent an electrical signal across the Thames in 1747; Joseph Bozolus suggested in 1767 that an alphabetic code could be worked out; but this was all theory.

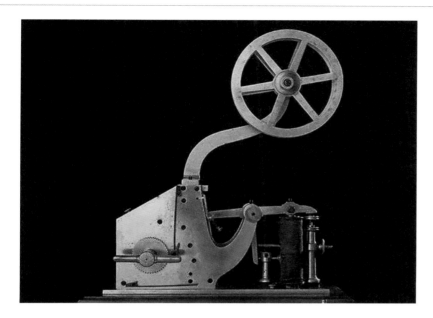

A telegraph key with a paper tape loop at the top.

Claude Chappé, inventor of a semaphore system (and also the person who invented the word "telegraph"), experimented with an unusual electrical system in 1790. Imagine that you have two clockwork dials, each with a single hand that points in turn to the numerals 0 to 9. Provided these turn in unison, if I ring a bell when my dial points to 3, you can read a 3 off your dial as well. Unfortunately, by the time you hear my bell from 300 yards away, a second has elapsed, and your dial probably says 4 or 5, not the 3 that I intended you to read. An electric signal is effectively instantaneous and might get around that, and this was what Chappé explored.

After the invention of the electric cell, it was inevitable that people would start thinking about sending signals by wire, but the big challenge was to find a way of encoding a signal. Having done that, the next challenge was to get the signal to travel any significant distance. Joseph Henry in America and Edward Davy in England each developed the electrical relay, an electromagnet that closed a switch and sent a fresh signal on the next stage of the line.

This was the secret to long-distance signaling, and the telegraph began in Britain with the Wheatstone and Cooke system of 1837, where two of five needles switched from their neutral up–down positions to point to one of twenty letters (C, J, Q, U, X and Z were all left off the display). In America, the Morse system of 1835 was developed at about the same time, using combinations of short and long signals to stand for the letters of the alphabet.

Originally, a small machine was supposed to copy the Morse messages onto paper strips for later decoding, but before long, experienced operators found they could understand the patterns of clicks as the writing device moved up and down. By the late 1850s, operators were expected to be able to receive "on the click." An expert could send or receive 2,000 words an hour, and entrepreneurs could start thinking about laying communications cables under the sea, wrapped in layers of gutta-percha insulation.

Chinese does not use an alphabet, but ideograms, which is one reason why the fax has been so popular in Chinese-speaking areas, even with the advance of the Internet. In the days of the telegraph, the Chinese Commercial Code was created, a set of 9,999 four-digit codes, each group of four digits indicating a single Chinese character.

It might not seem like much, compared with the Internet, but compared with a messenger on a horse (12 miles per hour), the telegraph was like greased lightning.

SHOWING THAT LIGHTNING IS ELECTRICAL

How we linked lightning to electricity and understood its power

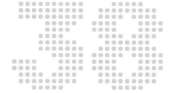

Date: 1750 or 1752.

Location: Marly, France; and Philadelphia, Pennsylvania, USA (perhaps).

Discovery: Lightning has all the same properties as static electricity.

Discoverer: Thomas-François Dalibard (1709–1799); or Benjamin Franklin (1706–1790).

Impact: Once lightning was shown to be electrical, tall buildings could be protected from it. More importantly, electricity could be seen to be more than a plaything.

In the mid-nineteenth century, electricity only existed as charges that stayed in one place—static electricity. The name "electricity" came from William Gilbert (17), the student of magnets. He based it on the term "electron," a Greek word for amber, reminding us that when you rub amber on cat fur or silk, it develops a static charge. Before synthetic fabrics and plastic shoe soles, few people could feel static charges as we now can on a dry day, so the amber sort of electricity was all people knew, and then mainly as a novelty.

We seem to like hearing trivial things about famous scientists, like Newton's apple, Einstein's habit of wearing no socks, or Franklin's flying of a kite in a thunderstorm. Perhaps it was that famous Currier and Ives print which makes us recall the famous kite. But maybe we mere mortals just like the thought of a famous scientist "playing" at kites.

We ought to be grateful to John Lining, because he asked Franklin what had made him think that lightning might be electrical. Franklin wrote in reply, quoting from his notebooks. The date of the notes was November 7, 1749.

Electrical fluid agrees with lightning in these particulars: (1) Giving light. (2) Color of the light. (3) Crooked direction. (4) Swift motion. (5) Being conducted by metals. (6) Crack or noise in exploding. (7) Subsisting in water or ice. (8) Rending bodies it passes through. (9) Destroying animals. (10) Melting metals. (11) Firing inflammable substances. (12) Sulphureous smell. The electric fluid is attracted by points. We do not know whether this

property is in lightning. But since they agree in all particulars wherein we can already compare them, is it not probable that they agree likewise in this? Let the experiment be made.

Lightning at night provides one of nature's most spectacular displays.

Franklin may not have performed the actual experiment, but his friend Thomas-François Dalibard certainly tried a version of it and survived. On the other hand, Franklin may have tried it, because he wrote a detailed description of how to perform "the Philadelphia experiment for drawing the electric fire from the clouds by means of pointed rods of iron erected on high buildings, etc.," and the description includes instructions for making a kite from strips of cedar and a silk handkerchief. That makes it sound as though he really tried it.

Still, if you are thinking of trying this, it might be safer to try making a nuclear reactor instead—the next two adventurers to try this experiment were killed! The average lightning bolt involves moving 10 coulombs across 10^8 volts, which means a million kilojoules. In extreme cases,

FAMOUS CONNECTIONS

Like Thomas Edison (43, 73), Benjamin Franklin had a son who became governor of New Jersey.

there may be 200 coulombs moving across moving across 10^9 volts in 200 microseconds, producing temperatures as high as 54,000°F. The surface of the Sun only reaches about 11,000°F!

Lightning develops in cumulonimbus clouds, which have fast currents of air traveling up inside them, often to a height of six or seven miles. When the charge in the clouds has reached a high enough voltage (called the *breakdown potential*, and usually equal to about 10,000 volts/cm or 25,000 volts/inch), a lightning flash happens. In other words, there is a serious voltage involved.

Franklin gave us the notion of positive and negative charge, those sayings about "death and taxes," and "Early to bed, early to rise …," a better stove, bifocal spectacles, and electrotherapy. He even improved the design of the rocking horse and introduced us to the term "battery" as a voltage source, although in his case, the battery was made up of primitive capacitors called Leyden jars. To top it off, he liked a good yarn and old Madeira. And as well as yarning, he corresponded, all over the place, and with all sorts of people.

Franklin was honored by the Royal Society, which awarded him its Copley Medal, and three years later elected him a fellow (a member) of the Society, unusually, without having to pay any fees. As well as being a man of science and an inventor, Franklin was also an ambassador for his young nation, a gun runner, and a publisher. Franklin found his bifocal glasses especially useful when dining in France, as he was able to focus on his food, and also on the lips of French speakers, which he found helped him to understand what they said.

Less well known is Franklin's part in founding Australia. Favoring a pointy-ended lightning conductor, the rebel American offended England's randomly batty King George III (who suffered from attacks of porphyria). George was convinced that blunt-ended lightning rods would be better, but the Royal Society agreed with Franklin. Its president, Sir John Pringle (1707–1782), aside from coining the terms "septic" and "antiseptic," told the king that "the prerogatives of the President of the Royal Society do not extend to altering the laws of Nature."

While we can see the funny side now, the whole business incensed King George, who at that time considered Joseph Banks, recently returned with Lieutenant James Cook from an exploration on board H. M. Bark *Endeavour*, to be a very fine fellow. In order to win back the King's favor, the Royal Society elected Banks their President, and from this power base Banks, a disciple of Linnaeus (39), was able to agitate even more effectively for the establishment of a colony at Botany Bay. Maybe, without Franklin's unintended shove along, Australia might never have been settled!

Scientists can never predict what effects their discoveries will have. Well, hardly ever.

INVENTING CLASSIFICATION

How we learned to name plants and animals in a systematic way

In the eighteenth and nineteenth centuries, there was a craze for collecting unusual specimens from faraway places and museums were crammed with fossils, skins, bones, and pickled and stuffed animals. At the same time, herbaria were being filled with dried plant specimens and packets of seeds, while botanical gardens were established, just to maintain the collections of new and interesting plants.

Without classification, those collections of specimens and other bits would have been as much scientific use as a flea market, but a system of classification, which included approved ways to extend the system by adding categories when necessary, changed all that. It opened the way for scientists to look at the diversity of life, and find the patterns left behind by evolution and plate tectonics. Without classification, those patterns would have been harder to spot.

Every time we identify a bird as a house sparrow, a rock sparrow, a rock pigeon or a passenger pigeon, we are doing something very natural. We are identifying the bird as part of a group of similar types, and then applying an extra word to indicate which one we mean. That sort of naming was common, even before Carolus Linnaeus, but there were no standards, and there are none for modern common names. The kairu of Pohnpei in Micronesia is the cane toad, the giant toad or the marine toad in other places, the sapo grande to Spanish speakers, and so on, but *Bufo marinus* covers all of them.

Then again, say "mountain ash," and different people may have very different ideas. An Australian would think of *Eucalyptus regnans*, the world's tallest flowering plant. A Texan would think of *Fraxinus texensis*, while other Americans might think of trees in the genus *Sorbus*. But British readers would assume you meant just one tree: the rowan, *Sorbus aucuparia*.

When Linnaeus started writing the first edition of his *Systema Naturae* ("The System of Nature") in 1735, he was still a medical student whose curriculum included compulsory studies in botany, because doctors were expected to be able to find and use medicinal herbs. By 1741, he had worked out most of the basics of his classification system, and in that year he took a chair at the University of Uppsala, where he reorganized the university's botanical garden, according to his own plans. He kept on refining the system until 1759, adding more detail and new groups across that time. By 1759, it was close to what we know and use today, though it has been expanded to include many more species since then.

Date: 1753–1759.

Location: Uppsala, Sweden.

Discovery: A system for naming and classifying living things that could expand to include new discoveries.

Discoverer: Carl von Linné (Carolus Linnaeus) (1707–1778).

Impact: Rapid storage and retrieval of information, because everybody used the same names.

Linnaeus had no intention of imposing a system that would become an international standard. That happened because people found his system so useful, and adopted it. So far, though, we have only used the lowest level, the binomial (two-name system) that classifies us as *Homo sapiens*. Here are a few examples, where you can start to see patterns in the beginnings and endings. It all sounds a bit like Latin, but when Linnaeus was working, many scholars still used Latin as a living language. Curiously, a form of Latin is *still* used today by taxonomists when they describe plants and animals, because it is a neutral, dead language.

	Human	**Chimpanzee**	**Dog**	**House sparrow**	**Garden web spider**	**Apple**	**Monterey pine**
Kingdom	Animalia	Animalia	Animalia	Animalia	Animalia	Plantae	Plantae
Phylum	Chordata	Chordata	Chordata	Chordata	Arthropoda	Magnoliophyta	Coniferophyta
Class	Mammalia	Mammalia	Mammalia	Aves	Arachnidae	Magnoliopsida	Coniferopsida
Order	Primates	Primates	Carnivora	Passeriformes	Araneae	Rosales	Coniferales
Family	Hominidae	Hominidae	Canidae	Passeridae	Araneidae	Rosaceae	Pinaceae
Genus	*Homo*	*Pan*	*Canis*	*Passer*	*Araneus*	*Malus*	*Pinus*
Species	*sapiens*	*troglodytes*	*familiaris*	*domesticus*	*diadematus*	*domestica*	*radiata*

There are other levels that are sometimes used: sub-orders, superfamilies, and more. Aside from that, there are a few catches: one botanist's Magnoliophyta may be another botanist's Angiospermae, and it is mostly a matter of opinion—fashion that leads in the end to a slow consensus. Most taxonomists, as serious classifiers are called, now believe that groupings should reflect a group's inheritance through evolution—but working out what originated where can be a problem.

There are two sub-orders of bats in the order Chiroptera: the Megachiroptera (fruit bats), and the Microchiroptera (insect-eating bats). Some zoologists think they are similar but unrelated, in which case, the sub-orders should be separate orders; it now looks as though most people who work on bats will agree with this division in the next few years, but nothing is certain. The lower down you get, the more stable things become. Names change very rarely at the species level, and it has to be within a set of international rules, and if the genus changes, the species part stays the same. That is why a Spaniard can speak to a Japanese, a German and a Pohnpeian about *Bufo marinus*, and be understood.

Linnaeus probably never anticipated that convenience, but he probably should have worked out that people would get upset when he emphasized the reproductive parts of flowers, which he used in his classification system. From a scientific point of view, it was an inspired choice, but his language was all about marriage beds and the like. It may have been poetic, but sensitive people did not approve when he wrote about it.

One rival botanist, Johann Siegesbeck, called the Linnaean sexual emphasis "loathsome harlotry." Linnaeus repaid this compliment by selecting a small and useless weed and naming it *Siegesbeckia*. Later systems used a wider range of characteristics, but around Linnaeus' time, people began, for the first time, to understand sexual reproduction.

Giving names to the germs causing disease would take longer. The first weapon against microbes, a trick called variolation, was already being used, far from the centers of science.

DISCOVERING VACCINATION

Edward Jenner took a chance observation and saved lives

The facts are simple: Jenner heard that cowpox provided immunity to smallpox. He infected James Phipps, a boy of eight years, with cowpox from a pustule on the hand of Sarah Nelmes, a milkmaid who had the disease, and some two months later, James was deliberately infected with variolous matter, part of a smallpox pustule.

People often express shock and accuse Jenner of endangering the life of a small boy, but he did no wrong. The critics who make the accusations do not understand medical practices in the late eighteenth century. While the facts are simple, the interpretation is more complex, and Jenner never used the child as a guinea pig. He was protecting James Phipps, not endangering him.

There was huge excitement when Jenner first announced his results, but nobody accused him at the time of acting unethically, because people understood what he had done. A year later, more than seventy of London's principal physicians and surgeons supported the Jenner method, and soon after, vaccination became as normal as the inoculation procedure that it replaced.

Today, we use "inoculation" and "vaccination" interchangeably. But once upon a time, the two words meant quite different things, though

Date: 1798.

Location: England.

Discovery: Being infected with harmless cowpox protected people from smallpox.

Discoverer: Edward Jenner (1749–1823).

Impact: For the first time, humanity had a chance to stop an epidemic.

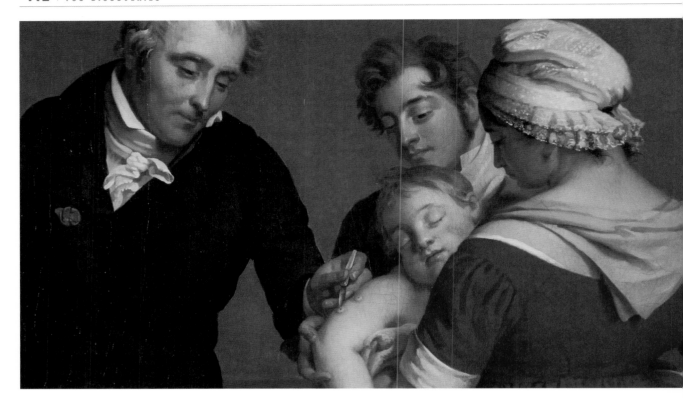

Detail of an oil painting showing Baron Jean Louis Alibert (1768–1837) performing the vaccination against smallpox in the Chateau of Liancourt, France.

both caused immunity. "Inoculation" originally described the act of grafting a plant bud, an oculus, onto a different plant. In medicine, inoculation involves grafting a disease onto a new patient. If a weakened form of the disease can be found, that's handy, but if it can't be found, at least we can choose the time to get the disease.

"Vaccination" has to do with cows. The Latin word for a cow is *vacca*, and the "vaccine disease," "vaccine pock," or *variolae vaccinae* were all names for the mild disease called cowpox by the people who suffered from it.

You could get smallpox once and once only. If you survived, you might be scarred, but you were safe from the disease forever. This is probably what gave us the idea of *variolation*. The trick may have been used first in Africa, but our first historical record comes in a letter from Adrianople in the Ottoman (Turkish) Empire, written by Lady Mary Wortley Montagu in 1717:

I am going to tell you a thing that will make you wish yourself here. The small-pox, so fatal and so general among us, is here entirely harmless, by the invention of ingrafting, which is the term they give it. There is a set of old women who make it their business to perform the operation every autumn, in the month of September, when the great heat is abated. People send to one another to know if any of their family has a mind to have the small-pox …

There is no example of any one who has died in it; and you may believe I am well satisfied of the safety of this experiment, since I intend to try it on my dear little son.

So the original treatment against smallpox was deliberately catching the disease at a time when the patients were otherwise healthy. In Boston, Cotton Mather recommended variolation before he died in 1728, and George Washington had his troops inoculated in 1776.

The death rate from variolation was far lower than from smallpox, probably because people chose "mild cases" as their source of germs. While they did not know about bacteria or viruses then, they knew about strong and weak poisons, and would naturally have chosen the weakest "poisons."

By 1790, variolation was commonplace, and the Reverend Gilbert White described variolation parties in his journal, showing that to the folk of Selborne in southern England, variolation was just part of the annual cycle, like spring gales or the strawberry crop.

A group—one of the ones he described included pregnant women, four-month-old babies, and adults who had not previously been exposed—would go into isolation. They would be given smallpox, and when the disease was finished, the survivors would emerge. A few people died, but most survived.

Perhaps we could accuse Jenner of being wrong in subjecting a young boy to the cowpox, but even *that* had been the subject of careful observation and testing. In 1798, after many other careful checks and tests, Jenner was satisfied that cowpox was safe. Note that when he says "virus," he means "poison," not the sort of virus we talk about today.

Case XVII. The more accurately to observe the progress of the infection, I selected a healthy boy, about eight years old, for the purpose of inoculation for the cowpox ... it was inserted on the fourteenth of May, 1796 .... In order to ascertain whether the boy, after feeling so slight an affection of the system from the cowpox virus, was secure from the contagion of the smallpox, he was inoculated the first of July following with variolous matter, immediately taken from a pustule ... no disease followed.

In short, James Phipps was to be variolated in any case, so Jenner treated him with liquid from a cowpox pustule. Then James was variolated, but did not develop smallpox.

Variolation was a much better risk than a genuine and unplanned attack of smallpox, but some people still died of it. Jenner realized that if suffering harmless cowpox was as effective as variolation with risky smallpox, it would be an even better treatment. Vaccination was better than inoculation.

For the first time, a killer disease was deliberately beaten in a skirmish, though the war would last another 200 years.

SOMETHING TO THINK ABOUT

Smallpox is a virus (in the modern sense), and it is now almost extinct, thanks to vaccination. Have humans the right to wipe out the last stocks of it? Some people say viruses aren't living, so there is no question. Others aren't so sure.

MEASURING THE UNIVERSAL GRAVITATIONAL CONSTANT

How one of the important physical constants was measured

- -

Date: 1798.

Location: London, England.

Discovery: The precise force of attraction between two known masses.

Discoverer: Henry Cavendish (1731–1810).

Impact: Among other things, this single experiment told us how much our planet weighed, which in turn allowed us to calculate the average density of the Earth.

- -

If you have ever fallen off anything, you will probably be surprised to learn that physicists call the force of gravity a weak force. The reality is that it takes an amazingly large lump of planet to pull the way that terrestrial gravity does. A golf ball, a horse or an ocean liner also exert forces of attraction on you and each other, but the forces are so tiny that we don't even notice them. Gravity is a weak force.

Newton (32) was able to tell us that the force can be represented by a mathematical equation that reads $F \propto m_1 m_2 / R^2$. We could also write this $F = G m_1 m_2 / R^2$, where G is a constant—but because gravity is a weak force, G is a very small number, and hard to measure.

When you start a pendulum swinging, it keeps going, either because it has a restoring force acting on it, or because it has momentum. Ignore the momentum, and concentrate on the restoring force—the force that pulls somebody on a swing down from the high point, and which slows them as they approach the next high point. By a stroke of luck for physicists, the restoring force is proportional to the distance away from the lowest point, a distance called the displacement, and that makes all the calculations easy.

A torsion pendulum is a horizontal bar, hanging from a thin wire. If you make the bar swing one way, the wire twists and tightens; after a while, the bar stops and swings back, moving past its starting point, and the wire twists and tightens again; then the bar stops and swings back to where it began, all over again. The same "restoring force" rule applies to a torsion pendulum: double the displacement, and you double the restoring force. That is the secret behind the discovery Henry Cavendish made with John Michell's apparatus.

If the bar is very heavy, it will swing very slowly, but the restoring force will always be proportional to the displacement. Now, turn that on its head: we can say just as truly that the displacement will always be proportional to the restoring force. John Michell (1724–1793) arrived at this realization before he died, and luckily, he had enough time to construct an apparatus which was later passed on to the immensely clever but slightly odd Henry Cavendish.

Cavendish made many discoveries, but he published few of them. James Clerk Maxwell later realized that Cavendish's papers included prior discoveries of many phenomena that we credit to Michael Faraday. This discovery, though, was one he *did* publish. Perhaps he thought he owed Michell that much.

The idea was simple enough: get the torsion pendulum at rest, safe from air currents, then bring a mass near each of the heavy balls hanging on a truss structure which he called a "wooden arm." Gravity is a weak force, but even weak forces have an effect, and the two weights attracted the balls, which moved, allowing Cavendish to measure the displacement as often as he liked, also recording the distances between the centers of the two balls (R in the equation). Later, the period of the pendulum gives the restoring force for a particular displacement.

Here is how Cavendish described the experiment:

The apparatus is very simple; it consists of a wooden arm, 6 feet long, made so as to unite great strength with little weight. This arm is suspended in an horizontal position, by a slender wire 40 inches long, and to each extremity is hung a leaden ball, about 2 inches in diameter; and the whole is enclosed in a narrow wooden case, to defend it from the wind.

As no more force is required to make this arm turn round on its centre than what is necessary to twist the suspending wire, it is plain, that if the wire is sufficiently slender, the most minute force, such as the attraction of a leaden weight a few inches in diameter, will be sufficient to draw the arm sensibly aside. The weights which Mr. Michell intended to use were 8 inches in diameter. One of these was to be placed on one side of the case, opposite to one of the balls, and as near as it could conveniently be done, and the other on the other side, opposite to the other ball, so that the attraction of both these weights would conspire in drawing the arm aside; and, when its position, as affected by the weights, was ascertained, the weights were to be removed to the other side of the case, so as to draw the arm the contrary way, and the position of the arm was to be again determined; and, consequently, half the difference of these positions would show how much the arm was drawn aside by the attraction of the weights.

In order to determine from hence the density of the earth, it is necessary to ascertain what force is required to draw the arm aside through a given space. This Mr. Michell intended to do, by putting the arm in motion, and observing the time of its vibrations, from which it may easily be computed.

Once you know the value of G, and the force acting on a mass at the Earth's surface, one Earth radius from its center, only the mass of the Earth remained unknown, and this could be worked out by arithmetic. From there, Cavendish calculated the density of the Earth, obtaining a value of 5.48, quite close to the presently accepted value of 5.52.

From this point, the enthusiasm for measurement in science could only increase as the eighteenth century gave way to the nineteenth.

A simple clock pendulum can keep accurate time, because the time it takes to complete its swing remains the same regardless of the angle it swings through, so long as the angle is small.

INVENTING THE ELECTRIC CELL

How a way was found to make electricity whenever and wherever it was needed

Date: 1800.

Location: Como, Italy.

Discovery: The Voltaic pile (or cell, or battery).

Discoverer: Alessandro Volta (1745–1827).

Impact: All of a sudden, scientists had a source of electricity that could be turned on and off at will. Now they could discover electrolysis, electric light, telegraphy, and more.

Sometimes, when ideas from two different directions intersect, science makes a leap ahead. This happened when static electricity and "animal electricity" became confused in scientists' minds.

Static electricity became really interesting around 1733, when Charles Du Fay (1698–1739) found he could charge sealing wax by rubbing it with cat's fur. He found that there were two kinds of electricity which repelled themselves, but attracted each other. He called the two types of electricity "vitreous electricity" and "resinous electricity." Then, in about 1747, Benjamin Franklin called the two kinds of electricity "positive" and "negative," giving us the expressions we use today.

Alessandro Volta started studying electricity in 1769, and by 1775, he had invented the electrophorus, a useful source of static electricity that could be used to charge up a Leyden jar. Then he heard about a discovery of another Italian scientist, Luigi Galvani (1737–1798).

Tradition says Galvani believed in "animal electricity," and that he thought the electricity came from muscles. Since Benjamin Franklin had shown lightning was electrical, he hoped lightning would make the muscle in a frog's leg twitch. So Galvani hung some frogs' legs out on brass hooks during a thunderstorm and saw that the legs twitched when they came in contact with a nearby iron rail.

There is just one catch: in a case like this, you need to make sure that the legs only twitch during a thunderstorm. In fact, the legs twitched every time they came in contact with the iron rail. We do know for certain that on September 20, 1786, Galvani took a fork with one copper prong and one iron prong, and touched a frog's leg with it. That twitch we know about, because it is recorded in his notebooks. He even refers there to "controlled conditions." The frogs'-legs-in-a-thunderstorm yarn, on the other hand, is probably just that—a fanciful story.

All the same, Galvani believed in animal magnetism, and given a choice between muscle and the metals as the source of the electricity, the anatomist chose the muscular source. And why shouldn't he? The electric eel had become a well-known European wonder, a living creature that produces electricity from muscle. There was a detailed report to the Royal Society on these eels in 1774, from Alexander Garden in South Carolina: in those days, the 's' looked more like an 'f.'

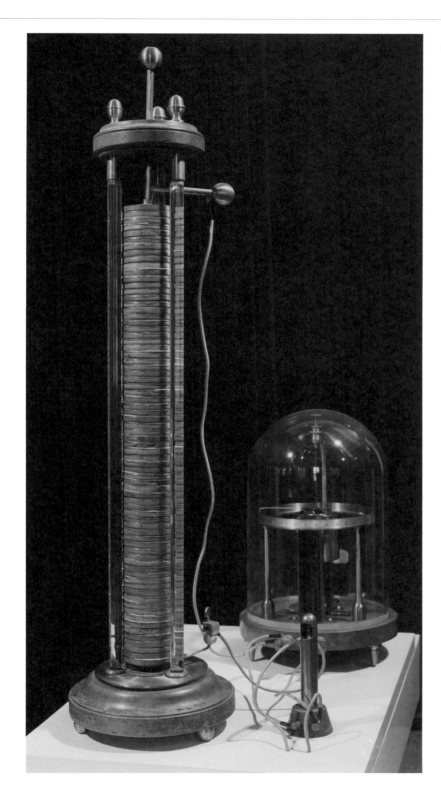

A Voltaic pile—the first electric battery.

But this fifh hath the amazing power of giving fo fudden and fo violent a fhock to any person who touches it, that there is, I think, an abfolute impoffibility of ever examining accurately a living specimen; and the perfon who owns them rates them at too high a price (not lefs than fifty guineas for the fmalleft) for me to get a dead fpecimen ... George Baker, mariner, who brought them here [from Surinam to South Carolina] intends to carry them to England ... The perfon to whom thefe animals belong, calls them electrical fifh; and indeed the power they have of giving an electrical fhock to any perfon, or to any number of perfons who join hands together ... is their moft fingular and aftonifhing property.

With animal electricity so well established as fact, small wonder Galvani believed in his theory! Poor man: within a few years, his friend and fellow countryman, Alessandro Volta, had shown that electricity came from lifeless metals, when he made his first pile. But why is it a "pile"? The answer is clearer when we read how Volta described his invention in a letter (in French) to Banks; the reference to "strata" tells us the pieces were piled up in a stack.

The apparatus to which I will allude ... is only the assemblage of a number of good conductors of different kinds arranged in a certain manner. Thirty, forty, sixty or more pieces of copper, or rather silver, applied each to a piece of tin, or zinc which is much better, and as many strata of water, or any other liquid which may be a better conductor, such as salt water, lees etc., or pieces of cardboard, skin etc., well soaked in these liquids; such strata interposed between every pair or combination of two differentials in an alternate series, and always in the same order of these three kinds of conductors, are all that is necessary for constituting my new instrument, which, as I have said, imitates the effects of the Leyden flask, or of electric batteries, by communicating the same shock as these do ...

Volta invented the "voltaic pistol," a small container of hydrogen and oxygen which could be set off by a very primitive spark plug. In about 1807, an otherwise unknown Swiss called Isaac de Rivaz used this in a way that I will explain later (65). Volta thought that with wires, the pistol might be a sort of one-shot telegraph.

Galvani's name lives on, however, in one of the most bizarre methods of corpse preservation ever, which was once called galvanoplasty. This method involved placing a corpse in a copper solution, and covering it all over with a millimeter thickness of electroplated copper. This was popular in France during the nineteenth century, but seems to have dropped out of use. These days, galvanoplasty is called electroforming, and was last heard of being used for mundane things like making the pressing masters for vinyl records. Remember them?

Then there were the other uses for electricity.

INVENTING ELECTRIC LIGHT

How a new use was found for Volta's cells

Before 1880, bright lighting depended on finding efficient oil lamps. Efficiency was important, because if you wanted a lot of light in your house, and you were burning hydrocarbons—especially large molecule hydrocarbons—you needed a big clean flame, free of smoke, and that meant getting enough oxygen into the flame.

Gas lighting started quite early in the nineteenth century, and it kept getting better. All the same, oil lamps and candles were the main sources of light. But there were other sources, too, and soon after news of the voltaic pile (42) got out, Humphry Davy started experimenting with them. In 1802, he found that if he used a high enough voltage, he could get a continuous spark to flow between two electrodes. He used 2,000 of Volta's cells and carbon electrodes to get an "arch," which later was called an "arc." Soon after, he showed it off at a meeting of the Royal Institution.

It took a while, but in 1846, the Paris Opera was lit by arcs. The power came from the more efficient Bunsen cells of Robert Bunsen (1811–1899), but the batteries still quickly lost their power. Arc lights did not really take off until about the late 1850s, with the first arc light in a lighthouse in late 1858, and more the following year. In the summer of 1859, a wagon with a steam engine, a generator (then called a dynamo), and an arc light trundled through the streets of Paris at night. It was the combination of these three elements (not necessarily on a wagon!) that made the arc light a success.

In May 1896, while many pioneers were still alive, a meeting of the National Electric Light Association was held in New York, at which listeners heard of the struggle to get multiple arc lights running from a single generator. Mr. H. L. Rogers told his audience that the US now had thousands of dynamos, each driving "125 arc lights of 2,000 candle power each." He neglected to mention the drawback: the stink of ozone. When domestic electric lighting with incandescent lamps became common in the 1890s, users who were likely to know about the ozone had to be reassured that electric light does not harm the health. A glowing filament in a sealed tube, after all, could produce nothing dangerous, people were told.

There were several problems to be dealt with, assuming an electricity supply was available. The filament had to be sealed in a glass bulb with wires running into it, and the bulb had to contain either a vacuum, or a gas that would not support combustion. Over time, the hot filaments burned out or evaporated, but that was slowly brought under control.

Date: 1802.

Location: The Royal Institution, London.

Discovery: A voltage between two electrodes can start a glowing current in the air.

Discoverer: Sir Humphry Davy (1778–1828). .

Impact: Arc light was brighter than any flame, turning night into day; but arcs were just the start.

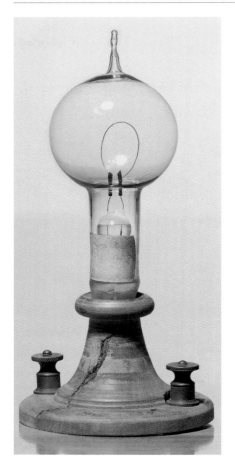

Thomas Edison's 1879 electric light bulb.

Two men, Thomas Alva Edison (1847–1931) in the USA (73), and Sir Joseph Wilson Swan (1828–1914) in England, usually share the credit for inventing the electric light bulb. More than a hundred years on, American books favor Edison as the prime inventor of the light bulb, while English sources favor Joseph Swan as the main inventor of electric light. Perhaps the best indication of the truth is that the two agreed to form the Edison-Swan Electric Company to work in Britain.

Swan certainly gave a public demonstration some eight months before Edison did, but by the time Swan got around to patenting his lamp in 1880, Edison had already lodged his patent application and secured the field—even though Swan's lamps were better, and even though Swan had both developed and demonstrated his lamps first. This was the legal context in which the Edison-Swan Electric Company was formed in order to avoid a long and messy battle.

Still, if Swan gets equal or greater credit over his light bulbs in Britain, Edison's bulbs gained the first prize at the Paris Exposition of 1881, with Swan's bulbs in second place. And it was Edison and his team who solved the practical problems, like variable loads on the grid as people switch on and off, and metering the supplies to each household.

Neither man's bulb would attract interest today, when compared with a modern tungsten-filament light bulb. Edison's bulbs were particularly low in efficiency, converting only 0.25 percent of the electrical energy to light. In fact, the incandescent light bulb continues to be an inefficient source of light, which is why it is now being targeted for elimination in favor of the more efficient fluorescent bulbs.

Even most Americans are unaware of the claims of another of their countrymen, who had light bulbs in operation at the same time the French were trundling their portable arc light through Paris. During July 1859, Professor Moses Farmer lit one room of his Salem, Massachusetts house with lamps using small pieces of platinum-iridium wire, which glowed dimly as the current from primary batteries passed through them. Batteries, however, were not the future. Electric power had to be delivered to each home, school, hall, and place of work.

The social effects of electric light were many. Those who know their Bible may recall this phrase: "The night cometh, when no man can work" (John 9:4). But all that changed when gas lights were installed in factories in the early 1800s.

And just imagine Times Square without electricity!

UNDERSTANDING FOSSILS

How we learned the meaning of the life-like shapes sometimes found in rocks

On April 29, 1962, President John F. Kennedy looked around at his guests, forty-nine Nobel laureates, and said, "I think this is the most extraordinary collection of talent and of human knowledge that has ever been gathered together at the White House—with the possible exception of when Thomas Jefferson dined alone." Even when Jefferson had guests, however, they were often excellent scientists.

Caspar Wistar (1761–1818) is a good example of the sort of friend Jefferson cultivated. He understood fossils, but he was not the first to have some idea of what they are. The Islamic scholar, Avicenna (980–1037), thought they were stones hidden by the Creator "for His own pleasure," though Albertus Magnus (1200–1280) said that Avicenna had also described them as animals "changed into stones, and especially salty stones."

Most fossils are small broken pieces of a long-dead animal, of a sort no longer living, and the fossils are often squashed out of shape by the pressures that formed the rocks the fossils lie in. How would you decide if the fossils came from animals, or were the work of a creator, or of some evil spirit trying to fool us? This was the problem scholars faced before the nineteenth century.

Georgius Agricola (1494–1555) was the first mining engineer/geologist to publish his views in *De Natura Fossilium* (1546, "On the Nature of Fossils"), and in his best-known book, *De Re Metallica* (1556, "About Metals"). He was born in Saxony as Georg Bauer, but took a Latin form of his name when he studied medicine (Bauer is "farmer" in German; Agricola is "farmer" in Latin).

Agricola identified many fossils and said they resembled various life forms, but he stopped short of actually suggesting they came from things which had formerly been alive. Aside from Steno (35), Robert Hooke and John Ray (1627–1705), who all said fossils were the remains of extinct creatures, people seemed to be shy of treating fossils as biological objects until the time of Caspar Wistar. It wasn't all that long since witches and heretics had been burned.

In 1787, on October 5, in the city of Philadelphia, the worthy Dr. Caspar Wistar described a large bone to the American Philosophical Society. It was, he said, a thigh bone of a large animal. This bone came from the Upper Cretaceous deposits of the New Jersey plains, a place where duck-billed hadrosaur fossils are common, even today.

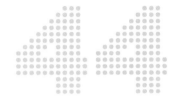

Date: 1802.

Location: Edinburgh, Scotland.

Discovery: Learning how to make sense of a sequence of fossils.

Discoverer: John Playfair (1748–1819).

Impact: The rocks were recognized as a "book" in which the history of the Earth is recorded, ready for us to read, once we learn the alphabet.

A fossil of *Sinornithos*, a small feathered theropod dinosaur ancestral to birds, found in Liaoning Province, China, in an area where a forest existed 130 million years ago.

Wistar's bone has long since been lost, but knowing where it was found, we can strongly suspect that it was a dinosaur bone. We know that Wistar wrote the first American anatomy textbook, and he would not mistake a thigh bone.

While people in the 1700s had begun to make sense of individual fossils, they still could not read them as they could a book. "Father of geology," James Hutton (1726–1797) saw them, and wrote *the* book about them. That is to say, he put words on a page. They were unreadable stodge, and few modern professional geologists have read Hutton. But he left the right ideas there, waiting for John Playfair to come along and explain them.

John Playfair was trained in mathematics before geology was invented, so he was largely self-taught. Like Hutton, Playfair learned from the stimulating geology of the area around Edinburgh, and he gave us "Playfair's Law," which says that rivers cut their own valleys.

There were other original contributions, but mainly, he translated and made the work of Hutton more accessible when he published his clear and easy-to-read *Illustrations of the Huttonian Theory of the Earth* in 1802. Still, Playfair's ideas did not gain wide acceptance until Charles Lyell (1797–1875) added them into his own *Principles of Geology*.

William Smith (1769–1839) became an expert canal surveyor in England, and as he was building canals, he took notice of the rocks he saw. More importantly, he saw many fresh exposures of rock, and he began to build up a pattern of the fairly simple sedimentary sequences that cover much of England, spotting the key fossils which identified each stratum. In 1815, he created a geological map of England at a scale of five miles to the inch (1:316,800), the first colored geological map ever drawn.

In Paris, Georges Cuvier (1769–1832) went further. He showed how the whole of an animal might be reconstructed from just a few small fossilized parts:

Every organism forms a whole … if, for instance, the intestines of an animal are so organized as only to digest fresh meat, it follows that its jaws must be constructed to devour a prey, its claws to seize and tear it, its teeth to cut and divide it, the whole structure of its locomotory organs such as to pursue and catch it; its sensory organs to perceive it at a distance …

Cuvier saw that each layer of rock beneath Paris could be identified by its fossil contents, wherever that rock outcropped on the surface. In 1822, he drew up an idealized stratigraphic column based on the fossils. All of a sudden, people realized that fossils were important, and rushed to apply the method to other geological areas.

Now people understood fossils and every student of science was interested in them, but the time was fast coming when there would be so many discoveries that scientists would have to specialize. The flood of interest began when people explored the electric cell (42).

DISCOVERING ELECTROLYSIS

How the power of Voltaic electricity to split compounds into their elements was discovered

Date: 1807.

Location: London, England.

Discovery: Salts can be split by electricity, producing a variety of amazing new metals.

Discoverer: Sir Humphry Davy (1778–1829).

Impact: In just a few years, there was almost enough information to start piecing together the patterns that would become the periodic table of the elements.

In March 1800, Alessandro Volta (42) wrote to Sir Joseph Banks about his piles. England and France were at war, and Volta's letters had to pass through France, so he sent them in two parts, written in French, probably so French censors could check them more easily. Anthony Carlisle was fluent in French, and Banks (who was poor at languages) passed the first four-page section to him, possibly for translation, while waiting for the second part to arrive. Excited by what they read, Carlisle and William Nicholson made their own pile and tried the same experiments.

In one experiment, they wanted to charge an electroscope, and because the contact was poor, they added a drop of water to improve the connection. When they saw bubbles forming in the liquid, they experimented further, and discovered the electrolysis of water. It took more experiments to find that hydrogen and oxygen came off at separate electrodes, and almost a hundred years to explain it, but the idea of electrolysis—splitting by electricity—was soon out there and available.

Their pile was a stack of seventeen silver coins—half-crowns—and an equal number of pieces of zinc, with each pair separated by cardboard soaked in salt water. This was enough, they reported, to produce a shock that was "abominably painful at any place where the skin is broken."

Nicholson also measured the amount of gas produced by weighing the water displaced by the bubbles, and found "72 grains by the gas from the zinc side, and 142 grains by the gas from the silver side." He found that the gas from the silver side was able to be exploded when mixed with air and lit. Just before Dalton proposed his atomic theory, here was a clear pointer that each water molecule was made up of two hydrogens and one oxygen, allowing for experimental error.

You can break down liquid water, and electroplating happens in solutions, but if you try electrolysis in a salt solution, you run into a problem: any sodium metal that forms will immediately react with the water in which the salt is dissolved. This will produce hydrogen gas and sodium hydroxide, and potassium salts will have the same effect. To form sodium and potassium metals by electrolysis, you need to avoid water.

These days, we understand that the solution of any "salt" is made up of large numbers of charged ions, both positive and negative. When two electrodes are placed in the solution and connected to a voltage source, the ions migrate: positive ions to the negative plate, negative ions to the positive plate. Once they reach an electrode, the positive ions gain an electron (or electrons), while the negative ions lose electrons to become neutral elements. Unless the material to be electrolyzed is in liquid form, ions cannot migrate, and no reaction happens.

This may be why it took Humphry Davy until 1807 to succeed in the electrolysis of potassium hydroxide and sodium hydroxide. He tried melting these substances, using a spirit lamp boosted by a stream of oxygen, but in the end, he settled for putting potassium hydroxide on a platinum plate, with a platinum wire leading in, attached to the 250-cell copper-zinc battery of London's Royal Institution.

If things had been different, Davy might have been a poet. He had a number of poets among his friends and Samuel Taylor Coleridge used to attend Davy's lectures, "to improve his stock of metaphors." Mary Shelley's 1818 tale of Frankenstein bringing life to his monster with a spark may have been inspired by the spectacular public demonstrations that Davy sometimes put on at the Royal Institution. In the nineteenth century, London was the center of the intellectual world, and the Royal Institution was London's scientific center, a place where society folk could attend inspiring lectures and demonstrations featuring the very latest science.

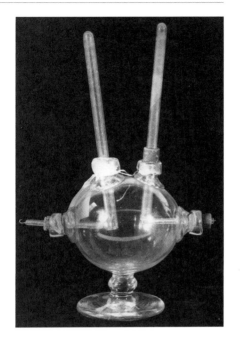

An electrobulb, a sample of the kind of equipment used by Michael Faraday in his studies of electrolysis.

A Cornish surgeon's apprentice at seventeen, Davy helped Thomas Beddoes, who treated the sick with nitrous oxide (laughing gas) in 1798 (55). Davy wrote up his observations, and in 1801 he was appointed as a lecturer at the Royal Institution. That gave him access to the Institution's equipment, and gave the Institution access to the talents of a remarkable showman who was also a highly effective investigator.

In a few short years, he had used electrolysis to prepare and describe potassium, sodium, barium, strontium, calcium, and magnesium. The name potassium was Davy's Latin form of "pot-ash": wood ash prepared in a clay pot. The symbol, K, comes from Latinizing *al kali*, the Arabic name for potash, into kalium. (And the alert reader may now see where "alkali" comes from!)

For all this, Davy's greatest discovery may have been the man who became his successor at the Royal Institution, Michael Faraday. Faraday proposed two laws of electrolysis which linked the mass of the products of electrolysis to the current passed, and to the atomic weight of a particular element, giving us a useful way to get relative atomic weights.

… I can have no doubt that, assuming hydrogen as 1, and dismissing small fractions for the simplicity of expression, the equivalent number or atomic weight of oxygen is 8, of chlorine 36, of bromine 78.4, of lead 103.5, of tin 59 etc., notwithstanding that a very high authority doubles several of these numbers.

As we shall see, George Johnstone Stoney (85) would later use those laws as evidence that electrons had to exist.

DETECTING ELECTROMAGNETISM

How we learned that electricity and magnetism were related

Date: 1820.

Location: København (Copenhagen), Denmark.

Discovery: There is a magnetic field associated with an electric current.

Discoverer: Hans Christian Oersted (1777–1851).

Impact: This opened the way for others to develop electrical motors and generators.

In 1600, William Gilbert (17) had carefully shown that electrical attraction ("amber") was completely different from magnetic attraction ("lodestone"). Two centuries later, people who studied that sort of thing were called natural philosophers, and they had begun to question everything, even the clever theories and proofs of those who had gone before them.

Hans Christian Oersted (Danes write his name "Ørsted") thought Gilbert might have been wrong, not for any good scientific reasons, but because he had trained originally in metaphysics, a branch of philosophy, and liked the idea that nature was unified and connected. In 1806, he became professor of physics and chemistry at Copenhagen, where he was the first to prepare metallic aluminum in 1825.

All the same, he is better known for his discovery of electromagnetism. He even coined the word "electromagnetic," and he gave his name to the unit of magnetic field strength, the oersted. In 1820, he was preparing for a lecture when he noticed that an electric current moving through a wire made a compass needle under the wire deflect, turning from its usual north–south alignment. Oersted wrote a report in Latin in July that year, in which he described this electromagnetism, and it was translated into French and other languages soon after.

Here is how he described it:

The first experiments … were set on foot in the classes for electricity, galvanism and magnetism, which were held by me in the winter just past. By these experiments it seemed … that the magnetic needle was moved from its position by the help of the galvanic apparatus … when the galvanic circuit was closed, but not when open, as certain very celebrated physicists in vain attempted several years ago …

The joining conductor may consist of several metallic wires or bands connected together. The kind of metal does not alter the effects, except, perhaps as regards quantity. We have employed with equal success wires of platinum, gold, silver, copper, iron, bands of lead and tin, a mass of mercury …

If the joining wire is placed in a horizontal plane under the magnetic needle, all the effects are the same as in the plane over the needle, only in an inverse direction …

That these things may be more easily remembered let us use this formula: the pole over which negative electricity [in modern terms, electron flow]

This kind of electrical transformer forms part of the AC adapters that provide useable power to homes and businesses.

enters is turned towards the west, that over which it enters is turned toward the east.

One of the great continuing challenges in science involves the need to justify research in advance, usually to bean-counters, by showing what it is useful for. Yet even the most useless-looking piece of science can become useful.

Here, Lord Kelvin reflects upon Oersted's researches:

Oersted would never have made his great discovery of the action of galvanic currents on magnets had he stopped in his researches to consider in what manner they could possibly be turned to practical account; and so we would not now be able to boast of the wonders done by the electric telegraphs. Indeed, no great law in Natural Philosophy has ever been discovered for its practical implications, but the instances are innumerable of investigations apparently quite useless in this narrow sense of the word which have led to the most valuable results.

Batteries were all very well for experiments and small applications, but no long-term practical users of electricity as a work-horse could rely on battery power. Even today, when so many of us rely on cordless phones and drills, MP3 players, laptops and digital cameras, we need regular access to mains power to recharge the batteries. The mains power in turn relies on generators (at first called dynamos), and a system of distribution.

> You can sometimes read that the writer Hans Christian Andersen was "named after Oersted." Andersen was indeed a friend of the Oersted family, but "Hans Christian" is quite common in Denmark: the naming was just a coincidence.

Distribution requires electromagnetic induction, where a current produces a magnetic field that induces a current in another conductor. Every battery charger has two components: a transformer to step voltage down, and a rectifier to convert it to direct current. Oersted's discoveries had no part in the development of the rectifier, but they had everything to do with the transformer.

At the other end of the supply line, in factories and homes, the use of electricity depends on transformers (sometimes called substations) to step the AC voltage down, and then on electric motors and solenoids, which basically rely on Oersted's discovery.

The link in all the development of Oersted's work was André Marie Ampère (1775–1836), who followed up Oersted's work and found that like currents attract. Ampère also discovered the solenoid, a helix or coil of insulated wire carrying a current that behaved like a magnet. The most common and audible household use of the solenoid is probably in the switching systems which commonly turn the water flow on and off in washing machines.

Ampère completed his work while believing incorrectly in two "magnetic fluids": a northern fluid and a southern fluid. So long as he observed correctly, and so long as his theory allowed him to make sensible predictions to test, it mattered little.

Sometimes, though, an error could hold back a whole branch of science. That happened when people argued that the planet was only a few thousand years old.

DISCOVERING THE AGE OF THE EARTH

How we slowly worked our way to a clear understanding of how old our planet is

Around 1700, the world of science lay open. Where today's scientists must specialize in one small area, people like Edmond Halley (1656–1742) could explain the nature of comets, sail the oceans studying variations in the Earth's magnetic field, and also invent a way of estimating the age of the planet from those same oceans. He suggested measuring the salinity of the sea, and then finding the rate at which salt was added to the sea each year.

Now if this be the true reason for the saltness of these lakes, 'tis not improbable but that the ocean itself is become salt from the same cause, and we are thereby furnished with an argument for estimating the duration of all things, from an observation of the increment of saltness in their waters.

The method always gives low estimates because it does not allow for losses of salt back to the land, either as salt spray, as halite (rock salt) deposits, or as subduction losses. Still, it was a start.

It took a while for anybody to try Halley's method, but the Irish physicist John Joly calculated in 1899 that the sodium content of the oceans was 1.5×10^{16} tons, yielding an age of ninety-seven million years. Sodium is now believed to be added at the rate of 6×10^7 tons per year, giving an estimated age for the oceans of about 250 million years—still much less than what we now take as the Earth's age, but closer to the age that was needed to explain all the evolutionary evidence.

The question of age arose slowly, starting with an estimate, based on the ages of the patriarchs in the Bible, of some 6,000 years, although many assumed, like Steno (35), that there had been a lifeless Earth before that. By 1753, a French naturalist, Georges Louis Leclerc, Comte de Buffon (1707–1788) saw that the horse and donkey were similar and decided that asses were just horses which degenerated over time, as the Earth cooled. He also suggested that large and more perfect ancient mammoths and mastodons were replaced by their descendants, the elephants.

Buffon believed in spontaneous generation, and performed experiments to show that tiny organisms can form in sterilized jars of meat gravy. He also carried out cooling experiments with large, hot, iron balls. From his data, he deduced the planet was at white heat 75,000 years ago, and had carried life for only 40,000 years. Jean-Baptiste Joseph, Baron de Fourier (1768–1830) also argued that the Earth's central heat, revealed in higher temperatures in mines and by volcanic activity, could best be explained

Date: 1830–1950.

Location: The planet Earth.

Discovery: The real age of the Earth.

Discoverer: Many scientists.

Impact: If life had evolved then the Earth had to be old. For quite some time, scientists could see evidence for evolution, but not for an ancient planet. But then the evidence was found.

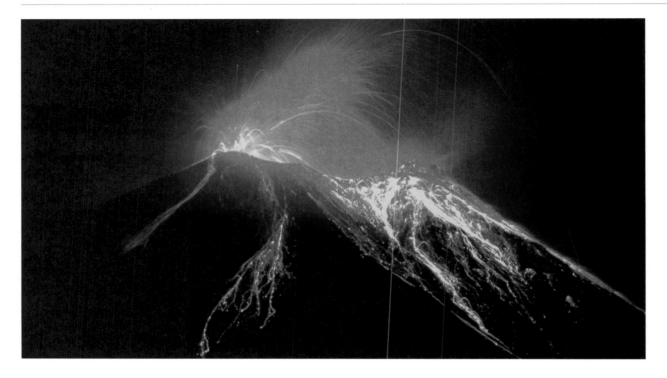

The Arenal Volcano in Costa Rica is considered one of the most active in the world. It spews out glowing red lava almost every day.

by assuming the whole Earth was once hot, and that the temperature of the Earth was now falling.

In 1862, Lord Kelvin estimated the age of the Earth, based on its cooling time, to be ninety-eight million years, but by 1897 he had lowered this to between twenty and forty million years, unless some other source of heat could be found. In May 1892, *Scientific American* reported an opinion from Sir Robert Ball that the Sun had existed for eighteen million years, and would burn out in another five million, still limiting the planet to a very short life.

The debate was a struggle between the biologists and the geologists on the one hand, who all demanded ever-longer ages for life on Earth as they saw it, and the physicists on the other, who could see no way of fueling the long, slow, steady-state Earth that we now accept. Then came the night in 1904 when Ernest Rutherford, a rising star of physics, was to lecture at the Royal Institution in London:

I came into the room which was half dark, and presently spotted Lord Kelvin in the audience and realized that I was in for trouble at the last part of the speech dealing with the age of the earth. To my relief, Kelvin fell fast asleep, but as I came to the important point, I saw the old bird sit up, open an eye and cock a baleful glance at me! Then a sudden inspiration came, and I said Lord Kelvin had limited the age of the earth, provided no new source of heat was discovered. That prophetic utterance refers to what we are now considering tonight, radium! Behold! the old boy beamed upon me.

Sadly, Kelvin was unconvinced and died still believing the planet to be about twenty million years old. In 1906, he wrote a letter, later published in the *British Weekly*, where, speaking of the Sun and the Earth, he said: "It seems almost infinitely improbable that radium adds practically to their energy for the emission of heat and light." At that time, "radium" meant not only the element radium, but also radioactivity in general.

Still, physicists were now able to say the Earth had cooled much more slowly than they once thought. The time-scale demanded by Charles Lyell for uniformitarian shaping of the Earth was possible, as Rutherford pushed the dawn of time back far enough to make room for Darwin's evolution and Lyell's geology. In 1913, Rutherford and Joly looked at radioactive decay in minerals and calculated an age that was more like 400 million years. By 1931, a combination of radioactivity and geological data gave the age of the Earth as at least two billion years, and by 1954, estimates were around five billion years.

Now we have settled on an age of 4.6 billion years, and nobody really expects that to change. In science, though, that sort of assurance is always a daring one.

THE FIRST ELECTRIC MOTOR

How we found a way to turn electrical energy into movement

In 1820, Hans Oersted (46) saw that an electric current produced a magnetic field. Later in the same year, André Ampère reported that two conductors exert a force on each other, and that a magnetic force moves in a circular motion around an electrically charged wire.

All of this fascinated a brilliant but unconventionally-trained young scientist who was working at the Royal Institution in London. Michael Faraday had originally trained as a bookbinder's apprentice. One day he was binding an encyclopedia and he read an article on electricity. He tried a few simple experiments; then, in 1812, went to hear Humphry Davy lecture at the Royal Institution to learn more.

He took notes about what he saw and heard, bound them, and sent them to Davy, asking for his assistance "to escape from trade and to enter into the service of science." The great man was impressed, and offered him a lowly job to see how he reacted. Faraday accepted the work, and quickly moved on to become an experimenter, then Davy's assistant, and, in 1833, a professor.

The range of Faraday's discoveries and innovations is phenomenal and is reflected in a legacy that includes scientific laws and experiments,

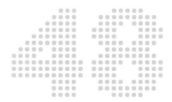

Date: 1831.

Location: London, England.

Discovery: An electrical current can cause a magnet to rotate, and vice versa.

Discoverer: Michael Faraday (1781–1867).

Impact: This revelation permitted the creation of the first electric motors and generators.

machines and implements, and technical and everyday terms. Faraday gave his name to laws of electrolysis, a law of induction, an ice-pail experiment, a tube, a disk, a shield, types of currents and even the Faraday cage (one that screens out electromagnetic radiation). His name lives on in the terms faradic current, faradism and the verb faradize, and he coined the words cathode, anode, electrode, ion, electrolyte, and electrolyze.

> Even if Faraday had no formal training as a scientist, he thought and worked like a scientist. Pondering Oersted and Ampère's work, he saw two interesting forces, electrical and magnetic, and tried to find out how they were related. It was a link that fascinated contemporary scientists and philosophers, who felt that all natural forces must be connected, and still fascinates scientists searching today for a so-called Grand Unified Theory of Everything.

In 1821, Faraday decided that a magnet which was free to move should rotate around a fixed conductor with a current in it, and that if the magnet was fixed down, and the conductor could move, the conductor would move around the magnet. He built two small models to prove this: one with a fixed magnet and one with a fixed conductor. These demonstrated the principle on which all electric motors would be based. Some motors today use an electromagnet, others use permanent magnets; but the basics remain the same, with a magnetic force pushing against a current in a conductor.

For a time, Faraday concentrated on chemistry, but he returned to his electrical experiments in 1831. To find out more about the interplay of electricity and magnetism, he wrapped two separate coils of wire around opposite sides of a simple iron ring. He attached one coil to a battery, the other to a current meter. When he closed the battery switch, current flowed around the first coil, magnetizing the iron ring. More significantly, the growing magnetic field generated a current in the second coil.

This was the first time anybody had observed what we now call electromagnetic induction. It became the basis of the electric transformer, which is used to increase or decrease the voltage of an electrical current—for example, to reduce the voltage of a power supply to operate low-voltage appliances, such as battery chargers for portable electronic items, or to boost voltage for transmission over high-voltage wires.

The power losses in high-tension (voltage) lines are relatively low, so power comes from the power station to the local area at high voltages; it is then stepped down to lower, safer voltages for use in homes (either 110 or 240 volts in most places). All of this relies on Faraday's discovery.

CONTROLLING ENERGY

Faraday knew that electromagnetism worked both ways. Electrical energy could create movement energy, but movement could also create electricity, as he showed by moving a bar magnet close to a coil of wire attached to a meter. In explaining this, Faraday planted the seeds for electrical generators, all of which, however they are powered, work on this principle. In 1832, Faraday also showed that static electricity, the electricity from electromagnetic generators, and the electricity from the kinds of batteries pioneered by Alessandro Volta, were all the same.

Faraday kept experimenting for another thirty years. He never built any practical applications of his discoveries—no working motors or generators—but he showed what was possible, and inspired others. Some of his other discoveries, like his laws of electrolysis, were applied much more rapidly.

Today, Faraday's innovations shape and direct all our lives. Look around your house and you will find electric motors everywhere, in fans and vacuum cleaners, in washing machines, computers and hairdryers. Almost every one of these devices will use electricity that has been modified by a transformer.

And they all run on electricity produced by generators working on the principles that Faraday elaborated.

The crude inductor used by Michael Faraday to discover the law of induction.

DISCOVERING THE INSIDE OF A CELL

How we realized that living things are made of cells, and that cells are made of still smaller things

Date: 1833.

Location: London, England.

Discovery: That each cell contains a nucleus.

Discoverer: Robert Brown (1773–1858).

Impact: Our understanding of life, physiology, and genetics relies on understanding cells.

The idea that living things are made of cells developed slowly, because while there were interesting observations, there was no earlier theory for the cell theory to replace. Usually, a new theory gains acceptance when an old theory raises questions that the new theory explains—but there was no predecessor here. Sometimes, we can pinpoint the moment of discovery, but it always takes time for a new discovery to be accepted.

Robert Hooke (31) described cells in his *Micrographia*, and over time, other people must have seen them too, but animal cells are hard to see because they are almost transparent. Hooke's cork cells had thick cell walls which stood out sharply, but they made no real sense to him. It was just an interesting pattern, and he thought it only applied to cork.

René Joachim Henri Dutrochet (1776–1847) served as a military surgeon with the armies of Napoleon Bonaparte until 1809, and then turned to science. He founded plant physiology, showed that plant and animal respiration are very much the same, studied osmosis, and discovered that chlorophyll was essential for photosynthesis. But his main claim to fame must be that in 1824, he was probably the first to offer us the theory that all life was made of cells.

We have seen that plants are composed entirely of cells, or of organs which are obviously derived from cells ... Thus all tissues, all the organs of animals are really one cellular tissue diversely modified. This uniformity of ultimate structure proves that organs really differ one from the other only in the nature of the substances which are contained in the vesicular cells of which they are composed.

Matthias Jakob Schleiden (1804–1881) and Theodor Schwann (1810–1882) usually get the credit for the cell theory, but they actually came to it later than Dutrochet, and by then Robert Brown (15) had already pointed out, in 1833, that each cell has a nucleus.

Yet you could not in all truth say that Robert Brown discovered the nucleus of the cell. There were plenty of others who had seen a nucleus before him (Franz Bauer had even drawn one in 1802), but Brown was the first to suggest that there was a nucleus in every cell, and he named it. This may sound like a small thing, but keep in mind that the nucleus is where the cell keeps its genetic material—the DNA that tells each cell what it is. Modern biology could not exist without an understanding of the nucleus. The first step, obviously, is to recognize that it is there.

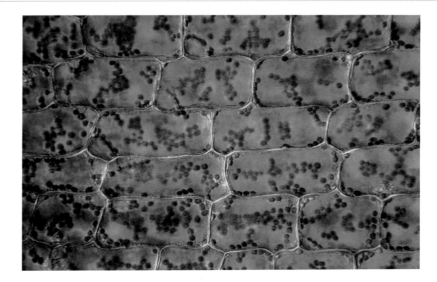

Photomicrography allows us to view detail like these epidermal cells, from the leaf of *Elodea* (a species of water weed).

Schleiden had been studying cellular tissues in plants and Schwann was doing the same with animals. When they talked to each other about their work in 1838, they realized they were both approaching the same conclusions. Schwann then published a book on cells in plants and animals, staking a claim to all the credit. When he published his own version later, Schleiden was basically wrong, claiming that the cell grew out of Brown's nucleus to full size.

One way or another, the idea was now out there, but people could not go much further until they could see what was inside cells. For this, they required better microscopes with achromatic lenses that corrected for the colored fringes around images and, most importantly, they required organic dyes which stained some of the transparent objects lying within the cells.

For the time being, all people could say was that cells were filled with cytoplasm which, as a colleague of mine used to say, is about as useful as saying that a television set is filled with teleplasm. The statement tells us nothing. The important components and activities in a cell—the genes, the ways the genes were expressed, the way they translated into enzymes in the cell, how proteins were formed, and much more—all of that remained hidden so long as the inner parts, the cell organelles, were invisible.

The organic dyes, most of them created from the by-products of making coal gas, coal oil, and petroleum products, changed all that. Take the genetic material that we now call chromosomes: the word just means "colored body," because the chromosomes absorbed certain dyes (59), and showed up brilliantly under the microscope. It seems that certain of the stains are able to fit the cell's surface chemicals, rather as a lock fits a key. One by one, the tiny and invisible organelles were made visible by complex chemistry.

Over time, as dedicated microscopists tried new combinations of stains, corrosive baths, and general maltreatment of slides of thinly sliced tissues, more organelles became visible. Our picture of the cell became more complicated and harder to explain, but ideas were taking shape.

As far back as 1890, German pathologist Richard Altmann suggested that the mitochondria had metabolic and genetic autonomy. Today, we believe that the mitochondrion was an ancient bacterium like *Rickettsia prowazekii*, which infected an early cell and became symbiotic.

In recent times, finer resolution from the electron microscope has revealed even more detail, and in 1971 Lynn Margulis proposed the idea of endosymbiosis. Under this complex theory, the mitochondria, plant chloroplasts, and perhaps flagella and cilia, all evolved as separate organisms which later joined together. If it is true, our understanding of evolution needs to take in a healthy dose of collaboration, as well as the combat aspect that we generally assume.

The story is not over yet.

DISCOVERING THE PRINCIPLE OF CATALYSIS

How we learned to speed up chemical reactions

Date: 1835.

Location: Stockholm, Sweden.

Discovery: The name for a process that had long been used without anyone understanding it.

Discoverer: Jöns Jacob Berzelius (1779–1848).

Impact: Many industrial processes use catalysts to make slow reactions happen faster.

To start with, we need a few definitions. First, chemistry is about equilibrium—the striking of a balance between reactants and products. Many chemical reactions can be reversed, and an end point is reached when the two changes balance out. There are exceptions: when you burn a candle, the products escape, and so does the energy, so combustion reactions are pretty much one-way changes.

Chemical reactions are sometimes slow. Some biochemical reactions could take a lifetime or more to reach an equilibrium. A catalyst is something which is added but does not change. It just speeds up the reaction, so equilibrium is reached much sooner. It is as though a catalyst provides an easier pathway to the final result—a tunnel through the reaction mountain. Salt is a catalyst that promotes the rusting of unprotected iron, which is why iron exposed to salt spray rusts quickly.

One of the more remarkable uses of a catalyst was in Döbereiner's Lamp, invented by Johann Döbereiner (1780–1849), and described in London the following year. It relied on platinum catalyzing the reaction of hydrogen and oxygen, releasing enough heat to start a hydrogen flame.

Amongst the ingenious novelties of the present day is a machine ... for the purpose of producing instantaneous light; which appears to be more simple, and less liable to be put out of order, than the Volta lamp, and other machines of a similar kind. It has lately been discovered that a stream of hydrogen gas, passing over finely-granulated platinum, inflames it. The whole contrivance, therefore, consists in retaining a quantity of hydrogen gas over water; which is perpetually produced by a mixture of a small quantity of zinc and sulphuric acid, and which, being suffered to escape by a small stop-cock, passes over a little scoop, containing the platinum, which it instantly inflames. From this a candle or lamp may be ignited ... it forms an elegant little ornament—of small expense, and easily kept in order; and, once charged, will last many months.

The Gentleman's Magazine, September 1824, p. 259.

Many domestic processes had used catalysts without the users knowing that catalysis was involved, just as people today use "enzyme" washing powder without realizing that enzymes are catalysts which speed up all the slow reactions of biochemistry—and cleaning.

Chemists' awareness of catalysts changed after 1835 when the Swedish chemist, Jöns Berzelius, proposed the name "catalysis" from Greek words meaning "down" and "loosen": the idea was that the catalyst somehow loosened links and allowed new links to form. When strong sulfuric acid converts starch to sugar, this is a catalytic reaction, because the acid is unchanged.

Catalysts have made all sorts of things possible. Late in the nineteenth century, Leo Baekeland (84) found that he needed a catalyst to make Bakelite, and we will visit that later. Indigo, the color we know best from blue jeans, was originally obtained from plants. But commercial synthesis became possible in 1897 when Eugen Sapper (1865–1901) accidentally broke a thermometer into the chemicals he was heating, and discovered that mercury could catalyze the reaction. Fritz Haber's process for making ammonia from a mixture of hydrogen and nitrogen required a catalyst (4). It was a key breakthrough in agriculture, but it also provided the nitrogen compounds needed for Germany's World War I munitions.

There is a rule of chemistry, called Le Chatelier's Principle, which says essentially that when you have a system, and you make some change to the conditions, the system will react in order to reduce the effects of your change. If you have three molecules of hydrogen and one of nitrogen, and you compress them, they are more likely to become two molecules of ammonia, which reduces the pressure. Heat also helps, because energy is needed to break the original chemical bonds, but a catalyst that lowers that energy requirement helps even more.

So the basis of Haber's process was a cylinder of hydrogen and nitrogen under a pressure of 250 atmospheres (that is, 3,500 pounds per square inch, or 25 megapascals), and at a temperature of 850–950°F. Under the right conditions, 20 percent of the reactants can be drained off as liquid ammonia, but the "right conditions" rely on an iron catalyst with small amounts of aluminum and potassium oxides. The Ostwald process then used another catalyst to form nitric acid from ammonia.

A graphic impression of a catalytic converter's molecular structure.

Today, a major use of catalysts is to be found in the catalytic converters placed in automobile exhausts, and in the catalytic cracking of petroleum products. A catalytic converter is classed as a heterogeneous catalyst, because it is in a different form (a solid) from the reactants, which are gases. The idea in these cases is to lower the *activation energy* for a reaction to take place. Metals like nickel, platinum and palladium, either as metals or as oxides, are used to provide a surface area on which reactions can occur.

Among other things, the catalysts allow the conversion of poisonous carbon monoxide to carbon dioxide, the complete burning of unburned fuel, and the breaking down of nitrogen oxides to nitrogen and oxygen. The catalysts can be easily "poisoned" by lead compounds, which is one of the reasons for leaded fuel being phased out around the world.

In science, ideas often need a catalyst as well—a push that gets them exposed. Louis Agassiz needed similar help to get others to see that his idea of ice ages was obvious.

DISCOVERING THE ICE AGES

How people came to accept that ice flows and climate changes

Irish tradition says that St Patrick banished the snakes from Ireland. When Irish adventurer, Sir Henry Hayes, was transported to New South Wales in 1802 for abducting an heiress, he was allowed to have his own house. He had a trench dug around the house and filled with turf brought from Ireland, to keep snakes out. Hayes should have filled the trench with ice, because just a few years after he died in 1832, the truth became apparent. The saint never cleared Ireland of snakes—if they were ever there, it was ice that drove them out.

North America and Europe both have large beds of gravel, and huge "erratics"—boulders made of rock not usually found in their locality, which must have been transported over large distances. Today, we have absorbed a uniformitarian view of the world: we assume that the geology we can see was formed by forces like those we see today. It took time, though, for that viewpoint to mature. Curiously, Louis Agassiz was a catastrophist, yet his theory helped make uniformitarianism popular.

Agassiz and Jean de Charpentier (1786–1855) both realized during the 1830s that the best explanation of many landforms comes from assuming that a thick sheet of ice had spread across the land, pushing rocks ahead of it and dragging others along underneath it. In 1840, Agassiz published the idea, and got most of the credit, but while he had the basics right, his theory assumed major glaciation everywhere, killing all life. In the Irish case, there probably never were any snakes in Ireland, but if there had been, the glaciers would certainly have pushed them out.

As a Swiss, Agassiz saw plenty of glaciers, and in 1839 he discovered that a cabin built on a glacier in 1827 had moved about a mile down the glacier. This led him to carry out a classic experiment, still performed today. He drove a series of stakes into the ice in a straight line across a glacier, and found that they moved into a U shape as the apparently solid ice flowed faster in the middle than on the edges. Only this movement of ice could explain the valleys that eventually formed:

Water may polish the rocks, but it nowhere leaves straight scratches upon their surface; it may furrow them, but these furrows are sinuous, whilst glaciers smooth and level uniformly, the hardest parts equally with the softest, and ... rub to uniform continuous surfaces the rocks upon which they move.

The effect of his comments was immediate, with scientists seeing the obvious fact which had been beneath their noses. Even Sir John Tyndall examined the theory of ice age glaciers, confirming that glaciers could be highly effective as agents of geological change.

Date: 1839.

Location: Switzerland.

Discovery: Confirmation of the suspicion that glaciers move.

Discoverer: Louis Agassiz (1807–1873).

Impact: The idea of ice ages explains a great deal about human history.

Spectacular mountains give rise to the Pietro Moreno Glacier in Argentina.

There were many ice ages, times when ice sheets and glaciers advanced from polar regions. The most recent ice age lasted from about one million years ago until roughly 10,000 years ago, when the ice retreated to its present limits, and modern human history began. There are traces of other ice ages going back as far as 250 million years ago. In the southern hemisphere, the ice ages created fewer and smaller glaciers, with the main effect being cooler and drier weather.

In an ice age, up to a third of the Earth may be covered by ice, flowing slowly across the land, pushing everything before it. With all that ice on land, the sea levels fall. When they accepted Agassiz' ideas, scientists began to think about the distribution of animals. Now they could see how migration might have been possible. The animals of Tasmania, Australia's island state, are mainly the same as those of the mainland, and Australian-type animals are common on the island of New Guinea, north of Australia. In the last ice age, all three were continuous land.

At the end of the last ice age, England was connected to France by low land, and snakes were migrating back from southern Europe. Three snake species were able to reach Britain, but Ireland was cut off by a rising snake-proof sea before the new arrivals could reach the island. The Bering Straits were then ice and dry land, providing a much easier route for humans finding their way out of Asia and into the Americas. That same link helps to explain why many of the animals of North America and Europe are either the same, or close relatives.

Alfred Russel Wallace (63) is best remembered as the other scientist who thought of evolution by natural selection. He also discovered and described a line that we now call Wallace's Line, in 1876. He drew this between the Indonesian islands of Bali and Lombok, and then between Sulawesi and Kalimantan (or Celebes and Borneo, to use the names of his time). To the west of his line, the fauna and flora are distinctly Asian; to the east, they are distinctly Australian. Today, we know that Wallace's Line coincides with a deep trench, far too deep to have ever been dry land, even during an ice age, but narrow enough for humans to cross in boats or on rafts.

But now comes the frustrating part, if you care about archeology. The early humans would have been mainly coastal, because the coastal plains are rich and flat, and there would have been plenty of fish in coastal waters. Now, though, all of those sites occupied by ice age humans are deep under water—very difficult to excavate!

Today, all scientists accept the idea of ice ages, but we have no agreement on what causes ice ages to begin.

INVENTING IMMUNOLOGY

How we discovered that our bodies can identify 'outsider' cells

There are several preferred dates among immunologists for the start of their profession: 1797, when Edward Jenner introduced vaccination (40) is one; a period in the 1850s, when Ignaz Semmelweis (67) identified hand-washing as a way of stopping childbed fever; or any of several dates when germs were specifically identified as the cause of disease (71). Others would date it from 1883, when Ilya (or Elie) Metchnikoff (1845–1916) discovered a form of phagocytosis, where leukocytes—white blood cells—attack various invaders.

In 1840, Jakob Henle was newly arrived in Zürich, when he published a paper called *On Miasmata and Contagia* (we might translate this as "On Disease-causing Smells and Contagious Diseases"). In it, he classified the known diseases. He identified those that were clearly miasmatic and never contagious, like ague (malaria); there were some that appeared to arrive miasmatically, but then spread by contagion, like smallpox, measles, influenza, and cholera; and finally, there were diseases which seemed never to spread except by contagion, like syphilis and scabies.

Today, there are effectively two branches of immunology. One seeks to boost the immune system to help it fight disease; the other seeks to restrict the immune system in some helpful way, to prevent the rejection of grafts and transplants of one sort or another. Each branch relies on understanding how the body identifies self and non-self. Until we knew that diseases were caused by invading cells that were recognized as foreign, we had no way of understanding what immunity was. Jenner

Date: 1840.

Location: Zürich, Switzerland.

Discovery: That the body reacts to disease in characteristic ways.

Discoverer: (Friedrich Gustav) Jakob Henle (1809–1885).

Impact: It led to better ways of fighting disease, as well as to skin and organ transplants, and more.

could use vaccination against smallpox without knowing why it worked, but other vaccines could not be developed without a good theory.

Henle's essay set a foundation for immunology, but understanding only came when Metchnikoff left Russia for a seaside work-break at Messina on the island of Sicily, in 1882. The Tsar had been assassinated, and a reactionary government was making life unpleasant in Russia, so Metchnikoff set to work on some experiments in embryology.

Even when the focus is on mammals, embryologists rely on studies in animals which develop outside the mother's body. After William Harvey (30), they understood that the similarities were greater than the differences, and that progress was much more easily studied in the "lower" animals.

Metchnikoff was living by the sea, and chose starfish (seastars) as his study animal. Like many marine animals, starfish release sperm and eggs into the sea, where they meet more or less randomly, and fertilization happens. The fertilized eggs then develop into larval stages, and eventually into small starfish. They are small, they are easy to obtain, and easy to keep—perfect subjects for this kind of study.

Metchnikoff was curious about how starfish absorbed food, so he had previously fed them small doses of carmine dye and watched the dye particles being absorbed. Then it struck him: could similar cells absorb "invaders" in us? He knew that a thorn in the flesh attracts lymphocytes, so he had the idea of inserting a splinter into a semi-transparent starfish larva. The next morning, cells had gathered near the splinter—unusual cells that he called "phagocytes," which means cell eaters.

In 1886, Metchnikoff became director of an institute established in Odessa to offer Louis Pasteur's rabies vaccine, but he came under fire because he was not medically trained; in 1888, he moved to the Pasteur Institute in Paris, where he stayed until he died.

In 1888, Charles Richet (1850–1935) discovered by accident that blood from dogs with a *Staphylococcus* infection made rabbits immune to the bacterium. Further studies showed that it was something in the serum of the blood which made the difference, and these unknown particles that we now call antibodies were dubbed anti-toxins. Richet had another lucky find in 1902, when he found that a tiny second dose of venom from a Portuguese man-o'-war would kill a dog which had previously survived a large dose. The dog had been sensitized, and died of what we now call anaphylactic shock.

The picture became clearer when Karl Landsteiner (1868–1943) took blood serum from one person and mixed it with blood corpuscles from another. Sometimes the corpuscles would clump, but at other times they did not. The era of blood typing had begun, and blood transfusion followed soon after, now that a simple test, outside the body, could confirm compatibility. During World War I, medical workers used stored blood to save lives.

Mid-1800s colored engraving of a man after a skin graft operation, which took skin from his forehead and grafted it tohis nose.

In World War II, Peter Medawar (1915–1987) became interested in the need for skin grafts, mainly for airmen who had been burned after their planes caught fire, but also for other servicemen. In the sixteenth century, people had skin from one part of their body grafted to another, but Medawar was working with donor grafts from other people. He found something rather like Richet's anaphylaxis, where second and later grafts from the same donor were rejected more quickly than the first one.

After the war, Medawar continued his studies in immunology, and learned of work done by Macfarlane Burnet (1899–1985), who had found that very early exposure to foreign tissue made an animal more tolerant, more receptive to a later graft from it. Further, he predicted that this tolerance might be reproduced in the laboratory. Medawar and his colleagues established that it was so, at least for mice: while it had no direct implications for organ transplants, it showed that transplants were not impossible.

It was a long road from pus in seastars to skin grafts in mice, but it was a successful one. Metchnikoff (1908), Richet (1913), Landsteiner (1930), and Medawar and Burnet (1960), all won or shared Nobel Prizes in Medicine or Physiology for their contributions to discovering how our immune systems work.

DISCOVERING GUTTA-PERCHA

How we explored the uses of the first plastic materials

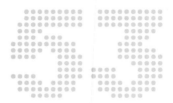

Date: 1843.

Location: Singapore.

Discovery: That people in Singapore were making knife handles from gutta-percha.

Discoverer: William Montgomerie (1797–1856), a British surgeon in Singapore.

Impact: It allowed the first undersea telegraph cables to operate, and much more.

Most of the things we did later or do now with rubber were first developed using the very similar but now rarely used gutta-percha. This was collected as a sap from a tree (*Palaquium gutta*) in much the same way as rubber, and it was chemically similar to rubber—but not the same. Despite the chemical similarities with rubber, gutta-percha was easier to work with and had different drawbacks.

Gutta-percha softens at about 160°F. It can be extruded at that temperature, and it is soft enough to cut at 140°F, which was cool enough that workers could handle it without protective wear. William Montgomerie sent notes, and samples of gutta-percha, to the Medical Board of Calcutta and also to the Royal Society of Arts in London, and triggered interest in it.

Investigators thought it was "just like rubber," and later noticed its plastic nature, its insulating properties, and its low efficient of expansion when it was heated or cooled, which made it ideal for molding and casting. Golf balls in the second half of the nineteenth century were "gutties"—gutta-percha balls that flew faster and were cheaper than traditional leather-and-feather balls.

Werner Siemens (1816–1892) began investigating the use of gutta-percha to insulate telegraph wires (37) in 1845, and by 1850, a gutta-percha cable had been laid from Britain to France. It failed, but a successful one was in place by 1851, as the telegraphic linking of the world began. By 1858, a cable with gutta-percha insulation briefly joined Britain and the USA before it failed, but an improved cable, also insulated with gutta-percha, opened a telegraphic service in 1866.

Irish children wore gutta-percha shoes when it was wet; New Yorkers could seal a roof with gutta-percha cement (the cost was "5 cents a foot"). The US cavalry had cloaks of gutta-percha; some of them had scabbards for their sabers and ammunition boxes made of gutta-percha; and biologists sent live seaweeds in the mails, sealed in gutta-percha envelopes. On the goldfields of Australia, a surgeon used gutta-percha in about 1860 to "stop" tooth cavities at a guinea ($5) a time. The material came from a gutta-percha bucket, bought at auction as part of a batch of old tools. He would cut a small piece, heat it and ram it into the gap. He estimated that his bucket would "stop" thousands of teeth before it ran out.

Once rubber could be vulcanized, it was much tougher than gutta-percha. Rubber was also much easier to obtain, and it started to take over some of gutta-percha's applications. Still, when the first rubber golf ball was invented in 1898, it had a coating of gutta-percha. The use of gutta-percha was only really killed off when artificial plastics began to reach the factories and stores of the world. It slipped out of general usage, yet many older people still have some in their teeth.

If you have root canal therapy, the hole will still be filled with gutta-percha, even today, because nobody has yet found a better material. At least it is no longer obtained from old buckets!

India rubber, alias cauchu, caoutchouc or gum elastic, was interesting stuff. It came from tree sap, like gutta-percha, and it worked rather like gutta-percha, but the rubber trees were more common. It was used by the Mesoamericans before Columbus, and the Spaniards who followed him must have seen games played with balls made of rubber, but the material did not interest them as much as gold and silver.

By the 1830s, the needs of industry were changing. Slow steam engines could use oiled leather to seal valves, and while shoes and inflatable canvas boats could be made with India rubber, steam valves could not, and the new faster engines needed better seals. Inventors everywhere hunted for ways of making the easier-to-obtain India rubber more weather-proof and tougher.

One of them was a bankrupt called Charles Goodyear (1800–1860), who had been mixing gum elastic with white lead and sulfur. The mix was unsuccessful until he had a stroke of luck in February 1839. Some of his gum elastic/sulfur mix landed by accident on a hot pot-bellied stove, and when he scraped the material off, he realized that the heat had produced an elastic rim.

Here was the secret to toughening rubber: mix it with sulfur and heat it. But how much sulfur, and how much heat? In the end, he found that to toughen the rubber, it had to be heated by steam under pressure, at a temperature of about 270°F, for several hours.

The molecules of rubber are natural polymers—long chains that can slip and slide past each other. The sulfur forms bridges between chains, tying them together and making a more stable product. At the time, there was no theory to explain this, so anybody seeing the material would have no idea of how the gum elastic had been changed.

Goodyear never benefited from his discovery. He died in 1860, worn out by patent battles and owing some $200,000. The giant Goodyear Tire and Rubber Co. may carry his name, but there is no family connection. It would be some time before rubber tires would soften the rides of wagons, bicycles, and automobiles, but by 1860, railway cars could be fitted with coiled springs embedded in vulcanized rubber.

People all over the world died as food crops were displaced by rubber plantations, or as Congolese rubber tappers were terrorized, beaten and killed to make them work harder. On the other hand, rubber has made

The leaves, bud and blossom of the gutta-percha tree, from an 1868 drawing.

our lives better, and it continues to save lives today. Catheters, surgical gloves, condoms, and other products are still made of rubber, as are the tires on vehicles and aircraft.

On balance, rubber has probably done more good than harm—just.

UNDERSTANDING ENERGY

How we learned what energy was, and how we learned to use and manipulate it

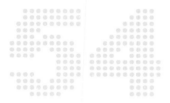

Date: 1845.

Location: Manchester, England.

Discovery: Mechanical energy (movement) can be converted to heat.

Discoverer: James Prescott Joule (1818–1889).

Impact: Our economy is based on energy: just imagine a world without oil, coal or electricity. All of the best bits came from humans mastering energy.

Thomas Savery's 1698 steam engine patent was for "raising water by fire," which tells us how energy was seen at the start of the 1700s. To sell their engines, James Watt and his partner, Matthew Boulton, had to invent ways to measure the efficiency of the machines before anybody even knew what work or energy were. As part of this exercise, Watt (36) introduced the horsepower (equal now to 746 watts, or 746 joules per second). The horsepower, seen as "what one horse can do," was a useful unit for practical folk. It told us nothing of what energy is, but it helped to boost sales.

All kinds of people explored the nature of energy, and some of them had surprising backgrounds. In fact, any writer telling the history of Benjamin Thompson, alias Count Rumford (1753–1814) as fiction would be laughed at. Born in America, he became a shop assistant, and then a teacher, before marrying a rich widow at nineteen. In the Revolutionary Wars, he became a major in the New Hampshire regiment, but fled to England in 1776, leaving his wife and a baby daughter behind. By 1781, he was a Fellow of the Royal Society and two years later, he was working in Bavaria where he introduced reforms like the steam engine and the potato. He later invented the coffee percolator to stop workers drinking so much beer, and developed a clevernew chimney design! He was probably also a British spy in both America and Bavaria.

Rumford did his best scientific work after he saw what happens when guns are being bored. Back then, cannon were cast as a block of solid metal, with the long hole (the bore) of the cannon being formed by a drill. Rumford noticed that as the bores were drilled out, a huge amount of heat was produced by the friction of the boring machine on the metal of the cannon.

The standard theory of the time said that converting the iron block into small shavings released lots of "caloric," which had been trapped in the iron and now escaped, making everything hot. Yet even if the drill bit was blunt and produced no metal shavings, heat was still produced. Rumford thought mechanical energy—the movement of the drill—was somehow being converted to heat. He carried out some accurate measurements, and showed that if "caloric" had mass, then one calorie had to weigh less than 0.000013 milligram—less than half of one-billionth of an ounce.

Joseph Black (1728–1799) was professor of Medicine and Chemistry at Glasgow University when he first distinguished heat from temperature. He mixed one measure of cold water with a measure of hot water, then repeated the process using the same measures, but adding hot mercury instead of hot water. He found that the much more dense mercury, even at the same temperature, contained less heat than an equal volume of water.

In France, Sadi Carnot (1796–1832) was well on the way to a good theory in 1824, but when he died of cholera, most of his possessions were buried with him (they did that back then to stop the cholera "poison" spreading). His work was largely lost.

By the 1840s, facts were needed more than theory. James Prescott Joule (1818–1889) was a rich member of a Manchester brewing family. He managed the brewery until 1854, and practiced science as an amateur. By then, the amateur scientists were giving way to professionals, but Joule had been educated by John Dalton (15), the originator of atomic theory, so he was a well-trained amateur.

Sometimes called the capacity for doing work, we know energy as a useful book-keeping device for analyzing processes. We know that energy can neither be created nor destroyed, but that it can be changed in its form. This is an understanding we have inherited from Joule, who showed that heat and mechanical movement were forms of the same thing.

He was an accurate measurer of small changes, even finding the length change in an iron bar as it is magnetized. But most importantly, he established the third law of thermodynamics when he showed us that energy comes in different forms, one of which is heat.

If you rub your finger backwards and forwards on a table, you can soon see and feel how friction produces heat, but the scientific proof of this proposition calls for careful measurement. Without measurement, people could still argue that the rubbing made some sort of "heat fluid" come out of your finger, just like sweat. You have to measure things, if you want to understand heat.

As a practical experimenter, Joule excelled at measuring things. In particular, he used the energy of falling weights to heat water, measuring how much heat we get from a certain amount of mechanical energy. And he found *he always got the same amount of heat from the same amount of mechanical energy:* this proved conclusively that the two were both forms of energy.

The fascinating perpetual motion machine!

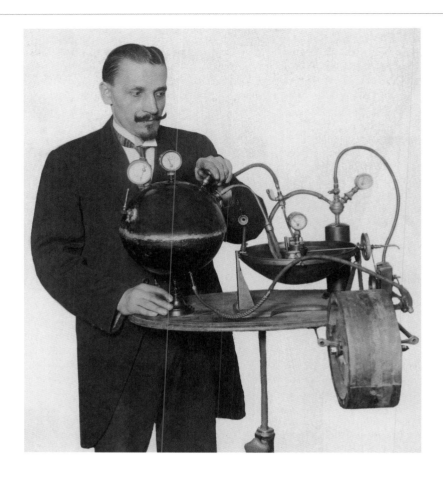

At about the same time, in Germany, the medically trained Julius Mayer approached the problem from another direction. He showed that, in theory, heat and mechanical energy ought to be the same thing. That helped, but Joule's work was better than a theoretical proof, because theory cannot say how much mechanical energy is needed to raise the temperature of a gram of water by 1 degree. Joule could tell us, and he did:

If my views be correct, a fall of 817 feet will of course generate one degree of heat; and the temperature of the river Niagara will be raised about one fifth of a degree by its fall of 160 feet.

Once we understood energy, we could work with it. In the future, with oil reserves running down and the global climate changing fast, we may need an entirely new understanding of energy.

DISCOVERING ANESTHETICS

How we learned to stop people feeling pain during surgery

The history of science might have been different if anesthetics had been available earlier, because sometimes the onlookers suffered as much as the patients. Charles Darwin (1809–18820 was a medical student in Edinburgh in the 1820s, and saw "two very bad operations, one on a child, but I rushed away before they were completed." It was the end of his medical days because this happened, he said, "long before the blessed days of chloroform."

And so Darwin pursued science, but he was wrong to some extent, about chloroform. Ether was used before chloroform, and other substances were used even before that to knock a patient out—William Morton may not have been the first to use anesthetics, though he was certainly *one* of the first.

In 1718, Johann Bernhard Quistorp (1692–1761) appeared for public examination at the University of Rostock, in what is now eastern Germany. His dissertation topic was "Anesthesia," a word that had come down from ancient times with two meanings: one being a lack of sense (as in stupidity), and the other a lack of sensation (as in stupor).

In the first century AD, Dioscorides used "anesthesia" when referring to a mixture of wine and mandragora, used for insomnia, chronic pain and "during cutting and cautery." To Quistorp, anesthesia was:

a spontaneous, deep, more or less persistent loss of sensation by the whole body, except by the organs supporting the pulse and respiration. The brain is plunged into a deep, strange, more or less pleasant trance.

To historians of anesthesia, the interesting bit comes in Quistorp's hypothesis 14, which reads: "Vapors (fumes) entering the body may produce anesthesia."

Opiates were widely used to treat those in pain, and it may reasonably be guessed that opiates were used to make surgical patients unconscious, just as alcohol was sometimes used. But the "vapors" are interesting because ether was well known from about 1275, and after nitrous oxide (laughing gas), ether was the second anesthetic of modern times. Humphry Davy (45) proposed that nitrous oxide might be used in pain relief in 1800, but Quistorp was well ahead of him.

Davy helped Thomas Beddoes (1760–1808) in his nitrous oxide studies, but Beddoes had used ether in 1794 in attempts to treat phthisis (tuberculosis), catarrhal fever, bladder calculus (bladder stones), and

Date: October 16, 1846.

Location: Boston, Massachusetts, USA.

Discovery: Surgery could be carried out without trauma on unconscious patients.

Discoverer: William T. G. Morton (1819–1868).

Impact: Now complex surgery could be carried out without undue haste.

William Morton administers ether before performing an operation.

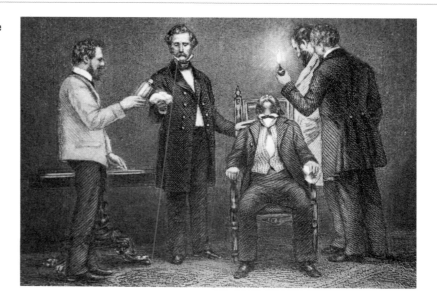

scurvy. Both Davy and Beddoes had seen the pain relief effects in animals, but they stopped short of trying ether on humans, possibly because they had been ridiculed over nitrous oxide.

Whatever the reason, the earliest known use of an anesthetic in the modern sense occurred when Dr. Crawford Williamson Long (1815–1878) removed a tumor from James Venable's neck under anesthesia on March 30, 1842 in Jefferson, Georgia (he may have made even earlier trials). Foolishly, he did not publish his results until 1848, and so largely missed out on any credit.

About 1844, a Hartford, Connecticut dentist named Horace Wells (1815–1848) tried nitrous oxide anesthesia on a patient, followed by a public demonstration in January 1845 at the Massachusetts General Hospital. The demonstration failed because the gas dosage was too low, but the idea was out. Another dentist, William Morton heard of Wells' attempts through physician Charles Jackson, who knew them both, and began his own experiments. On September 30, 1846, he removed a tooth, using ether as an anesthetic. The tooth was extracted without pain, and within three weeks, another successful ether trial occurred at the Massachusetts General Hospital. The operating surgeon, Dr. Warren, famously announced, "Gentlemen, this is no humbug," and soon after, a fight over the credit broke out between Jackson, Morton, Wells, and Long.

Morton and Jackson patented the invention and refused to say what vapor they used, but people soon recognized the smell, and none of the pioneers profited from their efforts. Wells died, aged thirty-three, when he slashed his thigh and bled to death after becoming addicted to chloroform. Morton died of a stroke aged forty-nine, leaving his wife and five children with nothing. Jackson suffered a stroke and spent seven years in an asylum for the insane before he died aged seventy-five.

Long died at the age of sixty-two, while administering ether to a farmer's wife during labor.

Queen Victoria, who famously observed that being pregnant was an occupational hazard of being a wife, was the mother to nine children. She had no time for the pain of childbirth, and allowed John Snow (58) to administer chloroform to her in 1853 and 1857 for her last two confinements. One of the daughters of the Archbishop of Canterbury followed Victoria's lead in 1854, and while there was a Biblical argument against avoiding the pain of childbirth, based on a close reading of Genesis 3:16, England's women were quick to follow their lead. Apparently, what was good for the titular head of the Church of England and the daughter of its actual head was also good enough for ordinary women.

Anesthesia allowed slower, more careful operations, and combined with antiseptic technique and antibiotics, it saved many, many lives. Science was progressing at the speed of light—whatever that speed was.

MEASURING THE SPEED OF LIGHT

How we learned that light travels very fast, but not infinitely fast

How would you measure the speed of light? Hero of Alexandria thought light shone out of our eyes, bounced off whatever we were looking at, and bounced back again. This does not explain, however, why we can't see at night unless somebody lights a lamp or a candle.

Now imagine you close your eyes while you are looking at some distant hills, or at the Moon, which a Greek astronomer called Hipparchus said was "30 Earth diameters away." On that estimate, the Moon is close to a quarter of a million miles away (bravo, Hipparchus!), yet we see it as soon as we open our eyes. That was easy to explain, said Hero: light travels at infinite speed.

Galileo Galilei (24) often doubted things, so he stood on a hill and got some friends to stand on another hill, five miles away, holding a covered lantern. Galileo also had a covered lantern, and when he uncovered it, his friends were to uncover theirs. Galileo knew the light we see by came from a light source and shone outwards, so he expected there would be a slight delay. But the time interval over five miles was too small, and he was similarly forced to conclude that the speed of light was infinite.

The next player was Christiaan Huygens (1629–1695) of the Netherlands. During a lunar eclipse, he said, the Sun, the Earth and the Moon appeared to line up. The alignment was so close that the Earth's shadow

Date: 1850.

Location: Paris, France.

Discovery: A close approximation to the accepted modern value for the speed of light.

Discoverer: Armand Hippolyte Fizeau (1819–1896), and Léon Foucault (1810–1868).

Impact: With a reliable speed of light, we could begin to estimate how large the universe was.

had to reach the Moon in 10 seconds or less. He thought the speed of light might be 100,000 times the speed of sound, which would be around 20,000 miles per second—about 11 percent of the value we accept today. For the first time, light was regarded as fast but limited to a finite speed.

The next hint came when a Dane called Ole Rømer noticed that the eclipses of Jupiter's moons were sometimes early, and sometimes late, and that the delay between earliest and latest was 996 seconds. The moons can be seen from Earth with a telescope, and they had to be orbiting at a regular rate, which should make the eclipses always happen at the same time. Something was slowing down the time taken for light to get from Jupiter to Earth.

Rømer reasoned that the difference was caused by Jupiter sometimes being on our side of the Sun (thus, closer to us), or on the other side, further away. The difference in distance would be the same as the diameter of Earth's orbit, so if we knew that distance, we would know the speed of light—or if we knew the speed of light, we could make a good guess at the distance across the Earth's orbit (which we now know to be about 186 million miles, on average, from one side to the other).

Sadly, we knew neither, but in 1676 Rømer made a stab at the distance, and from that, suggested that light traveled at 142,000 miles per second, about 76 percent of the accepted value today, which is nearly 186,000 miles per second. Then, in 1728, an English vicar and astronomer, James Bradley, used the same method to estimate it at 177,000 miles per second, and that was the accepted value until 1849.

In that year, Armand Fizeau tried a clever variation of Galileo's method. He shone light through the gaps of a toothed wheel, at a mirror, five miles away. If the wheel spins fast enough on this apparatus, the reflected light gets back, just as the next gap moves into position. If you know how many gaps there are in the wheel, and how fast the wheel is rotating, you have a fairly accurate estimate of the time taken for light to travel 10 miles.

Fizeau's result was about 5 percent higher than the value we accept today, but this was adjusted the following year, when Jean Foucault refined the method. Since that time other measurements have been taken that have refined the value for the speed of light in a vacuum, but it will never change from 299,792,458 meters/second, because we now define the meter as 1/299,792,458 of the distance traveled by light in one second (with the second defined by a cesium clock).

Discovering that light had a finite speed had a curious side-effect. On November 27, 1783, John Michell, who made the apparatus Cavendish (41) used to find G, shared an interesting thought with the Royal Society. Like most people at the time, he thought of light as a stream of tiny particles, and he assumed the particles had mass. If a body had enough mass, he said, then any particle of light leaving its surface would never escape. It would be pulled back down again.

The Royal Society was not really all that interested in the notion of invisible holes in space, but we must give Michell credit for thinking of a great idea first. Relativity tells us that even light waves are affected by gravity, so that tiny massive objects exist, from which no light escapes. We call them black holes, but they are exactly what Michell described.

While people say "nothing can travel faster than the speed of light," this is not entirely correct unless you add "in a vacuum." In water, the maximum speed of light is about three-quarters of the speed of light in a vacuum, and a fast cosmic particle, entering the eye of an astronaut, can be traveling faster than the speed of light in water. When this happens, it slows down, emitting a flash of Cerenkov radiation which lights up the inside of an astronaut's eye.

But however fast light goes, we now know how to capture it, thanks to the work of Frederick Archer and others.

Total eclipses of the Moon got people thinking about the speed of light.

INVENTING PHOTOGRAPHY

How we learned to make accurate and permanent images

Date: 1851.

Location: London, England.

Discovery: The development of the collodion process of photography.

Discoverer: Frederick Scott Archer (1813–1857).

Impact: It provided reliable illustrations and records that could be duplicated.

The first step came in the 1600s, when Robert Boyle noted that light makes silver chloride change from white to black. The first permanent photograph was taken in 1826 when Joseph Niepce (1765–1833) used asphalt to make a plate which could be used to make prints. The asphalt ("bitumen of Judea") was spread on pewter, and hardened over an eight-hour exposure, after which the remaining soft asphalt was washed away with lavender oil. Niepce later collaborated with Louis Daguerre (1787–1851) who developed daguerreotypes in 1839. Two years later, William Henry Fox Talbot (1800–1877) patented his calotype process in England. The daguerreotype was sharper, making a single positive image; Talbot's system made negatives, but the prints were more blurred.

Talbot charged people high fees for using his method. He later allowed amateurs to use the calotype system for free, but pursued professional photographers, even those using the far better collodion process that Frederick Scott Archer described in 1851. According to Talbot, people using the collodion process still required a calotype license, but in the end, the courts found against him.

Archer had been working as a sculptor, and began using photography as an aid. He was a gentle and unassertive person, and while his friends urged him to take out a patent, he did not, and died penniless, leaving a widow and three daughters. A public subscription raised an amount variously stated as £747 or £767, and two years after his death his family were granted a civil list pension of £50 (a year) in recognition of his contribution to photography.

Archer knew of collodion, a solution of nitro-cellulose (gun-cotton) in alcohol and ether, as a material that could be used to place a thin, clear film over wounds. His 1848 method was to mix collodion with potassium iodide and spread it on glass. The glass plate was then dipped in a silver nitrate solution. Both the exposure and the development happened in the camera while the plate was still wet, but the finely detailed negatives were transparent and only required exposures of a few seconds.

By 1857, wandering street photographers touting for custom were becoming a nuisance, and two years later, miniature painters were out of work. Specialist shops sold stereo pairs of photographs that could be viewed through a stereoscope to see a scene in three dimensions.

Clever painters like William Frith used photography to capture scenes, and his 1858 painting, *Derby Day*, drew huge crowds. Charles Baudelaire,

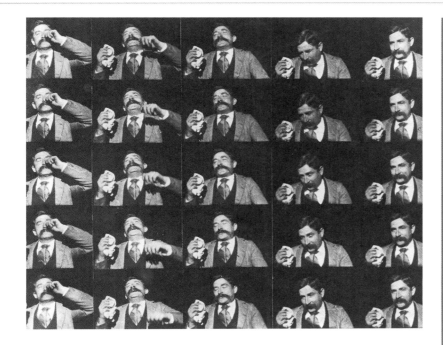

HIAWATHA'S PHOTOGRAPHING

First, a piece of glass he coated

With collodion, and plunged it

In a bath of lunar caustic

Carefully dissolved in water

There he left it certain minutes.

Secondly, my Hiawatha

Made with cunning hand a mixture

Of the acid pyro-gallic,

And of glacial-acetic,

And of alcohol and water-

This developed all the picture.

Lewis Carroll

writing as an art critic, argued that photography was not an art, that its duty was "the servant of the sciences and arts—but the very humble servant, like printing or shorthand, which have neither created nor supplemented literature." Baudelaire also noted that pornographers had taken to photography.

Classes were available everywhere, and in the mid-1860s, the poet Alfred Lord Tennyson, complained to his neighbor, Julia Cameron, that "I can't be anonymous by reason of your confounded photographs." The age of the paparazzi was dawning. In Massachusetts, where 144 banks issued their own bank notes in 1859, people were worried that photographic copies would be passed off, but the banks held photographic records of genuine notes, and so could detect the cruder copies.

Kinetoscope filmstrip of a man sneezing, taken in the 1890s.

Artists still had one advantage though: they could produce color, while photographs were monochromatic. In 1861, James Clerk Maxwell reproduced an image of a tartan from three separate filtered photographs—red, green, and blue—when these were recombined by three projectors. Maxwell's film did not react to red light, so the experiment shouldn't have worked, but it did. By sheer luck, the red dye in the tartan also reflected ultraviolet wavelengths, the red filter also passed ultraviolet light, and the film recording the red portion was also sensitive to ultraviolet. So the emulsion that supposedly showed red light indicated red in just the right places, but it was an unconscious fake.

Lewis Carroll, mathematician and children's author, is less well known as a photographer. In "Hiawatha's Photographing," he exercises his skill in parody while describing the collodion process.

In 1840, J. W. Draper photographed the Moon and invented astronomical photography, and by the end of the nineteenth century, astronomical photography was normal, starting with Edward Emerson Barnard at the Lick Observatory in 1888. He was the first to discover a comet with the aid of photography, and also the last astronomer to discover a planetary satellite *without* the use of photography.

Late in the nineteenth century, the cheap Kodak camera was available to all, and Baudelaire's demand that photography be "the servant of the sciences and arts" had been met. Radiography, micrography, and astronomical spectral photography were all part of the scientist's tool kit. Bubble chambers and mass spectrographs lay ahead. So did integrated circuits, which are made by photographic methods.

By the 1850s, the advances were beginning to feed each other.

DEVELOPING THE ART OF EPIDEMIOLOGY

How we learned to apply careful observation, logic, and mathematics to finding the cause of a disease

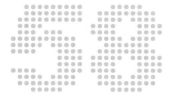

Date: 1853.

Location: Soho, London, England.

Discovery: That careful observation and recording can reveal where sickness comes from.

Discoverer: John Snow (1813–1858).

Impact: Once the source of a disease can be pinpointed, it can be attacked.

In early 2003, a disease called Severe Acute Respiratory Syndrome (SARS) emerged in China. At first, the Chinese authorities tried to keep it secret, and soon the disease spread in a major way to Vietnam, Hong Kong, and Canada, carried by air passengers who reached their destinations before any symptoms showed up. In those countries, it killed about 15–16 percent of those who were given good treatment.

Within a few weeks, virologists knew what caused the disease, and epidemiologists knew a lot about where it had come from (an animal), though even today we are unsure what the original source animal was. The disease was stopped because epidemiologists knew enough about the cause.

Epidemiologists are medically trained but they rely on knowledge, statistics, and logic. If children living on a river get bad diarrhea, if all the cases are in towns near the river, and the outbreaks spread down the river, this would give you a hint that there might be something wrong with the river water. Investigation might prove this suspicion wrong. It might be a disease-bearing mosquito that was being spread via the river, or something else. At least you could start testing some hypotheses.

There is a pub in Broadwick Street in London's Soho, just along from Carnaby Street. Called the John Snow, it does well from serving ales to epidemiologists, anesthetists—it is named after the same John Snow (55) who gave chloroform to Queen Victoria during her last two confinements—statisticians, and curious scientists. Just a little further along the street, there is a replica of a pump.

The original pump provided local people with water when Broad Street was there, but German bombs destroyed the area during World War II. Now, it is Broadwick Street, and local shopkeepers hush you if you say there was once an epidemic of cholera there. One must not alarm the tourists!

Tourists need not be alarmed—the outbreak was a long while ago: 1853, to be exact. In ten days, 500 people died of cholera in an area just 250 yards across. All the cases seemed to be in one small part of London, and centered on Broad Street. Snow, who had previously suspected that cholera was spread in drinking water, targeted that street.

The Broad Street pump took water from a well, and Snow suspected this water supply. But there were two puzzles he faced: some houses near the pump were free of cholera, and some cases were located quite a long way from the pump. By careful questioning, Snow found that some people from further away preferred to get water from the Broad Street pump because it "tasted better" than water from other pumps. These were just about the *only* distant people to get cholera. Then he found that the nearby people who used the pump but were cholera-free were tea drinkers, who never actually drank unboiled water from the pump.

"Infection" meant something different then. An infectious disease was caused by "infecting poisons," and on that model, boiling could work by destroying the poisons. It would be some years yet before people accepted that bacteria caused disease. But the match between pump and cholera was a convincing one, so Snow called for the removal of the pump handle, stopping people from using the water. This was done, and within days, the link was broken and the epidemic was a thing of the past.

Several years later, he famously drew and published a map showing the pattern of cholera cases near Broad Street. Each black dot indicated a house where somebody got cholera, and the local pumps were shown as well.

So why was the Broad Street pump polluted? Why weren't other pumps just as dangerous, when they were all taking water from the same chalk beds under London? Later research explained it for us. The outbreak started on August 31, three days after a baby at 40 Broad Street developed cholera. This was the house nearest to the well, and the toilet for this house was a cesspit, just like most of the other toilets in London. All human waste from the house went into this hole, right beside the well.

Cholera gives people a very bad case of the "runs" (or diarrhea, to give it its proper name). Cholera germs breed in the victim's small intestine, and they are flushed out with the "runs." This puts them into the cesspit, and from there into the well beside the cesspit. Leakage was inevitable.

In Hong Kong, at the height of the SARS outbreak, people wore protective masks as a precautionary measure.

Epidemiology demands subtle and creative minds, and the clever use of science and statistics. For example, the only visible difference between malaria-carrying mosquitoes and some related mosquito species which don't carry malaria is found in the hairs on their legs. Only careful and systematic microscopy can reveal details like that. Graphs, spreadsheets, maps, and tests can reveal more. Truth and honesty are essential, or any statistical analysis is a waste of time.

The World Health Organization figures on the SARS outbreak reveal something strange. In every country with a major SARS outbreak, except one, the mortality was closer to 15 percent: overall, the rest of the world (minus China) had a death rate of 14.4 percent. The Chinese authorities admitted to a death rate of just 6.4 percent. In a number of other ways, the Chinese data have the odor of manipulation about them. In Hong Kong, the mortality rate lifted at the end, as old cases died and no new cases arose, but in China, the death rate did not show this final upward flick.

The figures tell a grim story. Even at the end, it appears that somebody in China was still not facing up to the truth. Without absolute honesty, epidemiologists stand little chance in any future outbreak of disease. SARS was stopped in 2003, but only just, and it might not be stoppable next time.

Yet we know the epidemiologists will be out there, trying, and that has to be a step forward!

INVENTING ORGANIC DYES

How we learned to make dyes from coal tar

Coal gas lighting began slowly after William Murdock patented a process to make the gas in 1804, but by the 1850s, most cities and towns had at least street lighting running on gas. People could buy "village-sized" gas-making systems to supply small communities, and even a few hotels had their own gas-making systems.

In 1850, James Young gained a patent for making oil from coal, so even more coal was fed into retorts and treated to extract the valuable components. But that left a problem: coal tar. This was the by-product of both oil and gas making, and it had few known uses. This seems odd, as coal gas was discovered by accident in the 1790s when the ninth Earl of Dundonald was trying to make tar that could be used to protect ships' woodwork and rope rigging. The real problem was that there was just too much of the stuff being produced in the 1850s.

Many chemical elements were known by then. World trade was doing well, and quite a few clever minds could see that many new industries needed chemistry.

August Wilhelm von Hofmann (1818–1892) studied chemistry with Justus von Liebig, then took a post at London's Royal College of Chemistry in 1845, where he was able to teach technique while chemical theory caught up. By 1857–58, August Kekulé (in Germany and Belgium), like Archibald Couper (in Scotland), had begun to develop some models for structures in carbon chemistry, although Kekulé's solution for the structure of benzene, C_6H_6, would not be ready until 1865.

With no idea of molecular structures to go on, all chemists had were the empirical formulas—counts of atom ratios in compounds. Quinine is actually $C_{20}H_{24}N_2O_2$, but the empirical formula—a set of simplified ratios—is $C_{10}H_{12}NO$. That tells us the ingredients, but is useless as a blueprint; a bit like saying that a clock contains twenty-three gears, forty-nine screws, and two springs.

So when von Hofmann decided that he might be able to obtain quinine from the aniline extracted from coal tar, he was being orthodox, rather than naïve and eccentric. William Perkin joined the Royal College of Chemistry in 1853, and by 1856 he was Hofmann's assistant. When he tried adding a single oxygen atom to allyl toluidine, $C_{10}H_{12}N$, to produce quinine, $C_{10}H_{12}NO$, this was standard chemistry for its time. Instead of quinine, he got a reddish powder, so he followed the same procedure again, but this time he started with aniline, and got a black powder which turned mauve when it was dissolved in alcohol.

Date: 1856.

Location: London, England.

Discovery: New chemicals can be derived from coal tar, a by-product of making coal oil and coal gas.

Discoverer: William Henry Perkin (1838–1907).

Impact: The dyes opened up a whole new world of chemistry.

Organic dyes derived from coal tar transformed fabric colors.

This would not have been all that surprising, because various chemists had been finding colored products based on aniline. But Perkin wondered if the color might serve as a dye. He tried it on a piece of silk, and tested to see if washing or sunlight would fade it. The dye stood up to these simple tests, so he sent some off to a Scottish dye works, and mauve received an enthusiastic response.

A year or so later, the commercial release saw mauve taken up by the Empress of France, Britain's Queen Victoria, and her daughter, the wife of Prussia's Crown Prince—and Perkin's fortune was made. Others followed his lead, and the 200 or so chemicals in coal tar were sorted, tested, treated with indignity and tested again, all in the name of finding new colors for the fashionable to wear.

A good dye remains fast. It attaches to fiber by forming a lock-and-key bond that withstands soaking, chemical attack and sunlight. Scientists realized that some of the materials that make up cell walls and cell membranes are similar to the silk, cotton, wool, and linen on which the dyes were used. There were subtle differences, though, and microscopists soon discovered that the new dyes attached strongly to certain types of cells, tissues, or cell parts, identifying them reliably. The textile dyes of the fabric makers became the stains of the histologists studying tissues in thin slices, and also of the bacteriologists.

One basic division in bacteriology, which is still used today, is between the Gram-negative bacteria (like *Salmonella*, *Legionella* and *Helicobacter*) on the one hand, and the Gram-positive bacteria (like *Staphylococcus* and *Streptococcus*) on the other. Gram-negative bacteria stain red or pink, while Gram-positive bacteria stain blue or violet. The new dyes helped researchers and medical workers identify different kinds of bacteria.

Paul Ehrlich (1854–1915) argued that if a stain could attach to a cell, and also to a drug molecule, it might help deliver a drug to a bacterial cell, killing it. He called this potentially impressive development a "magic bullet," and set out to find a magic bullet that would hunt downand kill the spirochete which caused syphilis. He famously succeeded with his 606th compound, which became known either as "606" or Salvarsan.

In the 1930s, Gerhard Domagk (1895–1964) found a dye called prontosil which killed bacteria, all by itself. He had proved its effectiveness on mice when his daughter developed a life-threatening streptococcal infection in her arm, which in those days could only be treated by amputation. He famously treated her with prontosil, and saved her arm. Antibiotics (89) would soon do even more, but the sulfa drugs like prontosil offered medical workers the hope of new weapons against bacteria.

And those dyes and drugs all came from evil-smelling waste stuff!

INVENTING STATISTICS

How we learned to deal with large masses of data

"If your experiment needs statistics, you ought to have done a better experiment," Lord Rutherford (86) is supposed to have said. Yet statistical analysis reveals the underlying truths in complex situations—the sorts of messes that true physicists used to shy away from.

It spoils the story, but Rutherford sat in on Horace Lamb's lectures on mathematical statistics so that he could improve his statistical analysis of alpha particle deflections, work which demanded serious work with statistics. Simple patterns lent themselves to simple analysis, with simple mathematics revealing the laws that lay beneath the patterns. But by the nineteenth century, nothing was quite so simple any more. The patterns were more complicated, and even physics needed statistics.

Many people helped invent statistics, but Florence Nightingale makes an excellent case study. While we may know her as the Lady of the Lamp, few people know that after she returned to London in 1857, she used statistics to argue for reforms in nursing.

First, aiming to rally public support, she prepared a pamphlet based on the report of a Royal Commission about the Crimean war campaign, where Britain and France had fought Russia. Her pamphlet, *Mortality in the British Army*, showed very clearly where the problems lay, and featured the first use of pictorial charts to present data. In fact, she was

Date: 1857.

Location: London, England.

Discovery: That large amounts of information can be easily organized and summarized.

Discoverer: Florence Nightingale (1820–1910).

Impact: Most medical and biological research, all social science research, and many other areas of scientific enquiry can only work by the use of statistics.

the originator of those kinds of diagrams we now find routinely in the financial pages, with wheat bags, or oil barrels, or human figures lined up like so many paper dolls to make a graph or chart.

She hammered away again in 1858 in her *Report on the Crimea*:

It is not denied that a large part of the British force perished from causes not the unavoidable or necessary results of war ... (10,053 men, or sixty percent per annum, perished in seven months, from disease alone, upon an average strength of 28,939. This mortality exceeds that of the Great Plague) ... The question arises, must what has here occurred occur again?

In 1858, Nightingale was elected to the newly formed Statistical Society and turned her attention to hospital statistics on disease and mortality. You could never, said Miss Nightingale, discover trends unless figures were kept systematically. She prepared a plan, published in 1859, for the keeping of uniform hospital statistics. Her aim—ambitious for those times—was to compare the mortality figures for each disease in different hospitals, which could not be done without a standard recording system.

Others could equally be listed as founders of statistics. John Graunt (1620–1674) published his *Observations on the Bills of Mortality of the City of London* in 1662. This has sometimes been attributed to Sir William Petty, but in 1939, George Udny Yule published a statistical analysis (what else?) to show that the sentence length in *Observations* did not match known samples of Petty's writing.

Graunt's figures became the basis of the first life insurance tables, but he also revealed some of the problems with the record system. For a small fee, a death from "French-pox" could be listed as "consumption," saving the family of the deceased much embarrassment, but hiding a medical truth.

Before the nineteenth century, statistics were just numbers describing the state of a nation, and this is what Mark Twain had in mind when he spoke of "Lies, damned lies, and statistics." Now, statistics began to take on a whole new meaning, with a statistic as a representative summary figure for a large number of measurements. The mean and standard deviation of a set of measures gives an experienced person an immediate impression, although lay people still say statistics cannot be trusted.

The simple fact is that figures don't lie, but liars can figure. "Statistics" always need to be looked at carefully, but the use of statistics in science is fully justified. Statistical analysis can reveal such things as Mendel (66) probably massaging his data, dishonest SARS figures (58), or Cyril Burt's fraudulent work on twins and inherited intelligence, where he faked his data. Statistics can also reveal amazing patterns, laws, and truths.

Adolphe Quetelet (1796–1874) was a brilliant mathematician who learned about probability in Paris, then returned to his native Belgium, where he started to explore the ideas of "social physics" and "moral

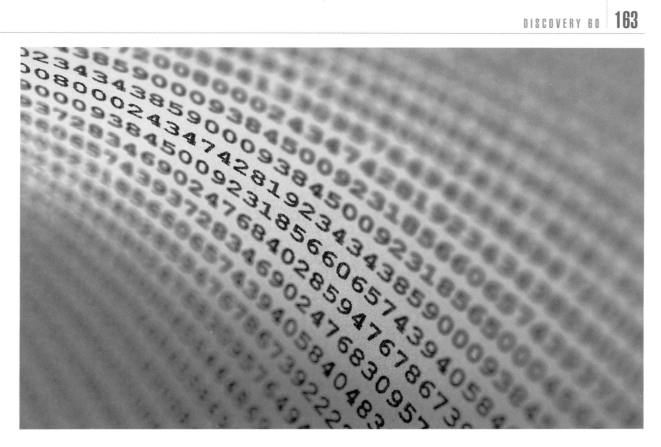

statistics." Quetelet was struck by the idea that there were many predictable sets of data. Crimes, suicides, and marriages all involved individual free choice, and yet happened at predictable rates in different age groups, giving him the starting point for his moral statistics.

Sad condition of the human race! We can tell beforehand how many will stain their hands with the blood of their fellow-creatures, how many will be forgers, how many poisoners, almost as one can foretell the number of births and deaths.

Statistics would end up being the glue that would bring together evolution and genetics in the 1920s, helping biologists to understand what was going on in large populations. In time, ecology would absorb pattern analysis as a powerful tool, just as numerical methods would find a place in biological taxonomy and classification.

Tied in with this were the tests of significance for a set of results, tests which provide an estimate of how likely the results are to mean something. It took statistics, wielded by epidemiologists, to prove what people suspected in the nineteenth century: that tobacco causes lung cancer and other diseases.

You *can* trust statistics—if they are properly used.

When numbers tell a story ...

INVENTING THE SPECTROSCOPE

How we found a way to look at bright and dark lines in a spectrum to learn new things

Date: 1859.

Location: Heidelberg, Germany.

Discovery: Chemical salts cause a flame to radiate light of characteristic wavelengths.

Discoverer: Robert Bunsen (1811–1899), and Gustav Kirchhoff (1824–1887).

Impact: It led to the Bunsen burner becoming popular, but it also gave us a way to identify chemicals and elements in small samples and distant stars.

As a close approximation, glass is sodium silicate. No chemist who has heated glass in a flame would doubt the sodium part—like common salt, glass gives a distinctive yellow color to the flame. We know now that there are actually two colors, with wavelengths of 589.592 and 588.995 nanometers, but for the moment, we can treat them as a single color.

The spectrum had come a long way since Isaac Newton's (34) examination of the "celebrated phenomenon of colors." While Newton's light source was an open hole, by the early 1800s scientists were using a narrow slit, in order to keep the colors as pure as possible. They examined the result through a small lens system, traditionally referred to as a telescope.

In 1802, an English chemist named William Hyde Wollaston (1766–1828) noticed a number of black lines in the spectrum of the Sun. Joseph von Fraunhofer (1787–1826) saw the same lines in 1814, and mapped them in more detail. He found 570 lines, and gave them names, according to their prominence. These days, better instruments can detect thousands of Fraunhofer lines across the solar spectrum, and Fraunhofer's D line can be distinguished as three separate lines.

Fraunhofer's newly-discovered lines seemed to make no real sense, because they were being viewed as gaps in the spectrum. In fact, each line represented a subtraction—the removal of a key wavelength—from a continuous spectrum, but the mystery stood for more than forty years before Gustav Kirchhoff and Robert Bunsen sorted it. Kirchhoff noted the similarity between some of the "dark" lines in the solar spectrum, and some of the "bright" lines of emission spectra. What happened next is best described in Kirchhoff's own words:

While engaged in a research carried out by Bunsen and myself in common on the spectra of colored flames, by which it became possible to recognize the qualitative composition of complicated mixtures from the appearance of their spectra in the flame of the blow pipe, I made some observations which give an unexpected explanation of the origin of the Fraunhofer lines and allow us to draw conclusions from them about the composition of the sun's atmosphere and perhaps also that of the brighter fixed stars.

Fraunhofer noticed that in the spectrum of a candle flame two bright lines occur which coincide with the two dark lines D of the solar spectrum. We obtain the same bright lines in greater intensity from a flame in which common salt is introduced. I arranged a solar spectrum and allowed the sun's

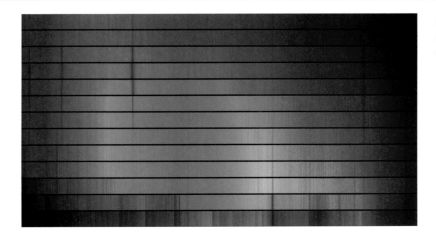

Comparison of the visible light spectra of thirteen types of stars. The dark spectral bands show stellar composition.

rays, before they fell on the slit, to pass through a flame heavily charged with salt. When the sunlight was sufficiently weakened, there appeared in place of the two dark D lines, two bright lines; if its intensity, however, exceeded a certain limit the two dark D lines showed much more plainly than when the flame charged with salt was not present.

As we understand it today, sodium ions in the flame absorb energy. The energy goes into moving an electron from a lower-energy orbital to a higher-energy orbital. According to some ideas we will look at later, that quantum—that very precise packet of energy, the exact energy difference between the two orbitals—is associated with a particular wavelength.

If light passes through a cloud of sodium ions, light of exactly the frequency of the sodium line (and only that frequency) will be extracted and used to "excite" electrons. Later, if the electrons drop back down to a lower energy level, they will emit light of exactly the same frequency. Kirchhoff then described other similar experiments in which flames "doped" with either sodium or lithium act as either absorbers or emitters on limelight and sunlight.

I conclude from these observations that a colored flame in whose spectrum bright sharp lines appear so weakens rays of the color of these lines, if they pass through it, that dark lines appear in place of the bright ones, whenever a source of light of sufficient intensity, in whose spectrum these lines are otherwise absent, is brought behind the flame.

Later, Anders Ångström used this method to show there was hydrogen in the Sun, and Norman Lockyer would find helium there as well, while William Crookes detected thallium, without ever seeing it, by finding a green line in a spectrum from some residues in a sulfuric acid factory.

Kirchhoff and Bunsen got the credit for inventing spectroscopy, based on the flame of the Bunsen burner (which was originated by Michael Faraday (48) and made by laboratory technician Peter Desaga). Bunsen just demonstrated its effectiveness and made it popular. Desaga made quite a lot of money from selling the things, so everybody came out all right in the end, except, maybe, Faraday.

According to legend, Bunsen suspected his landlady had used leftover meat in her stews, so one night he sprinkled some scraps on his plate with lithium chloride. The next night, he tested a sample of the stew in front of witnesses and showed that it gave off the brilliant red flame characteristic of lithium. This element, he noted, is not meant to be found in stews. Exit left one highly embarrassed landlady, I imagine.

The spectroscope would one day prove to be a basic tool for a revolution in cosmology, but 1859 had a few rather more immediate revolutions to deliver.

DISPROVING SPONTANEOUS GENERATION

How Louis Pasteur showed that life only comes from existing life

Date: 1859.

Location: Paris, France.

Discovery: That life only arises from life.

Discoverer: Louis Pasteur (1822–1895).

Impact: Once spontaneous generation was ruled out as a possibility, the only source for new species had to be evolution.

When Johann Baptista van Helmont (27) said a sweaty shirt and wheat could give rise to mice, most people accepted this. Most people, but not everybody. And it was the same when people said that maggots just grew out of old food. A few scientists might fall for that, but practical people knew to cover their food to keep the flies off.

Francesco Redi (1626–1698) believed that adult flies came from maggots which came from eggs laid by adult flies, and he had support from a Greek poet named Homer, who lived around the eighth or seventh century BC and wrote the *Iliad*—the story of the Trojan wars.

Towards the end of the story, the hero Achilles was encouraged by his mother, the sea nymph Thetis, to put on the special armor made for him by the god Vulcan, and to get back into the battle. Achilles had stopped fighting because his best friend Patroclus had been killed, and he told Thetis he was unwilling to fight, because if he left his friend's body, the flies would attack it and worms (maggots) would grow in it. Thetis told him she could deal with that.

Here is how Alexander Pope translated the story of what Thetis did, once Achilles had marched off into battle:

Then in the nostrils of the slain she pour'd
Nectareous drops, and rich ambrosia shower'd
O'er all the corse. The flies forbid their prey,
Untouch'd it rests, and sacred from decay.

Redi read his Homer in 1668, understood it, and tested it out.

A flask used by Louis Pasteur during his experiments with bacteria, in Pasteur's original laboratory, now part of the Pasteur Institute, Paris, France.

I put a snake, some fish, some eels of the Arno, and a slice of milk-fed veal in four large, wide-mouthed flasks; having well closed and sealed them, I then filled the same number of flasks in the same way, only leaving these open. It was not long before the meat· and the fish in these second vessels became wormy and flies were seen entering and leaving at will; but in the closed flasks I did not see a worm, though many days had passed since the dead flesh had been put in them. Outside on the paper cover there was now and then a deposit, or a maggot that eagerly sought some crevice by which to enter and obtain nourishment. Meanwhile the different things placed in the flasks had become putrid and stinking.

Not content with these experiments, I tried many others at different seasons, using different vessels. In order to leave nothing undone, I even had pieces of meat put under ground, but though remaining buried for weeks, they never bred worms, as was always the case when flies had been allowed to light on the meat.

As we can see, well before 1700, there were clear indications that life did not pop up out of nowhere. Still, as long as people believed life could just appear, there would be no scientific understanding of why food went "off." People thought it was the nature of food to turn into worms after a few days. And if mice could develop from wheat and sweaty shirts, there was no reason to wonder where the species came from.

Around 1748, science went backwards for a while when Georges Louis Leclerc, Comte de Buffon (1707–1788), in Paris, and John Needham (1713–1781), in England, declared that they had seen micro-organisms spontaneously springing up in jars of sterilized meat broth which had been boiled to kill all life. Buffon was satisfied with this as proof that organic particles had some special power which allowed them to form living things.

Lazzaro Spallanzani (1729–1799) showed in 1770 that some organisms could stand forty-five minutes of boiling, but that a broth, carefully boiled, and sealed from the air, would not develop life until it was unsealed again. Opponents argued that the long boiling had destroyed the "vital principle" in the air inside the flasks, and people believed this until Louis Pasteur's experiment, which he published in 1860.

Pasteur had been asked to look at souring in wine. Lactic acid was forming in the wine, and it seemed to be a chemical problem. After microscopic studies, he saw that the problem came from tiny yeast cells in the wine—one type produced alcohol, the other produced lactic acid, and continued to do so after the wine was bottled. His answer was to recommend a gentle heating of the wine to kill the lactic acid yeast. The wine growers were horrified but tried it, and it worked.

Perhaps somebody asked him where the yeast came from, but whatever happened, he turned next to the question of spontaneous generation. He prepared flasks of clear broth which remained open to the air, stopping any arguments about vital principles, but he added an extra twist: each flask ended in a long, drawn-out glass tube which was heated and bent like a swan's neck, so as to stop any spores drifting along through the air and falling into the broth. Spores might enter the tube, but they would stick to the sides, and there was no chance of them ever reaching the broth.

At any time, the glass tube could be snapped off short, and soon the clear broth would turn cloudy as spores fell through the opening. It was neat, it was repeatable, and people repeated it, over and over, all around the world, always with the same results. So long as the neck was intact, the open flasks had no organisms in them.

Spontaneous generation was dead. Pasteur was ready to start fighting infectious diseases—those we now regard as being caused by microbes.

UNDERSTANDING EVOLUTION

How Charles Darwin explained the way evolution happens

Most people think Charles Darwin "invented" evolution, but what he did was far cleverer: he worked out how evolution happened. He was not the first to suggest evolution by natural selection, but he was the first to explain it in fine detail, and the first to present detailed evidence for natural selection as the force driving evolution.

Biology was now better understood. Spontaneous generation theory was out, and scientists knew that cells arose only from previous cells, so the idea of species evolving was reasonable in 1859. Some thought species were unchangeable, because in the lifetime of a human, no real change can be seen. But other people not only accepted that species changed: they also had ideas about what made the changes happen.

In 1680, Edward Tyson dissected a porpoise and showed it was a mammal, not a fish. He later dissected a young chimpanzee which had died, and published illustrations which showed just how close humans were to the other animals. Copernicus had removed the Earth from the center of the universe, but Tyson removed *Homo sapiens* from a central position in creation. This was the "missing link" between humans and the whole of "lower" creation, and the idea, based on the fish-shaped porpoise, that environment shapes appearance, was up for discussion.

Darwin's grandfather, Erasmus Darwin, thought exercise or disuse caused people to change, and these changes were inherited. A blacksmith with heavy muscles often had strong children, and Erasmus thought the muscles acquired by exercise were passed on somehow. Today, we would assume that the blacksmith took up his profession because he had good muscles, and passed his genes for good muscles to his children.

In Paris, Jean Baptiste Pierre Antoine de Monet Lamarck (1744–1829) had a similar idea about the inheritance of acquired characteristics. Even Charles Darwin thought there might be something in it. At least it was better than the notion of the Comte de Buffon (1707–1788), who thought species changed by degeneration. To Buffon, a donkey was a horse gone bad, and the mammoths and mastodons whose fossil remains were then being found in Siberia and North America were more perfect forms which had been replaced by their descendants, the "degenerate" elephants of Africa and India.

So long as the Earth was considered to be very young, so long as the fossils of extinct animals could be dismissed as the losers during Noah's flood, and so long as people did not travel and collect specimens from around the world, many of the patterns of life would be hidden. While

Date: 1859.

Location: Down, Kent, England.

Discovery: Natural selection is all we need to explain why the evidence of evolution is all around us.

Discoverer: Charles Robert Darwin (1809–1882).

Impact: A viable explanation of how evolution works is essential to understanding the history of the planet, ecology and, more importantly, the interaction between humans and disease.

Darwin's close study of Galapagos finches was instrumental in his development of the idea of natural selection.

species obviously changed, most people could not work out where new species came from.

A few people could see it, though. In the second edition of *On The Origin of Species*, issued about six weeks after the first, Darwin listed many writers who had proposed evolution by natural selection before him, starting in 1813, with the frequency getting greater as time went by.

Darwin first realized that nature might favor some varieties over others in the late 1830s, but he hesitated to say anything in public. In 1844, he shared his ideas with botanist John Hooker (1817–1911), who is supposed to have shouted, "Why did I not think of that?" He also discussed it with geologist Charles Lyell (1797–1875), and from about 1856 he corresponded with American botanist Asa Gray (1810–1888) on the topic, still gathering more evidence, still hesitating.

In 1858, Alfred Russel Wallace (1823–1913) wrote a letter to Darwin which forced the issue. Wallace had reached much the same conclusion, and drew up a neat essay explaining it. He sent the essay to Darwin, suggesting that he might like to read it and, if appropriate, pass it on to the Linnean Society of London, the most important natural history society in Britain. Dismayed, Darwin discussed the letter with his friends, proposing that he should simply put forward Wallace's essay.

Wallace had come up with the idea of natural selection, as Darwin had, after reading Malthus, but unlike Wallace, Darwin had been collecting evidence and examples for a decade and a half. So Darwin's friends wrote a covering letter, signed by Lyell and Hooker, and put together a package that included Darwin's 1844 outline, extracts from a letter to Gray, written in 1857, and Wallace's essay. They delivered this package to the Linnean Society. In the end, Darwin got the lion's share of the credit, because having been "outed," he now settled down to write his book, *On The Origin of Species*, which spread the idea to a much wider audience.

The main thrust of Darwin's book—the favoring of certain varieties by natural selection—has never changed, though we change some of the details of the theory as we learn more.

Some people oppose evolution because they think life is too improbable to occur by chance, but as Sir Ronald Fisher (1890–1962) said, linking statistical genetics and evolution, "natural selection is a mechanism for generating an exceedingly high degree of improbability."

Science is made up of a number of basic ideas which often depend on and confirm others in the same basic set, but evolution is central to almost everything. Evolutionary assumptions even tell petroleum geologists where to search.

DISCOVERING PETROLEUM

How we learned to get oil from beneath the ground

We had oil long before we had oil wells. People used whale oil, tallow (animal fat), linseed oil and other vegetable oils, and from 1850 onwards, there was crude oil. Not crude oil from an oil well, but crude oil distilled from coal, and which could be refined to different oils that could be used in different ways.

The major need was for bulk quantities of something that would provide both lighting and lubricants. Gas lights were fine if you had the pipes to deliver the gas, but for portable lights, people used either a lantern with a candle in it, or a lamp with a wick that brought some sort of oil up from a reservoir to be burned. Old steam engines and the wheels of carts turned slowly, so they only required an occasional dab of tallow. But as faster engines and locomotives were developed, better lubricating oils were needed.

Some vegetable oils like linseed oil were useless as lubricants because they were "drying oils." They left a gummy surface that could seize up an engine or wheel bearing. Whale oil was a good lubricant and it did not smell when it burned in a lamp, but the cost was high: even in the 1850s, the Atlantic whale population was falling fast, and the Pacific whales were headed the same way. Coal oil was beginning to fill the gaps, but in 1859, Edwin Drake decided to improve the yield of "rock oil" that he was extracting from an oil spring.

Date: 1859.

Location: Titusville, Pennsylvania, USA.

Discovery: That oil can be obtained by drilling into underground reservoirs.

Discoverer: Edwin Drake (1819–1880).

Impact: There was now a new source of energy and raw materials for industry.

Finding oil was easy at first. People went to places where oil seeped out of the ground, places they called oil springs. They just collected the material in buckets as it oozed out. The Pennsylvania Rock Oil Company had bought rights to one such oil spring for $5,000 and leased it to Edwin Drake in exchange for a royalty of 12.5 cents a gallon.

By the time Drake decided to sink an oil well, American engineers at Louisville, Kentucky had already sunk an artesian well shaft 2,086 feet deep, so Drake's Pennsylvania drilling exercise was relatively easy. He had a small hole drilled down some 70 feet at the oil "spring," raising the yield from 400 gallons of oil a day to 1,600 gallons.

Understanding oil geology took time and subtle methods. Drillers had to obtain samples of the rock being drilled, and then look at microfossils which indicated the age of the rock they were drilling. Over time, an orthodox theory grew up, which said that oil was formed from the remains of prehistoric plants and animals, in much the same way that coal is formed. On that theory, oil is an organic substance, laid down in sedimentary rocks. It is a theory which has worked very well for oil companies for a century and a half.

Now the global demand for oil is enormous, and known supplies are running low. Even accepted orthodoxies can be questioned, especially at times like this. We will see how the "steady state" model of the universe, proposed by three astrophysicists, was overthrown by the "Big Bang" model in the 1960s (97). Each of the steady state people later adopted a maverick position on some part of science. Fred Hoyle and Chandra Wickramasinghe claimed that diseases come from space; Hoyle was also convinced (wrongly) that the fossil *Archaeopteryx* was a fake. And Thomas Gold (1920–2004) argued that oil did not come from former living things.

Science is full of "way out" ideas and, just occasionally, one of them is accepted. Think of black holes, Darwinian evolution, plate tectonics, the wave theory of light, quantum physics, or Pasteur's germ theory, all now accepted. In the 1990s, I listened to Gold in lectures and debates, I met him twice and interviewed him once. I am *sure* Hoyle and Wickramasinghe's ideas about diseases were wrong. I *suspect* Gold's idea is wrong—but it is still there, waiting for proper testing.

Gold said the Arabian Gulf oil fields have no common features at any depth, except that they all lie over an area of great seismic activity. The area contains 60 percent of the world's recoverable hydrocarbons. From the mountains of south-eastern Turkey down to the Persian Gulf, the plains of Saudi Arabia and the mountains of Iran, there is a continuous band of oil fields, but nobody can find an adequate supply of source rocks to account for the oil being there.

Gold thought the true source was about 100 miles down, that it had seeped up through cracks opened when the Earth moved, and that the hydrocarbons had been down there since the planet formed. He argued that when we first discovered petroleum back in the 1800s, it was close

to the surface, and chemists thought the only place you found carbon chemicals was in living things. They even named carbon chemistry "organic chemistry," because it was the chemistry of organisms. The theory was that oil was made of organic chemicals, so it obviously had to come from organisms.

But comets contain "organic" chemicals, and so does Jupiter. Nobody says the methane on Jupiter came from giant Jovians breaking wind, or that little green people on the comets produce the organic stuff there. If we discovered oil today, claimed Gold, we would never say it came from plants and animals, not with what we know about other planets in the solar system.

I asked him why we have never found oil in igneous rocks. He grinned, and told me that 12 tons of oil had been taken from one hole in granite (a very common igneous rock) in Sweden. I asked why oil companies don't try drilling in granite and his grin grew broader. Any geologist who suggested that would be judged mad and sacked for wasting money on a futile search, he told me.

It remains a fascinating idea. We desperately need oil for energy, and as a raw material: I wonder how long it will be before somebody is desperate enough to start Granite Oil Inc?

If they do, I don't think I will buy any shares, but it might be interesting to watch what happens. You can never tell which weird ideas about science will turn out to work.

In the not too distant future, oil wells like this could become a thing of the past.

INVENTING THE INTERNAL COMBUSTION ENGINE

How we acquired an engine which did not make us wait until the boiler heated up

Date: 1860.

Location: Paris, France.

Discovery: A cylinder with a spark plug, and filled with an explosive mixture, can power a vehicle.

Discoverer: Jean Joseph Etienne Lenoir (1822–1900).

Impact: This was the start of the practical internal combustion engine, found in motor vehicles, aircraft, water craft, and diesel locomotives. Our society would collapse without the internal combustion engine.

The idea of a self-powered vehicle, literally, a "locomotive," is an old one. The earliest locomotive was a lumbering steam-powered giant which ran in the streets of Paris in 1769. It was invented by a military engineer, Nicolas Joseph Cugnot (1725–1804), who hoped to use it to haul heavy guns into place on the battlefield. As well as being very slow, it kept running out of steam and had to stop to build up pressure again. It was also highly unstable, and development soon stopped.

In 1807, the world's first internal combustion vehicle may have moved under the control of Isaac de Rivaz (1752–1828), but first we need to look back to 1777, when Alessandro Volta invented his "pistol." This was a container that could be filled with gas and air, and then exploded with a static electric spark. Volta's idea was to use the device to study the composition of gases, but it quickly became a popular novelty.

Once Volta's batteries (42) were announced, people toyed with laying wires to fire off a "Voltaic pistol" at a distance, to send a signal. Others used hydrogen–oxygen mixtures to make alarming bangs. A few even used Volta's pistol to fire projectiles, though the force was weak.

Isaac de Rivaz believed the force that could throw a lead ball 20 feet might also push a wheel around. Some accounts say that in 1807 he actually got a vehicle to cross a room, but the plans show that the gases had to be mixed by hand, and the spark had to be set off by hand. It was an impractical device, but it contained the idea of internal combustion.

During the next half-century, mechanics developed many new tricks before Jean Lenoir, a French-speaking Belgian, settled in Paris. From an interest in electroplating, he turned to electrical telegraphy, and from there, he created a sparking system which could keep a two-stroke engine running. This was not a two-stroke engine as we understand it, because the fuel/air mix was not compressed before ignition. It ran on coal gas, then called "illuminating gas" because it was mainly used in gas lights. The first model was noisy and inefficient, and the engine tended to overheat and seize up, but it ran.

In September 1860, *Scientific American* reported on Lenoir's "new caloric engine." Even the French Emperor had examined it, and the journal

quoted a French newspaper, *Cosmos*, which declared the age of steam dead. The engine could be started when needed, and *Scientific American* thought the invention would be useful for driving sewing machines in the home, where a piped gas supply was becoming more common.

As it happened, the age of steam was not quite over, but the *Scientific American* reporter was clever to think of using Lenoir's engine on sewing machines. Because Lenoir engines used coal gas, most of the early versions were stationary power supplies which drove pumps and printing presses. But the new world order was visible, and the way was open to make improvements, most of them using spark plugs. In 1863, a Lenoir vehicle traveled 12 miles in eleven hours, showing that by then it could keep going, even if at slower than walking pace.

Others thought about the principle of the fire piston (1), the method used in South-East Asia to make fire. If a cylinder is compressed quickly, the contents get very hot, and if those contents are a suitable mix of fuel and air, the fuel will ignite. In time, a great deal of heavy haulage would rely on diesel engines which used the fire piston principle.

In 1876, Nikolaus August Otto (1832–1891) built the first practical four-stroke internal combustion engine. He called it the "Otto Cycle Engine," and installed one in a motorcycle. All later engines running on liquid fuel were based on his design—and it is worth stressing the "liquid fuel" part. Although Drake's oil well (64) started producing oil just as Lenoir was putting the finishing touches on his design, even in 1901, when fifty vehicles joined the Paris to Roubaix rally, the preferred fuel was a 50-50 mix of gasoline and ethanol (often made by fermenting beet-sugar), with some vehicles still using pure ethanol.

In time, as gasoline distribution improved, it took over from other options as the standard fuel, though there remain pockets of resistance: in the Kimberley region of north-western Australia, for example, diesel is the fuel of choice, and drivers hoping to buy gasoline can find themselves stranded.

As engines became more demanding, chemicals like tetraethyl lead were added to fuel, wasting a valuable resource and poisoning two generations, to a greater or lesser extent. Even though we fixed that problem when catalytic converters were added to cars to reduce the nitrogen oxides and other exhaust pollutants, carbon dioxide continues to escape. There are many sources for atmospheric CO_2, but automobile engines are significant contributors.

If global warming overtakes us, what will our descendants think of internal combustion (or steam, for that matter) as a "great discovery"?

DISCOVERING GENETICS

How the everyday knowledge of practical plant and animal breeders became a set of scientific laws and then a science

Date: 1865.

Location: Brno, Austro-Hungarian Empire (now the Czech Republic).

Discovery: Inheritance is delivered to offspring in ways that obey mathematical laws.

Discoverer: Gregor Mendel (1822–1884).

Impact: Once they were understood, Mendel's laws of inheritance allowed others to develop modern genomics.

The son of a peasant, Gregor Mendel looked after the fruit trees of his father's master. When he became an Augustinian monk, he was sent to Vienna to study mathematics and science, and became a teacher in 1854. In 1857, he began the experiments that would make him famous. These involved growing pea varieties, and investigating the offspring of various crosses. Here is an excerpt from Mendel's original paper:

Experience with artificial fertilization, such as is effected with ornamental plants in order to obtain new variations in color, has led to the experiments which will here be discussed. The striking regularity with which the same hybrid forms always reappeared whenever fertilization took place between the same species [i.e. hybrid forms] induced further experiments to be undertaken, the object of which was to follow up the developments of the hybrids in their progeny.

In brief, what he found was that inheritance is not blending: there are separate characters—the things we now call "genes"—and one of these is usually dominant over the other. This meant that what we call a mutant—the thing Charles Darwin (63) called "a sport"—would not be swamped under the mass of other genes in the population.

Imagine a population of fair-haired people, where a single mutant for black hair shows up. Darwin believed that blending would occur; that as the generations passed, the "dark hair" characteristic would spread, like a drop of ink in a bucket of water, so that everybody would have hair just a shade darker than before. On this basis, after the first appearance, there would never be another person with truly black hair, until another mutant arose.

What Mendel showed was that the genes do not blend; that the original character, in its original form, can return in a later generation. From the way he planned his experiment, it is probable that he already knew, from earlier trials, the results he would get from the test crosses that he carried out. Many nineteenth century plant breeders seem to have assumed something similar.

While Darwin was still puzzling the matter, Mendel had provided the answer and published it, but nobody noticed, for almost forty years. Then, in the one year, 1900, three different scientists—Carl Correns, Hugo de Vries, and Erich von Tschermak-Seysenegg—all rediscovered Mendel's work, but only after each of them had repeated some of Mendel's discoveries.

Suddenly, the world was ready for Mendel's genetics. Well, more or less ready—there were misinterpretations all over the place, which is why G. H. Hardy had to step in with his mathematical interpretation, which we now call the Hardy-Weinberg Law. Biology had been all about observation and natural history, and now, all of a sudden, people needed to have a sophisticated understanding of probability and statistics.

Within fifteen years, Thomas Hunt Morgan (1866–1945), the first giant of genetics, was on the scene, and the advances of twentieth century biology were under way. It would be a dizzy ride, but it began with peas in a monastery garden. Morgan won the 1933 Nobel Prize for Physiology and Medicine, mainly because he established the famous Columbia fly room, where the first serious laboratory genetics research took place. Given Mendel's results, and a firm faith in the existence of mutants (based on some wrong assumptions by Hugo de Vries), Morgan's team bred fruit flies (*Drosophila melanogaster*), checked the progeny for mutations and eventually found some, then used these to test inheritance.

Most importantly, they gathered the proof that the genes, whatever they were, were found on the chromosomes. They did not know it, but they were taking the first steps to modern genome mapping as they identified groups of genes that seemed to be linked together. Here, Morgan uses the fruit fly's old name, *Drosophila ampelophila*, as he discusses linked genes.

If the factors in heredity are carried in the chromosomes and if the chromosomes are definite structures, we should anticipate that there should be as many groups of characters as there are kinds of chromosomes. In only one case has a sufficient number of characters been studied to show whether there is any correspondence between the number of hereditary groups of characters and the

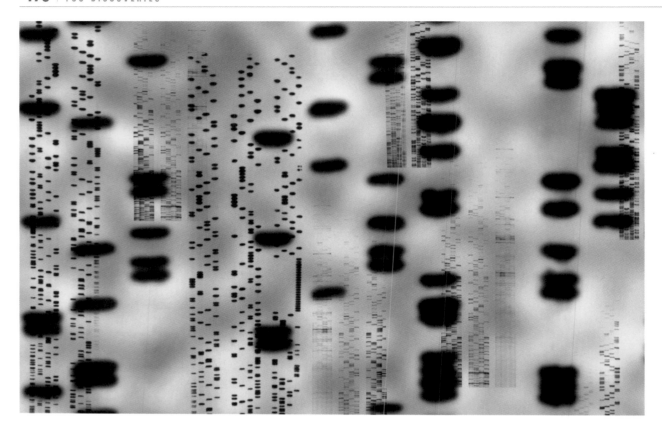

This autoradiogram image shows detail of DNA sequences. DNA sequences can be used for almost anything, from identifying criminals or dead bodies to identifying the source of ivory or drugs, or even to spot the different species of lizards which appear identical.

number of chromosomes. In the fruit fly, Drosophila ampelophila, *we have found about a hundred and twenty-five characters that are inherited in a perfectly definite way …*

If the factors for these characters are carried by the chromosomes, then we should expect that those factors that are carried by the same chromosomes would be inherited together, provided the chromosomes are definite structures in the cell.

In the chromosome group of Drosophila *there are four pairs of chromosomes, three of nearly the same size and one much smaller. Not only is there agreement between the number of hereditary groups and the number of the chromosomes, but even the size relations are the same, for there are three great groups of characters and three pairs of large chromosomes, and one small group of characters and one pair of small chromosomes …*

With the chromosome identified as the place where genes were located, the stage was set for genes to be mapped, for DNA (94) to be understood, and for genomics (100) to develop.

Without Mendel showing us that inheritance "factors" existed, none of that could have happened.

DISCOVERING ANTISEPSIS

How we learned to carry out surgery and cure more than we killed

There is a disease of cattle called rinderpest. When it caused an epidemic in Britain in 1865, the British just called it "cattle plague." It had been seen in England before, but this was the worst outbreak ever, thanks mainly to the railways. It showed up first at London's Islington cattle markets in June 1865, but within a month it had reached East Anglia, Shropshire, and Scotland. A combination of free trade and railway cattle cars meant diseases like rinderpest could spread further and faster, especially as nobody knew how or why cattle plague was spreading.

Something had to be done, declared the people who wrote *The Times* editorials, and the public agreed. Unfortunately, the editorial writers did not only demand action. They also insisted that some sort of poison was spreading and causing the disease, but at that time, they were not alone in holding this theory. Most of the leading medical men still regarded infection as something that was poison-based.

A Royal Commission was set up. By then, the germ theory was starting to catch on, yet the Commissioners repeatedly referred to a poison causing the disease: "the blood contains the poison of the disease, so that serum obtained from it will give the disease by inoculation," and a little later, "the poison contained in a minute portion of the mucous discharge ... multiplies when it is injected into an animal, and so causes it to sicken in turn."

To us, any poison that "multiplies" can only be alive, but like biology, chemistry was a bit weaker back then, and people could believe that poisons might multiply in some way. Still, if we read what the Commissioners said about disinfection, they were close to the mark:

Disinfection, in the sense in which the word is used here, implies the destruction of an animal poison in whatever way it is accomplished. To find a perfect disinfectant for the Cattle Plague poison would be to stop the disease at once.

Antiseptics, as the name implies, were used "against rottenness," whatever caused it. An infectious disease was originally one caused by an unhealthy house, so a disinfectant was something which got rid of the infecting poison, just like the bouquets of flowers held by English judges to ward off "jail fever," which they thought was caused by the evil smells that were common in prisons.

From 1854 onwards, "McDougall's Powder" had been sold as a sewage deodorant. It was mainly carbolic acid, a poisonous material that could

Date: 1865.

Location: Glasgow, Scotland.

Discovery: That surgery could be carried out without patients becoming infected.

Discoverer: Joseph, Lord Lister (1827–1912).

Impact: The work led to much higher survival rates from surgery.

Early surgery was made safer by Joseph Lister's antiseptic methods.

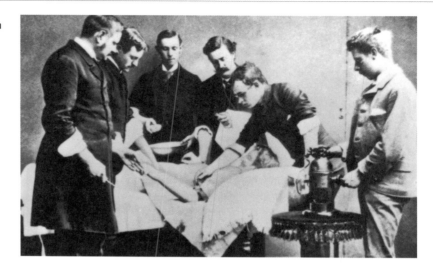

be extracted from coal-tar, and Alexander McDougall had tried using it against parasites of cattle in 1864. When Joseph Lister heard of this, he used a carbolic spray in antiseptic surgery. But was he targeting a poison, or bacterial parasites? He knew Pasteur's work and he must have understood how the carbolic acid "disinfected." His method worked, and by 1867, an exultant Lister wrote in the *British Medical Journal*:

But since the antiseptic treatment has been brought into full operation, and wounds and abscesses no longer poison the atmosphere with putrid exhalations, my wards, though in other respects under precisely the same circumstances as before, have completely changed their character; so that during the last nine months not a single instance of pyaemia, hospital gangrene or erysipelas has occurred in them. As there appears to be no doubt regarding the cause of this change, the importance of the fact can hardly be exaggerated.

An 1866 report by the Royal Commission pointed to evidence that chlorine, ozone, sulfurous acid and the tar acids "all actually do destroy the Cattle Plague poison." The poison model gave results, but in the long term, people did best when they assumed a microbe model of disease; by then, all the evidence indicated that microbes cause disease.

By the 1860s, anesthetics were standard, but the theory of infection was still hazy. A Hungarian physician, Ignaz Semmelweis (1818–1865) targeted the problem when he made students wash their hands after carrying out post mortems, and before touching live patients. This blocked the transmission of deadly puerperal fever ("childbed fever"). You could explain it by saying the washing had removed the "poison." But germs were close to being accepted. Here is Lister from that same 1867 article:

… I arrived, several years ago, at the conclusion that the essential cause of suppuration in wounds is decomposition, brought about by the influence of the atmosphere upon blood or serum retained within them … But when it had been shown by the researches of Pasteur that the septic property of the atmosphere

depended, not on the oxygen or any gaseous constituent, but on minute organisms suspended in it, which owed their energy to their vitality, it occurred to me that decomposition in the injured part might be avoided without excluding the air, by applying as a dressing some material capable of destroying the life of the floating particles.

Lister carried out operations while spraying the wounded area with carbolic acid. He used it first on a compound fracture of the lower leg, a break where bone had pierced the skin. In 1865, the normal treatment for such a wound was amputation, because bacteria in the wound would invariably make it "go septic," killing the patient. In 1869, Lister started using a steam spray to kill bacteria, but he always operated in his street clothes. The modern protocols of antisepsis took time to work out.

Over time, the germ theory gained support and the reforms that were introduced to kill smells were extended to fighting germs and preventing infections. Surgery could now proceed, limited only by the lack of antibiotics to fight escaped infections.

DISCOVERING THE CONCEPT OF ECOLOGY

How we realized that life forms all interact and depend on each other and on the environment

Ask scientists when ecology first started, and they are more likely to say 1966 than 1866. But by 1866, competent biologists could see how evolution was driven by species interacting with each other, while physicists could see that all life got its energy from the Sun, which drove photosynthesis for plants, which fed animals, which fed other animals. Many of the fine details were missing, but the basic outline of ecology was there.

Ecology became a science when the interactions of evolution (63) were viewed as a question of the energy (54) needs of organisms. In the late 1850s, the energy needs of humans were seen only in terms of warmth. The reality is, however, that humans and other animals need food not only to maintain body temperature, but to power body systems and muscles—and also for growth and replacement of tissues.

In 1893, John Burdon-Sanderson (1828–1905) was a physiologist interested mainly in electrical changes in tissues, but he could see the future. In his Presidential Address to the British Association for the Advancement of Science that year, he observed that "oecology" was, along with physiology and morphology, one of the three great divisions of biology. He said Ernst Haeckel had coined the word some twenty years earlier, but it was now one of the central tenets of biology.

Date: 1866.

Location: Jena, Germany.

Discovery: Species are interdependent, forming balanced communities.

Discoverer: Ernst Haeckel (1834–1919).

Impact: Modern environmental awareness stems from ecological science.

He added that it was in some ways the most attractive of the three, because it came closest to the spirit of what had once been called the "philosophy of living nature." In other words, natural history was back again in a new and scientific suit of clothes. The accepted modern spelling of "ecology" was used at the International Botanical Congress in the same year, and Eugenius Warming published the first textbook of ecology (he used the Danish *økologiske*) in 1895. *The Journal of Ecology* began in 1912, while the American journal, *Ecology*, was first published in 1920.

When you look back, people were thinking about ecology well before those dates. In 1801, a Prussian polymath called Alexander von Humboldt (1769–1859) was scrambling up the northern Andes with a French botanist, Aimé Bonpland (1773–1858), and unlike those who had gone before them, they noticed changes in the types of plants which were found at different levels: they had detected what we now call altitudinal zonation.

With a local companion and guide, they set an altitude record when they reached 18,096 feet on Chimborazo. Stopped there by a crevasse, the trio had discovered "mountain sickness," and were bleeding from the gums. But close to his highest point, Humboldt sketched the summit, and added to it the names of all the plants and their relative heights. Then and there, he developed the idea of plant associations: groups tied together by environmental factors like climate and soil.

More importantly, he wrote an account of what he had seen, and in 1831, a fresh young Cambridge graduate, Charles Darwin, read Alexander von Humboldt's *Personal Narrative of Travels to the Equinoctial Regions of the New Continent*. Later, Darwin said that reading the *Personal Narrative* was the foundation of his whole career.

There was another significant base for ecology in the growing art of measurement and statistics. No doubt a few natural historians of the old school were as affronted by this as William Harvey's opponents were when he "doffed the habit of the anatomist" (and measured blood flow) (26), but good science can only come from measurement and investigation. The results needed to be quantified, and even if much modern ecology is about quality, it is nevertheless a quality that can be measured.

Three years after Burdon-Sanderson praised and promoted ecology, a Swedish chemist, Svante Arrhenius (1859–1927), suggested in 1896 that using fossil fuels might lead to global warming. He was investigating possible causes for the ice ages, and realized that the surface of our planet only remains habitable because we have a blanket of carbon dioxide. Doubling the amount of CO_2, he said, could produce a 9°F rise in average temperatures. At the time, nobody worried much. Humans did not seem to be shaping the Earth to any great extent, and even if they did, there was a sense that it was the manifest destiny of humanity to shape the planet to make it more convenient for humans and their civilizations.

In the year that Arrhenius was born and Darwin published *On The Origin of Species*, one of the great ecological disasters was set in motion when rabbits were released in Australia. The same year, the Royal Geographical Society was told in London that Australian soils were loose and sandy, and needed the tread of hoofed animals to tamp them down.

In 1860, Alfred Russel Wallace (63) described the boundary we now call Wallace's Line, and made it abundantly clear that islands are curious and unique, with their own balances among the flora and the fauna. But still people insisted on introducing exotic species into islands. On much of Oahu and the Big Island of Hawaii, native plant species are rare until you get above 2,000 feet.

There are many horror stories, and few successes. Cane toads were introduced into Hawaii and Australia to control cane beetles in introduced sugar cane; mongooses were taken to islands to kill snakes or rats, and ended up killing birds instead. One estimate says that 42 percent of rare and endangered species are at risk from invasive species, many of them introduced unknowingly.

A little ecological knowledge was a dangerous thing. Like a Ming porcelain vase, an ecosystem is exquisitely beautiful and amazingly fragile. We know that now, and all too often, we have the broken pieces to prove it.

It is said that when a butterfly flaps its wings in one part of the world, it affects the weather somewhere else. The idea is that small variations in an ecosystem can generate large variations in the long term.

DEVELOPING THE PERIODIC TABLE

How we learned to understand the chemical properties of elements

Date: 1869.

Location: St Petersburg, Russia.

Discovery: There are repeating patterns in the chemical elements.

Discoverer: Dmitri Mendeleev (1834–1907).

Impact: The patterns could be used to identify undiscovered elements, and even to predict the properties of the unknown elements.

The Greek philosophers mostly believed everything was composed of four elements: earth, air, fire, and water. Some of them disagreed, and tried to make the number larger or smaller. Thales (27) believed there was just one element: water! They liked the idea of atoms, but only because they were uncomfortable with the idea that you could keep on cutting something in half.

Today, a single atom, by definition, belongs to one element. All of the stuff we see around us is made up of atoms of different sorts, combined in different ways. Each atom can be identified as belonging to a specific element—and if we want to know about those atoms, we can look them up in the Periodic Table of the elements.

Until 1869, there was no such table. There were simply not enough elements for anybody to make any sense out of the gaps. The ancient world knew nine of our elements (seven metals, plus sulfur and carbon); five more were found before 1700, and two more by 1750. Then, between 1751 and 1800, the sixteen known elements of 1750 became thirty-three. Another thirteen were found in the first eight years of the nineteenth century, and seventeen more, to make sixty-three elements by the time Dmitri Mendeleev approached the problem. Another twenty-one had been found by the end of the nineteenth century, but by 1868, Mendeleev's clever mind had enough information to see the patterns. More of him a little later.

In fact, some parts of the pattern were visible forty years earlier. In 1829, Johann Döbereiner (50) described a "law" of triads of elements. Looking at the elements in order of atomic weight, he found several sets of three elements, including chlorine, bromine, and iodine; calcium, strontium, and barium; sulfur, selenium, and tellurium; and iron, cobalt, and manganese. In these sets, the chemical properties of the central member could be estimated from the outsiders. Usually, Mendeleev gets the credit for seeing that there must be gaps to be filled with unknown elements, but Döbereiner was there first:

For the group including phosphorus and arsenic, the third member is missing. Mitscherlich, the discoverer of isomorphology, will know how to find this if it exists.

By 1843, Leopold Gmelin (1788–1853) had published three tetrads, and even a pentad—nitrogen, phosphorus, arsenic, antimony, and bismuth—today's Group V of the periodic table. Future development, though, depended on working out the atomic weights, which were still in a mess.

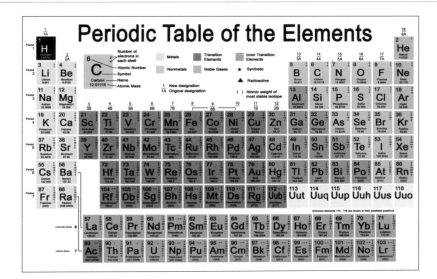

Especially where an element had a valency greater than one, or multiple valencies, the atomic weight could be one of several values.

Michael Faraday (48) pointed out that the same amount of electricity, passing through several electrolytic cells, always formed the same amount of a given metal on each electrode. Today, we understand that each metal ion lacks electrons in its outer shell. When these are replaced, an atom of metal is formed, but the number of electrons an ion needs varies for different metals: magnesium ions need two electrons, sodium and silver ions each need one electron to form an uncharged atom, and so on.

It seemed to Faraday as if an atom of each particular metal was always produced by the same amount of electricity. If the same current gives us 12.15 grams of magnesium in one cell, and 107.9 grams of silver in a second cell hooked up in series with the first, this would give us the relative masses of magnesium and silver atoms, since each product in each cell contained the same number of atoms.

The problem: as we know now, magnesium has two positive charges, sodium and silver have one, others are missing three or even four electrons. In our modern terms, a trivalent ion needs three times as many electrons to deposit it on a cathode as a monovalent atom does. While silver has an atomic weight of 107.9, magnesium is not 12.15, but 24.3.

In 1819, Dulong and Petit's law linked atomic weights and specific heats (75). In modern terms, they said that all elements have the same heat capacity: about 25 joules per mole per kelvin. (They actually said that when you multiply the specific heat and the atomic weight of an element, the result is a constant.) This rule was a useful approximation, but it was based on faked data: their atomic weight for tellurium was half the correct value, cobalt was two-thirds: in each case, they took a guess that was wrong, and fudged the specific heat values to match. Still, it worked, and modern values confirm their "law." Chemists could now combine electrolytic data with specific heat, and proceed with confidence.

Back to Mendeleev. In 1869, he drew up a table of elements with fifteen columns. In 1871, he amended this to something closer to the table we know today, with seven columns (the inert gases would come later). He also predicted three unknown elements—gallium, scandium, and germanium—all of which were found before he died, after a full and rewarding life.

As new elements were found, they fitted into the table, but how many new elements were still to be found? On the eve of World War I, Henry Gwyn Jeffreys Moseley (1887–1915) bombarded small samples of elements with X-rays, and examined the spectra that came back. He found gaps and predicted three elements: one between molybdenum and ruthenium (technetium); one between neodymium and samarium (promethium); and one between tungsten and osmium (rhenium). Promethium has never been found in nature, but it has since been made; and the other two have been discovered. Sadly, Moseley never knew. After pointing them out, he went off to war and died in a futile invasion attempt at Gallipoli in Turkey. What a waste!

INVENTING THE TELEPHONE

How we learned to communicate over distance, without telegraphers

Date: 1876.

Location: Boston, Massachusetts, USA and Brantford, Ontario, Canada.

Discovery: An operating telephone.

Discoverer: Alexander Graham Bell (1847–1922).

Impact: The telephone changed the way we communicate.

Bell's father and grandfather were both teachers of speech and elocution. This played a part in Bell's development of the telephone, and the family made even more of it in their patent battles. It also helped to show how Bell was unlike all the other inventors who were hunting around after the same thing at that time. As often happens in stories of discovery and invention, there seems to have been a certain amount of myth making. This can happen for a number of reasons, but the main aim of this kind of myth making is to strengthen a person's position in court cases over patents.

This motive is ignored in most popular accounts of Bell's work, which take the family's personal histories at face value. Sadly, this sort of embroidering makes the life of scriveners like me infinitely more difficult. But Bell's goal was to get patents—and there was a definite risk from competing claims regarding the telephone. On the very same day on which Bell's patent claim was lodged ("for telegraphy"), another American, Elisha Gray (1835–1901) from Barnesville, Ohio, lodged a caveat—a limited claim—for the same thing. It was pure good luck that Bell's attorney lodged first, without consulting Bell, just a few hours ahead of Gray.

Both Gray and Bell had started out trying to improve ordinary telegraphy, and had chanced on the idea of the telephone. Anxious about their competitors, the Bells stressed the ways in which they as a family were associated with the scientific study of speech. Presumably, they thought this would differentiate the young electrical amateur, Bell, from the established electrical inventor, Gray.

Alexander's father, Melville Bell, had developed a method of representing speech with symbols, known as "visible speech." George Bernard Shaw was a friend of Melville's brother, and we can see something of Melville in Shaw's character Henry Higgins, especially in the opening scenes of *Pygmalion* (and also in *My Fair Lady*), where Higgins is shown writing down the speech of Cockney Londoners in his own notation. Melville Bell is also mentioned by name in the preface to the play.

Using the family's visible speech notation, the young Bell succeeded in squeezing human-like sounds from a Skye terrier, and decided to try making an artificial "talking figure." At this point, Melville and Alexander called on an elderly Sir Charles Wheatstone (1802–1875) (37), who had created a talking device when he was nineteen, and asked him to show it to them. Wheatstone obliged, but there were no immediate results beyond the seed of an idea planted in the young Bell's mind.

The Bell "visible speech" was a useful aid in teaching the deaf to speak, so when the family moved from England to Canada, and then to the United States, they continued this work. They were successful, and by the age of twenty-six, Alexander Graham Bell was appointed as Professor of Vocal Physiology and Elocution at Boston University.

Joseph Henry (1797–1878) had also seen Wheatstone's talking device demonstrated, but he had seen another design as well, created by a German called Faber. This model was operated by strings and levers. Henry, the inventor of the electromagnet, realized immediately that the strings and levers could be operated at a distance with wires and electromagnets. What a great way, he suggested, to get the sermon given in one church distributed to other churches nearby!

This was the social context in which Bell developed his telephone. At least in part, he was thinking of the needs of the deaf, but he also saw the value of a device for speaking over distances.

The story is that Bell spilt acid on himself one day, and said, via his prototype telephone, "Watson, please come here. I want you." Thomas Watson, his assistant, heard the message and came running, according to legend. Whatever the truth of the story, Bell's telephone worked. It was patented in 1876, and the tale has persisted.

By 1885, Thomas Alva Edison (1847–1931) (73), the American inventor of improvements to the telephone, was able to predict that we might be able to telephone over considerable distances. Here is what he wrote in *Scientific American*:

Telephony has come a long way since the days of these switchboard operators c. 1915.

The efforts made with a view to long-distance telephoning have already proved quite satisfactory in a commercial way, and promise excellent results. Conversation has been conducted between Cleveland and New York, and is now daily carried on between New York and Boston to a limited extent. The great difficulty in long-distance telephoning is the loss of the current by static induction on the earth and wires in close proximity. If a single wire could be placed sufficiently high as to amply clear all the mountain tops, one could whisper around the world with perfect ease. One thing, however, is now certain: that the time is close at hand when the telephone will be perfectly successful in an unbroken circuit for a distance of at least 300 miles. It is probable that by means of repeating stations communication can be had over all parts of the United States.

He was right. In 1915, the first trans-continental telephone line in the United States was opened. In the east, Bell spoke into the telephone, and in the west, Thomas Watson heard the words "Watson, please come here. I want you," and this time it was said in front of witnesses, so we know that it was said at least once.

By the way, we remember Bell's earlier work every time we use the term "decibel" as a measure of sound intensity, because it is named in his honor. A decibel is one-tenth of three-quarters of his name, if you think about it.

DISCOVERING GERMS

How we stopped blaming smells and the environment for infectious diseases

Anthrax was a fearful disease in the nineteenth century. Anthrax spores can lie dormant in the soil for at least fifty years, and still spring back to life, infecting animals. The spores could also lurk in skins and fleeces, so its other name was the "Woolclasser's Disease." With no synthetic fibers to make fabrics and no plastics available to make things like saddles, tool handles, shoes, and containers, industrial countries imported vast amounts of wool, and incredible numbers of hides—and anthrax spores.

By 1877, the germ theory was well established, but humans contain and carry billions of bacteria at any one time. Many of these are good for us, so we cannot just kill them all; finding out how to prove which germ caused which disease was the challenge Robert Koch took on. The main aim was to get an effective diagnosis, but once Pasteur had shown you could create vaccines from weakened strains of disease organisms, the search became ever more urgent.

Most living things contain many different micro-organisms, so how do you identify the single "guilty party" species that causes a particular disease? Robert Koch came up with an effective experimental model, known to this day as Koch's postulates.

1. The organism should always be found present in an animal suffering from the disease being studied, and should never be found in one not suffering from the disease.
2. The organism must be cultured in a pure culture away from the animal body.
3. When the culture is inoculated into a susceptible organism, typical disease symptoms should appear.
4. The organisms re-isolated and cultured from the experimental animals should be the same organism.

Later, people who were "carriers" but who did not have the disease were identified—people like "Typhoid Mary"—and the second part of the first postulate was scrapped, but we use Koch's model, even today. It breaks down though, when something only attacks humans, like the AIDS-causing HIV (human immunodeficiency virus), where there is no ethical way to satisfy postulates 3 and 4.

This has allowed self-styled "HIV skeptics" to challenge the orthodox view that HIV causes AIDS. While they have every right to think as they do, they then use their irrational beliefs as an excuse not to promote safe

Date: 1877.

Location: Wollstein (Wosztyn), Poland.

Discovery: The isolation of the anthrax bacillus.

Discoverer: Robert Koch (1843–1910).

Impact: Now scientists could culture, identify and perhaps defeat disease-causing bacteria.

Anthrax bacteria viewed at very high magnification.

sex, not to provide antivirals such as AZT to HIV-positive pregnant women, and to act in other ways that endanger public health. In particular, the skeptics encourage the view that polio vaccine contains something that causes AIDS. This generates panic and avoidance of polio vaccine that otherwise saves many lives.

True proof that HIV causes AIDS would involve implementing postulate 3—taking human volunteers and deliberately infecting them with HIV—but this is unthinkable. In 2000, however, the Durban Declaration was endorsed by over 5,000 medical experts from eighty-three countries:

1. Patients with acquired immune deficiency syndrome, regardless of where they live, are infected with HIV.
2. If not treated, most people with HIV infection show signs of AIDS within 5–10 years. HIV infection is identified in blood by detecting antibodies, gene sequences or viral isolation. These tests are as reliable as any used for detecting other virus infections.
3. People who receive HIV-contaminated blood or blood products develop AIDS, whereas those who receive untainted or screened blood do not.
4. Most children who develop AIDS are born to HIV-infected mothers. The higher the viral load in the mother, the greater the risk of the child becoming infected.
5. In the laboratory, HIV infects the exact type of white blood cell (CD4 lymphocytes) that becomes depleted in people with AIDS.
6. Drugs that block HIV replication in the test tube also reduce virus load in people and delay progression to AIDS. Where available, treatment has reduced AIDS mortality by more than 80 percent.
7. Monkeys inoculated with cloned SIV [Simian Immunodeficiency Virus] DNA become infected and develop AIDS.

But Koch did far more than just propose a set of postulates. He also developed methods of isolating and culturing bacteria, and the familiar Petri dish of the microbiology laboratory was invented by Koch's assistant, Richard Julius Petri (1852–1921).

Agar is extracted from kelp seaweed and used to thicken ice cream, paints, and many other things, but it is most useful when it makes agar jelly. Agar is added to boiling water with carefully chosen nutrients, and poured into sterile Petri dishes. Growing the bacteria on the flat surface of nutrient agar in Petri dishes made it possible to see individual colonies and to sub-culture them. Louis Pasteur (62) used flasks of clear "broth," which were far less effective, especially in the isolation stages. On the right agar plate, individual bacteria become colonies with shapes and colors that help identify them. Microbiologists can select a pure colony and easily sub-culture it, or examine bacterial cells.

The anthrax bacillus, a bacterium that looked like a rod under the microscope, was seen first in 1849, when Koch was six years old; twenty-seven years later, he showed that it caused anthrax. Five years after that, given the start, Louis Pasteur had created a vaccine against anthrax. But the strained relations between France and Germany, and Pasteur's hatred of all things German, were an unfortunate side story. In 1882, Koch used similar methods to identify the cause of tuberculosis (a discovery that won him a 1905 Nobel Prize), and the cause of cholera, after taking a team to Egypt in direct competition with the French.

HARNESSING ALTERNATING CURRENT

How we learned to get electricity from generator to user without losing most of the energy

Over the years, I have talked on radio, and written a great deal about science, and the people who made science work. I have found that Tesla always generates more comments and letters than all the rest put together. He was certainly the greatest scientist from the former Yugoslavia, but this is no mere nationalism, since few of his admirers come from that area.

As a group, Tesla's supporters exhibit a determined enthusiasm close to obsession, but they strike me as people who rely on the evidence. They are engineers, technicians, and physicists, people who demand concrete evidence, and they share my belief that Tesla has never been given due credit. He was certainly one of the most original thinkers of his time, and his cleverness justifies the adulation his name still generates among his technical heirs. His detractors point to his instability; his supporters point to his genius, and the incredible stress he was placed under.

The secret to his success and the admiration he gets lies in electromagnetic induction. This is the effect that produces a current when "magnetic lines of force" cross a conductor. I need the quote marks there, because lines of force do not exist, but it is convenient to

Date: 1881.

Location: Budapest, Hungary.

Discovery: How alternating current can be manipulated and used.

Discoverer: Nikola Tesla (1856–1943).

Impact: The world's power supplies all use alternating current because Tesla made it possible.

assume they do, because the idea makes a very useful model. Fictional lines of force let us explain and predict a great deal about electromagnets and electric motors.

What about the lines of force you can map by sprinkling iron filings on paper? Each of the iron filings is magnetized, so it attracts and repels all of its neighbors. When you tap the paper, the iron filings clump into long chains. The direction of any "line of force" just tells you what direction a compass needle would point in, if you held one at that place, but there is no line of force.

The earliest electric lighting systems used batteries, but soon people were using dedicated generators which were driven either by steam or by falling water. It did not take too much effort to see that if you needed a light in the middle of the night, you would not want to go outside to the engine shed, fire up the boiler and get a supply of steam to drive the generator—not to mention the cost! The answer would be electricity distribution from central generators.

This proffered two significant problems: efficient transmission, and reliable metering of the power used. Efficient transmission was deemed the bigger problem of the two, because power lost was profit lost, but the answer had been found by James Joule (54) back in the 1840s. In a nutshell, power losses are proportional to the square of the current, but voltage and current are inversely proportional. So if you double the voltage, you halve the current, and power loss is reduced to a quarter! Clearly, high voltages are good, over long distances, but the earliest systems used direct current, and it was difficult to alter the voltage. In any case, lighting, fixed motors, and transport motors all needed different voltages.

Now, back to the fictitious lines of force: if an alternating current—an electron flow that reverses at regular intervals—runs through a coil, the magnetic field of the coil varies continually. That means the lines of force (which don't exist, but we are pretending they do) can cut through a second conductor, if there is one. If the number of turns in each coil is different, we have a transformer, which can be used to step up or step down the voltage.

Michael Faraday (48) made the first transformer in 1831. Transformers work on any varying current, but under normal conditions they operate best with alternating current. Lights work successfully on alternating current, but the standard electric motor operated only on direct current. If the electrical supply delivered AC, the motors of the day would not run.

Now back to Tesla. In 1881, he was in Budapest, working for the Austro-Hungarian imperial telegraph system. One day, he went for walk with Antal Szigeti in Budapest's Varosliget city park when he had a vision, almost, of a rotating magnetic field, while watching the sunset and reciting from Goethe's *Faust*. His enthusiasts believe that, and so do I: Tesla was like that.

Jump forward a few years. Tesla has traveled in Europe, reached the USA with four cents in his pocket, worked for Thomas Edison (73) who promised him large amounts of money but failed to pay up, and worked as a ditch digger in 1886–87 to raise some capital before filing his first patent in 1887. In the later part of that year and early 1888, he invented an AC induction motor.

On May 16, 1888, he gave an astounding address to the American Institute of Electrical Engineers. Called *A New System of Alternating Current Motors and Transformers*, the talk outlined the equipment which allowed efficient generation and use of alternating currents, including the use of polyphase AC. Seven weeks later, he sold the patents to George Westinghouse in exchange for cash, shares and a royalty.

Thomas Edison was an exquisite politician. Westinghouse had AC, and Edison was stuck with DC, so he attacked alternating current. It was dangerous, he claimed, and tried to have the word "electrocuted" replaced with "Westinghoused," with special reference to the electric chair, which Edison either inspired or designed. The attack failed, and by 1896, the first three-phase AC power plant had opened at Niagara Falls, and power was being transmitted to Buffalo, New York.

In 1960, the SI unit of electromagnetic induction was declared to be the tesla. That was deserved. But back in 1917, the IEE, the Institute of Electrical Engineers, awarded Tesla the Edison Medal, and both men were alive to see it. Now *that* was justice!

Nikola Tesla in his laboratory at Colorado Springs around 1900.

DISCOVERING THE THERMIONIC EFFECT

How we discovered the way to amplify a variable current, and started the electronic era

Date: 1883.

Location: Menlo Park, New Jersey, USA.

Discovery: A positively charged electrode or plate in a high-vacuum light bulb attracts electrons from a glowing filament, but a positive filament does not produce a reverse current from a negative plate.

Discoverer: Thomas Alva Edison (1847–1931).

Impact: Thermionic valves or vacuum tubes made amplifiers, and then all of electronics, possible.

When a metal wire is hot enough, some of its electrons are active enough to leave the wire. This gives the wire a slight positive charge, so most of them are pulled back again, but we say the electrons are "boiled off." In the atmosphere, some of the electrons may attach themselves to charged particles, but the mean free path—the average distance traveled—is so small that most of them are drawn back again.

In the partial vacuum of an early light globe, the mean free path was longer, so electrons could escape to any nearby positively charged object. If the hot wire and the nearby positive plate have a small voltage permanently applied to them, electrons will stream across continuously. In a good vacuum, the flow is even greater.

The current only goes one way, because even if the plate has a negative charge, it is too cold to lose electrons. The emission from the hot lamp filament or cathode involves charged particles ("ions," in nineteenth century terms) being forced out by heat, so it is called thermionic emission, and because the system works like a one-way valve, speakers of British English call it a thermionic valve, or just "a valve." The standard types are always in the form of a tube (of glass, ceramic, or even metal), and they contain a high vacuum, so in North America they are called vacuum tubes. As we will see, they were once called "valves" in both countries, but "tube" is a marginally more accurate description, once grids are added.

Most tubes had at least a heater filament and a separate cathode, as well as an anode. The heater filament just gets the cathode up to a sufficient temperature to start thermionic emission. A simple tube with only those elements is called a diode. A diode can only operate like a valve in a vein or a pump, as a one-way rectifier that lets current go one way only. But if you were hoping to use a valve to provide DC power for a motor, think again, because the total current is still tiny.

That is probably why Thomas Edison was unexcited in 1883 when he saw what was happening in a simple diode rig. It was interesting, but with no obvious use. So he patented what others later called the "Edison effect," and moved on to the next interesting thing.

In fairness to Edison, he was investigating the way carbon particles "boiled off" the carbon filaments used in light globes at the time. In any case, his patent may not have stood up, given that Frederick

Guthrie (1833–1886), physicist and poet, who held a chair at the Royal College of Science in London, had described the effect in 1873. In any case, as nobody was trying to make money from it, the issue never arose.

That changed when John Ambrose Fleming (1849–1945), a former student of Guthrie's, was working for the Marconi Company in London in 1904. He had repeated Guthrie's work and set it aside, but now a "detector" was needed to receive radio signals. Crystal sets would use a cat's whisker—a fine wire touching a crystal, usually of galena—which made a simple diode, but Fleming recalled and revisited the curious effect of the lamps. He described his "oscillation valve" to the Royal Society in 1905, but the Marconi Company was happy with the galena crystal and, as they held the patent rights for it, that was that for a while.

In New York in late 1905, Lee de Forest (1873–1961) patented a "static valve" which was very similar to Fleming's (de Forest claimed to know nothing about Fleming or Edison, but he almost certainly did). Still, by November 1906, de Forest had a genuinely original invention, the triode, which had a third element, known as the "grid." He called this tube the audion, and its task was to amplify.

Think of a garden hose running full blast. If you apply a small pressure to the hose with your foot, you can stop its flow or let it start again. A voltage on the grid was like the foot on the hose, producing a large variation at the output for a small variation at the input. Amplification and the electronic age had arrived.

Later tubes included more complex tetrodes and pentodes, some of them needing such a hard vacuum that they contained "getters"—materials such as barium that would react with any stray oxygen atoms that remained.

The power demand was huge, because vacuum tubes were extremely hungry. The first computer (92), the Colossus 2, used 1,500 tubes (later raised to 2,000, but often said to be 2,400 or 2,500). The design was made "Top Secret" after World War II, and while a few engineers seem to have kept plans (as engineers do), the lack of agreement is understandable.

Colossus 2 was used, like the later copies, to crack the new codes of the German military during the war. Like incandescent light globes, its tubes were most likely to fail when the machine was powering up or powering down. The failure of even one tube took the whole machine out of commission, so each of the ten Colossus 2 machines was kept on all day and all night, powered by two redundant diesel generators. At least the workers would have been warm in winter: each of the ten machines drew 15 kilowatts, day and night, and almost all of that power was used in the tube heater filaments.

So when the tube or valve was replaced by the low-power transistor, people were understandably ecstatic. But that is another story.

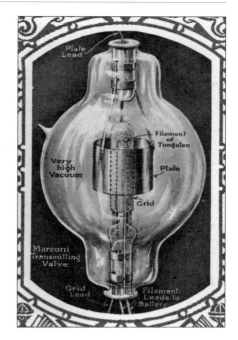

1920s drawing of a thermionic valve.

DISCOVERING NUTRITION

How we learned, just as everybody started believing in germs, that some diseases are caused by diet

Date: 1884.

Location: Japan.

Discovery: That some diseases are caused by a poor diet.

Discoverer: Kanehiro Takaki (1849–1920).

Impact: While scurvy was known to be cured by eating certain kinds of food, so long as it was the only deficiency disease, researchers had no idea that there were others to look for.

In English-language mythology, scurvy is seen as a maritime disease that was cured after Captain Cook made a discovery. In reality, Vasco da Gama's crew suffered from scurvy in the Indian Ocean in 1497–99, and were told by Arab traders that fresh vegetables cured the condition. In 1535–36, Jacques Cartier was over-wintering along the St. Lawrence River in North America when he witnessed the local cure—an infusion of Eastern White Cedar needles. Even then, if people had paid attention, they would have realized that scurvy was not a maritime disease, caused by salt spray.

Trials carried out by Cook on his crew demonstrated that James Lind (1716–1794) was correct in believing that some foods cure scurvy but, away from the sea, the lesson was poorly absorbed. In outback Australia in the second half of the nineteenth century, "Barcoo rot" (scurvy by another name) was a common problem for explorers and settlers.

Even at sea, some people were slow to catch on. When the First Fleet reached Australia in 1788, convicts and crews were healthy, but the Second Fleet arrived in June 1790 with a 26 percent death rate among the convicts. In time, sailors learned better. Out in the Pacific Ocean, scurvy may no longer have been a problem, but another deficiency disease was attacking sailors of the Japanese Navy. It was called beriberi, and it was also a problem in the Dutch East Indies (modern Indonesia).

Dr. Kanehiro Takaki was the Director General of the Japanese Naval Medical Services, and in 1884, he spotted a link between the diet of sailors and beriberi. He ordered more vegetables, barley, fish, and meat, and less rice, in the sailors' diets and in just six years the incidence of beriberi fell from 40 percent to zero. That was fairly convincing; by 1890, the Takaki diet was Japanese naval law. The idea of deficiency diseases was now on the agenda, but it took time for people to accept it.

Today, that sort of news would spread fast. But medical communications were slower back then, and so Dr. Christiaan Eijkman (1858–1930) began independently investigating beriberi at a military hospital in Batavia (modern Jakarta) on the island of Java. By the 1880s, Pasteur's germ theory held sway, and Eijkman was hunting the microbe responsible for what he called "polyneuritis."

Then he saw some chickens in the hospital grounds which appeared to have polyneuritis. A combination of records and experiments

revealed that chickens which were fed white (polished or milled) rice developed polyneuritis. Chickens fed partially polished rice, unhusked rice and rice hulls did not, and if they were already diseased, this diet cured them.

By 1911, Kazimierz (Casimir) Funk (1884–1967) crystallized an amine substance from rice bran. He thought it was the "vital amine," the missing anti-beriberi factor, but he gave it the classier name "vitamine." He had probably crystallized a different substance, but the name stayed around as "vitamin." The real factor was isolated in 1926 and synthesized in 1936. Today, we call it vitamin B1.

The battle was still not over. The disease pellagra had been reported in Spain in 1735. It seemed to be associated with eating corn, which had been brought to Europe from the Americas to become the main diet of the poor people of Europe. Much later, the disease was found in poor southerners in the USA in 1907, though it had probably been around since the 1820s.

Fresh vegetables on display at the Kandy markets in Sri Lanka.

Joseph Goldberger (1874–1929) inquired into pellagra in a Georgia asylum and two Mississippi orphanages. He worked like an epidemiologist: children between six and twelve years old got the disease, but staff, younger and older children were free of it. He found later that those under six were given plenty of milk, and those over twelve were given more meat. But since diet was not the popular villain at that time, he kept searching for a microbe as the culprit. Why, he wondered, did it only attack children in a particular age group?

Goldberger showed that he could cause the symptoms of pellagra in healthy convict volunteers, by feeding them just on maize. Then he "cured" the victims by returning them to a better diet. They stayed healthy, so he began to realize that pellagra looked very much like a deficiency disease.

Next he assembled sixteen volunteers, including himself and his wife, and they tried to infect themselves with pellagra. They tried blood transfusions from pellagra sufferers and "swabs" from the noses and throats of victims, applying these to the same parts of the "guinea pigs." They even swallowed pellets of dough made from the victims' urine, feces, and scrapings from the pellagra sores, mixed with some flour—but they all stayed healthy. There were critics still, but Goldberger had won. Now nutritionists know that pellagra is a deficiency disease caused by a lack of vitamin B3 (also called niacin).

Today, we all accept that bad diet causes disease, but can we go too far the other way?

As the twentieth century "progressed," famine became more common, and more deficiency diseases, including kwashiorkor, were identified. Kwashiorkor is common in Africa, and can easily be related to particular diets, so the link seems clear, but there are some odd things about kwashiorkor: the symptoms are not quite right for a deficiency disease. Many scientists suspect that kwashiorkor is really caused by one or more aflatoxins—poisonous chemicals made by fungi which sometimes grow on the food eaten by young children in some parts of Africa. The jury is still out.

Only time and more evidence will tell us whether or not scientists have been sticking to the wrong theory once again. The beauty of the scientific method, of course, is that sooner or later, we always do find out when we are wrong!

EXPLAINING THE SPECTRAL LINES

How we learned the meaning of the various lines seen in the spectrum

By the mid-1880s, spectroscopy (61) had come a long way. The lines in the absorption spectrum had been pinned down, one by one, so the exact wavelengths of the hydrogen lines could be identified. That left a major puzzle: why did the lines appear where they did in the spectrum?

Johann Balmer set out to make sense of a jumble of numbers. In this, he was like Johann Bode (1747–1846), who found a pattern in the distances of the planets from the Sun; or Pierre-Louis Dulong (1785–1838) and Alexis-Therese Petit (1791–1820) (69), who found a mathematical rule that tied specific heats and atomic weights together; or even Maria Goeppert Mayer (1906–1972), who found certain "magic numbers" of neutrons and protons that were associated with very stable nuclei.

They all engaged in a form of statistical analysis which its users often call data-snooping. In the real world, laws do not leap out at you; they are usually found when somebody goes data-snooping. That means making lists of measurements, and poring over them to see if there is any pattern to offer a hint about a rule lying beneath the measurements.

Data-snooping assumes there is an unknown rule to be found. Finding it means trying everything. Measured values, their squares, cubes, square roots, cube roots, products, differences, progressions, logarithms, sines, tangents, and other exotic mathematical functions are all thrown in—even fractions and combinations of functions. Heavy stuff, but worth it if we can make a breakthrough. It's easy enough today with a spreadsheet, but it was a lot harder in the nineteenth century.

If there is a pattern, the next step is to explore the relationship further. Are there any missing values in the range being studied? Can we extrapolate beyond the range? If so, we can predict some values, and then go looking for confirmation. Johann Balmer found a relationship linking four of the hydrogen lines in the visible spectrum. It seemed to him there should be another line, right on the edge of the ultraviolet, a line of which he had no knowledge. He checked, and the line was there, as predicted, so Balmer's rather odd little equation was confirmed. Score one point to data-snooping.

Balmer had some trouble reconciling the numerical values reported by different observers. Could it be that the observers were looking at stars with differing degrees of red shift? As we will see later (90), the red shift was important, once people detected it and chased it down. To track down his formula, Balmer found a common factor, deduced from Anders Ångström's measurements on the first four hydrogen lines, which gave

Date: 1885.

Location: Basel, Switzerland.

Discovery: A mathematical formula can account for the "hydrogen lines" in the spectrum.

Discoverer: Johann Jakob Balmer (1825–1898).

Impact: When Niels Bohr outlined his model of the atom, Balmer's empirical formula suddenly made sense.

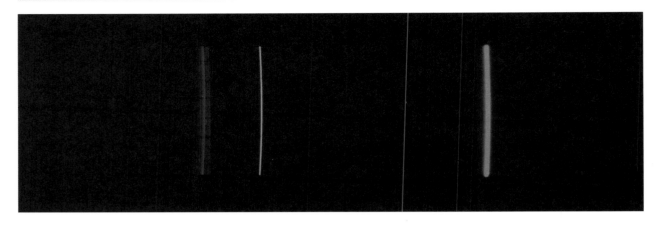

The emission spectrum of hydrogen.

him a value, b = 3645.6 mm/10⁷—and he then applied this. Here is his explanation of it, in translation:

The wavelengths of the first four hydrogen lines are obtained by multiplying the fundamental number b = 3645.6 in succession by the coefficients 9/5; 4/3; 25/21 and 9/8. At first sight, these coefficients do not form a regular series; but if we multiply the numerical values in the second and the fourth numbers by 4, we see a consistent regularity appearing [the series becomes 9/5, 16/12, 25/21, 36/32] and the coefficients have for numerators the numbers 3^2, 4^2, 5^2 and 6^2 and for denominators a number that is less by 4 [than the numerator].

For several reasons it seems to me probable that the four coefficients which have just been given belong to two series, so that the second series includes again the terms of the first series; and so I am able to present the formula for the coefficients in the more general form $m^2 / (m^2 - n^2)$, in which m and n are whole numbers.

That is to say, the wavelengths of the hydrogen lines are given by λ = b $(m^2/(m^2 - n^2))$. Now back to Balmer:

For n = 1 we obtain the series 4/3, 9/8, 16/15, 25/24 etc., for n = 2 the series 9/5, 16/12, 25/21, 36/32, 49/45, 64/60, 81/77, 100/96 etc. In this second series the second term is already in the first series but in a reduced form.

Balmer compared the first four hydrogen lines as measured by Ångström with calculated values. In Ångström units (10^{-10} meters), the values are:

Alpha line: Balmer: 6562.08, Ångström: 6562.10, Difference: +0.02
Beta line: Balmer: 4860.8, Ångström: 4860.74, Difference: -0.06
Gamma line: Balmer: 4340, Ångström: 4340.1, Difference: +0.1
Delta line: Balmer: 4101.3, Ångström: 4101.2, Difference: -0.1

Clearly, the model is a close fit to reality. But Balmer went looking for the fifth hydrogen line—this was the acid test. He calculated that it would be at 49/45 x 3645.6 = 3969.65 Ångström units.

I knew nothing of such a fifth line, which must lie within the visible part of the spectrum ... and I was compelled to assume that the temperature relations were not favorable to the development of this line or that the formula was not generally applicable.

On reference to Professor Hagenbach he informed me that many more hydrogen lines are known which have been measured by Vogel and by Huggins ... [and] he was kind enough to make a comparison of the wave lengths thus determined ...

There was something going on here. This sort of close fit has to have a reason behind it, but for the time being, all people could do was look out for a cause.

In time, they would find it.

DISCOVERING RADIO WAVES

How simple curiosity about electromagnetic waves changed the way we communicate

Posterity has been unkind to Heinrich Hertz. He is often seen as a tinkerer who found radio waves more or less by accident, when sparks mysteriously appeared in a spark gap that just happened to be sitting around in his laboratory. In fact, he knew exactly what he was doing. His experiments seem simple because his work is explained in simple terms, leaving the sense that Hertz was fiddling aimlessly. In reality, he wanted to test a complicated piece of theory, and did so.

In 1870, James Clerk Maxwell (1831–1879) deduced that light and other forms of radiation must be electromagnetic: they must have an electrical part and a magnetic part, and they would both travel at the speed of light. Until 1886, nobody had set out to generate and detect Maxwell's waves, even though George FitzGerald (1851–1901) had explained how to do it in 1881. Some people had seen sparks in spark gaps, just as Hertz did, but they missed the importance of what they saw.

Hertz was seeking the waves that we now call radio waves. He had no thought of applying them; he merely wanted to show that they existed. He needed to generate waves by sending an oscillating current around a circuit and across a spark gap. By analogy with electromagnetic induction, if a current in a circuit generates radiation, then the radiation ought to generate a current in a second, resonant coil. Of course, the gap needed to be smaller, and the spark was much smaller, but it could still be detected.

Date: 1886-88.

Location: Karlsruhe, Germany.

Discovery: Electromagnetic waves can be generated which are quite different from light waves in some respects, but quite like them in other crucial ways.

Discoverer: Heinrich Hertz (1857–1894).

Impact: In the short term, James Clerk Maxwell's theory of electromagnetic radiation was proven; in the longer term, we acquired a new way of communicating.

A crystal radio set with headphones. Notice the cat's whisker (93) on the sloping panel near the top. The lever on the right was used to probe the crystal for a good contact point.

As Hertz described his experimental rig, it sounds like something from a 1950s monster movie. There was an induction coil to deliver a high voltage to a small gap between two wires, and then there was the spark gap itself, where miniature lightning bolts crossed the gap. "More power, Igor," you can almost hear him saying. This spark gap was placed at the focus of a parabolic reflector that Hertz had made by bending some zinc sheet. It might have been a bit crude, but this parabolic mirror was the forerunner of all those dish antennas that we see on communications towers today. Hertz, remember, knew exactly what he was doing.

After creating a focused beam of waves, Hertz moved a small wire contraption—his detector—along the beam, looking for sparks in a second small spark gap that was built into the detector. The sparks were very tiny, but he could *just* see them if the detector was only a few meters from the source. Well, that was interesting—but it might just have been an induction effect, such as we see in a transformer. It didn't do very much, or prove anything new, but the next step did.

He set up a flat mirror—a sheet of metal—some distance from the parabolic dish, to reflect the waves back again. A wave reflected back through itself makes a standing wave. Do this with light waves, and you get interference, and bright and dark bands, with any two successive bright bands separated by half a wavelength. You can do the same thing with sound in an organ pipe, but instead of bands, you get high and low pressure zones.

With Hertzian waves, you get "bright" spots, where the spark in the detector is strong, and "dark" spots, where the spark completely disappears. Once again, the bright spots in the standing wave are half a wavelength apart.

Hertz observed precisely this effect, finding bright spots at 33 cm, 65 cm and 98 cm from the source, suggesting a 33 cm half-wavelength, giving "1.1 thousand-millionth of a second as their period of oscillation, assuming that they travel with the velocity of light." Hertz does not seem to have had much doubt they would: he showed that the "electric rays" shared with light the properties of rectilinear propagation (they traveled in a straight line), polarization, reflection, and refraction. Only rarely do we see a set of experimental results so complete and so convincing.

Here is the conclusion to his 1888 paper describing his experiments, where he shows clearly that he knew exactly what he had been studying: "light of very great wavelength."

We have applied the term rays of electric force to the phenomena which we have investigated. We may perhaps further designate them as rays of light of very great wavelength. The experiments described appear to me, at any rate, eminently adapted to remove any doubt as to the identity of light, radiant heat, and electromagnetic wave motion. I believe that from now on we shall have greater confidence in making use of the advantages which this identity enables us to derive both in the study of optics and electricity.

Hertz reported his work in German at the end of 1888, and by mid-1889, French scientists had improved on the apparatus. There was even an article about it in *Scientific American*. Before long, everybody was doing it, and it seems amazing it took so long for Marconi's important breakthroughs to occur, beginning with the first transmission in September 1895 (over just 2 miles), leading to the first trans-Atlantic broadcast in December 1901.

The long delay is more understandable, though, when you realize that better detectors had to be found, more sensitive detectors which would work over longer distances. Sadly, the radio breakthrough came too late for Hertz. Just before his thirty-seventh birthday, two years before Marconi's first patent, he died of blood poisoning, with little idea of the practical applications he had made possible.

Unfortunately, his early death prevented him witnessing some extraordinary radiation discoveries.

TRYING TO FIND THE ETHER

How a failure to find something was one of the most important discoveries of the nineteenth century

Date: 1887.

Location: Cleveland, Ohio, USA.

Discovery: That no ether could be detected in the vacuum of space.

Discoverer: Albert Abraham Michelson (1852–1931), and Edward Williams Morley (1838–1923).

Impact: It became necessary to find another way of explaining how light traveled across a vacuum.

So long as light was thought of as a stream of particles, nobody had a problem with light traveling through a vacuum. Christiaan Huygens (1629–1695) thought light was a wave, so he suggested that there must be "ether" to carry the light. Scientists knew waves needed something to travel through, and the notion of "ether" was a handy explanation. Most people, though, preferred to think of light as particles.

In 1803, Thomas Young (1773–1829) showed the Royal Society evidence that light was a wave, and the wave model of light was formally proposed by Augustin Fresnel (1788–1827) in 1818. Young's proof depended on light beams interfering with each other, sometimes adding together, sometimes canceling each other out. Only waves cause interference: if light beams interfered, they were waves.

Fresnel also offered a model of how waves behaved when light hit a circular obstacle. Siméon-Denis Poisson (1781–1840) tried to ridicule this theory, saying interference would produce a bright spot in the center of a circular shadow. François Jean Dominique Arago (1786–1853) went to his lab and showed soon after that the spot existed, confirming the wave theory of light. Some people call the spot the Poisson bright spot, others more justly call it the Fresnel bright spot, or the Arago bright spot. Light was a wave, no doubt about it—the ether was back in vogue.

People wanted desperately to know what ether was like, how it behaved and what effects it had. Today, it seems odd for sane physicists to believe in stuff that passes right through us, stuff that is almost impossible to detect, but neutrinos are like that, and we still believe in them! A lot of science sounds crazy, but scientists are polite: they just say it is counterintuitive, while they look around for a better idea.

Armand Fizeau (1819–1896) (56) was expert at measuring the speed of light. He was accurate enough to show by measurement that a moving medium affected the velocity of light traveling in it, which made people think. The Earth orbits the Sun, the Sun rushes through space. They figured that even if the ether was traveling at the same speed as the planet at the beginning of the experiment, in six months' time, when the Earth is on the other side of the Sun, going the other way, there should be a difference. On top of that, the planet is spinning, so even if the ether is stationary, relative to where you start out, in twelve hours' time, there must be a relative movement that can be measured. It seemed that whether they could detect ether or not, they could measure its effects.

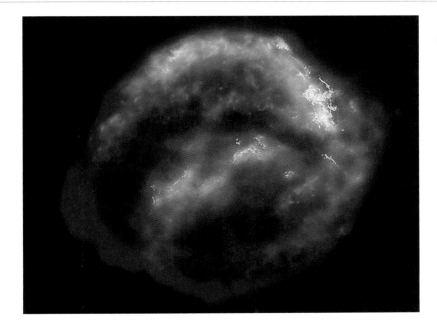

This bubble-shaped shroud of gas and dust that is 14 light years wide is expanding at a rate of 4 million miles per hour.

In short, ether could be detected by measuring the speed of light, day and night, and season by season, and spotting the systematic variations. In 1887, Michelson and Morley tried to detect the effect of a moving ether on the velocity of light in different directions.

In 1864, James Clerk Maxwell had shown that the movement of the Earth through the ether should be detectable, with variations of the order of 10^{-8}. There were no suitable instruments for the task, but Lord Kelvin gave a series of lectures at Baltimore in 1884, and both Michelson and Morley went along. Kelvin urged Michelson to repeat an inconclusive experiment he (Michelson) had carried out three years earlier in Potsdam, and Michelson and Morley agreed.

First, they repeated Fizeau's experiment on the speed of light in moving water, because if Fizeau had been wrong, this would explain Michelson's earlier failure. But Fizeau's result was confirmed. Michelson had encountered problems with traffic vibrations in Germany, and the expected changes were small, so modifications were made to the rig, which sat on a stone slab.

The apparatus … rests on an annular wooden float … 1.5 meter outside diameter, 0.7 meter inside diameter, and 0.25 meter thick. The float rests on mercury contained in the cast-iron trough 1.5 centimeter thick, and of such dimensions as to leave a clearance of about 1 centimeter around the float. A pin … fits into a socket … attached to the float … This pin keeps the float concentric with the trough, but does not bear any part of the weight of the stone …

In short, the system was vibration-free. There was no need to *measure* the speed of light: they just compared the relative speeds of two "pencils" of light at right angles to each other. The two light streams were separated and then brought back together again, where they would interfere with each other. If the speed changed with direction, rotating the slab and the apparatus would change the interference pattern in a systematic way.

The idea was that the light "pencil" bouncing back and forth across the ether flow should get to the end sooner than a light "pencil" going *up and down* the direction of the ether flow. This can be seen clearly from the limiting case, where the ether, relative to the Earth, has the velocity of light: if that happened, the up–down light would never get there!

Michelson and Morley expected only a small difference, detectable only by a shift in the interference fringes. As the apparatus rotated, so one "pencil" should go from the "across" orientation to the "up–down" orientation, and back again. This ought, they reasoned, to move the fringes. In fact, the fringes did not move at all. The Michelson-Morley experiment failed, and as a result, did away with the idea that the ether existed. That part of physics had to start again, but now they knew where not to look.

DISCOVERING X-RAYS

How a chance observation triggered a large number of applications

Date: 1895.

Location: Würzburg, Germany.

Discovery: An invisible radiation, able to pass through many solid objects, existed.

Discoverer: Wilhelm Conrad Röntgen (1845–1923).

Impact: The discovery opened up a new branch of medicine, inspired the discovery of radioactivity, and allowed X-ray diffraction to be invented.

X-rays have become an important tool for medical diagnosis, but their discovery in 1895 by the German physicist Wilhelm Conrad Röntgen had little to do with medical experimentation. Röntgen was studying cathode rays—the phosphorescent stream of electrons used today in everything from (older) televisions to fluorescent lights. One earlier scientist had found that cathode rays can penetrate thin pieces of metal; another showed that these rays could light up a fluorescent screen placed an inch or two away from a thin aluminum "window" in the glass tube.

Röntgen wondered if he could detect cathode rays escaping from a glass tube completely covered with black cardboard. During this experiment, he noticed that a glow appeared on a detector screen in his darkened laboratory some distance away from the tube. At first he thought the cardboard was torn, allowing light from the high-voltage coil attached to the cathode ray tube to escape, but he soon realized he had chanced upon something entirely different. Rays of light were passing right through the thick paper and appearing on a fluorescent screen over a yard away.

He found that this new type of radiation had many properties unlike those of the cathode rays he had been studying. It could penetrate solids

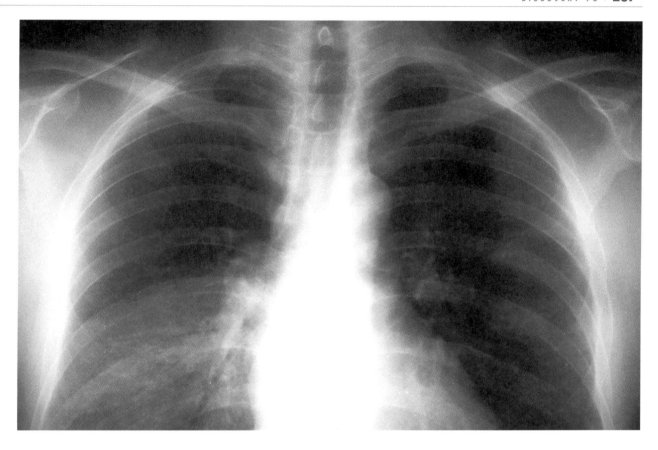

and even record the image of a human skeleton on a photographic negative, but it was blocked by metal.

X-rays like this one of the human thorax have transformed diagnostic procedures.

Röntgen was born in Prussia (part of modern Germany), grew up in the Netherlands, and trained at universities in the Netherlands and Switzerland. While he discovered an effect which Hendrik Lorentz called the Röntgen current, we remember him now because he was the first to see and describe the effects of X-rays. He described them so thoroughly that an English scientist, Sylvanus Thompson, complained later that Röntgen had left others very little to do, apart from verifying the results he had listed, but that thoroughness paid off. In 1901, the first year of the Nobel Prize, Röntgen won the prize for physics for his accidental discovery and later deliberate pursuit of what he called the "X-ray," which physicians worldwide soon adopted as a standard medical tool.

The names which appear in Röntgen's description of how the rays are generated remind us that it was only a matter of time before somebody found X-rays. After the event, Sir William Crookes (1832–1919) realized that he had detected the rays some time before, when some photographic paper had been fogged by being too close to one of his tubes. Here is how Röntgen described it:

If the discharge of a fairly large induction coil be made to pass through a Hittorf vacuum tube, or through a Lenard tube, a Crookes tube, or other similar apparatus, which has been sufficiently exhausted ... and if the whole apparatus be placed in a completely darkened room, there is observed at each discharge a bright illumination of a paper screen covered with barium platinocyanide, placed in the vicinity of the induction coil ...

Having found the effect in early November, 1895, Röntgen locked himself away and pursued the problem until a few days after Christmas, when he produced a ten-page paper for the Physico-Medical Society of Würzburg, from which this selection is taken:

The most striking feature of this phenomenon is that an influence capable of exciting brilliant fluorescence is able to pass through the black cardboard cover, which transmits none of the ultra-violet rays of the sun or of the electric arc, and one immediately enquires whether other bodies possess this property. It is soon discovered that all bodies are transparent to this influence, but in different degrees. A few examples will suffice. Paper is very transparent, the fluorescent screen held behind a bound volume of 1000 pages still lighted up brightly; the printer's ink offered no perceptible obstacle.

Fluorescence was also noted behind two packs of cards; a few cards held between apparatus and screen made no perceptible difference. A single sheet of tinfoil is scarcely noticeable. Only after several layers have been laid on top of each other is a shadow clearly visible on the screen ...

Glass plates behave differently, depending on whether they contain lead (flint glass) or not; the lead-containing ones are much less transparent than the others. If the hand is held between the discharge tube and the screen, the dark shadow of the bones is visible within the slightly dark shadow of the hand ...

A wooden rod, 20 x 20 mm cross-section, painted white, with lead paint on one side, behaves in a peculiar manner. When it is interposed between apparatus and screen, it has almost no effect when the X-rays go through the rod parallel to the painted side, but it throws a dark shadow if the rays have to traverse the paint. Very similar to the metals themselves are their salts, whether solid or in solution.

In his last sentence, Röntgen leaves an important clue that was not really picked up on until Marie Curie noticed that radioactivity was the same in both salts and elements: some physical properties, including X-ray absorption, are independent of the state an atom is in, because they are properties of the nucleus.

The discovery of X-rays led to X-ray diffraction (which has been a major tool of science ever since), computer-assisted tomography, and much more.

And it all started with a lucky accident, just like the discovery of radioactivity.

DISCOVERING RADIOACTIVITY

How physicists suddenly learned that physics was far from complete

Henri Becquerel was the grandson and son of famous French physicists, and the father of yet another excellent researcher. His discovery of radioactivity was driven by the French hatred of all things German. Wilhelm Röntgen (78) had shown that cathode rays cause fluorescence, and that the associated X-rays also cause fluorescence, receiving radiation of one wavelength and glowing at another. The Becquerel clan had always been interested in fluorescence in minerals.

By the mid-1890s, five empires were jostling their way toward World War I: Britain, France, Germany, Russia, and Austria, but the strongest rivalry was between France and Germany. If Germany had an amazing new ray, France demanded one of its own, and Becquerel thought sunlight on a fluorescent salt, uranium potassium sulfate, might deliver that new radiation.

He thought light rays might be "converted" into penetrating rays like X-rays, just as the cathode rays seemed to be converted into X-rays. He wrapped photographic plates in black paper, thick enough to keep out sunlight. He then put a crust of the uranium salt on the wrapped plates, and left them in sunlight. When he developed the plates, he found images of the salt on them.

This seemed to confirm that sunlight makes fluorescent salts generate a penetrating radiation. He also noted that coins and metal objects blocked the radiation, just as with Röntgen's rays (78). Then came a startling discovery, thanks to bad weather. There were two cloudy days, on February 26 and 27, so he put the film and crystals away in a drawer. When the sun still failed to show through, he developed the plates on March 1, expecting a weak image because the crystals had been exposed to only a small amount of sunlight, but he found very clear images.

Others might have assumed a mistake at this point, but Becquerel saw an opportunity: "I at once thought that the action might be able to go on in the dark," he said in his account of the work. He repeated the experiment in a darkroom, got similar images, published his results, and then gave Marie Curie her doctor's thesis topic: finding the source of the radiation and explaining it.

Maria Sklodowska (1867–1934) was brought up in Poland, which was then divided between Russia, Austria, and Germany. She had arrived in Paris to study at the Sorbonne (the University of Paris) in 1891. She married a well-known physicist, Pierre Curie (1859–1906) in 1895. Pierre and his brother had become well known for studying piezoelectricity:

Date: 1896.

Location: Paris, France.

Discovery: Certain elements emit radiation.

Discoverer: (Antoine) Henri Becquerel (1852–1908).

Impact: In the longer term, this led to nuclear weapons and nuclear power, but it also gave some important insights into the structure of the nucleus of the atom.

Pierre and Marie Curie in their laboratory.

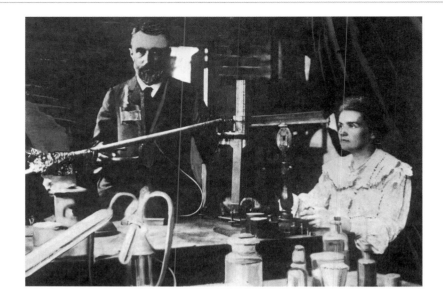

the way crystals under varying pressure produce varying charges (or conversely, the way in which crystals under varying voltage vibrate to generate a varying pressure).

They combined to work on Marie's experiments, with Pierre contributing the instrument with which they measured radioactivity. By 1898, she had named alpha, beta, and gamma rays, and together they had isolated and named two new elements: polonium (celebrating her native Poland), and radium. Their methods would horrify any modern radiation safety officer. After almost a century, their laboratory notebooks are still dangerously radioactive, and people wishing to look at them in Paris must sign a release form absolving the Sorbonne of any responsibility.

Here is part of an account Pierre gave in London in 1903, the year Marie finished her thesis, and the year that she, Pierre, and Becquerel shared the Nobel Prize for Physics. She was present—probably the first woman scientist to appear at the Royal Institution—but Pierre spoke.

These rays which are emitted spontaneously from some substances are called Becquerel rays, and we call the substances emitting these rays radioactive.

Mme Curie and I have discovered new radioactive substances which are present as traces in certain minerals, but from which the radioactivity is very intense. We have separated polonium, a substance with similar chemical properties to bismuth, and radium, a close chemical neighbor to barium. Since then, M. Debierne has separated actinium, a radioactive substance similar to the rare earths.

Polonium, radium and actinium produce radiation a million times more intense than that of uranium and thorium. With these substances, the phenomena of radioactivity may be studied in detail, and many researches have been carried out by various physicists in recent years. Tonight I wish to speak of radium, because we have recently proved that it is an element which we have isolated in the pure state.

In the later nineteenth century, inventors fought terrible battles over patents. Today, administrators and bean-counters with no knowledge or love of science infest universities, surrounding researchers, trying to extract profit from every discovery while contributing nothing. Going on her comments on the patenting of radium, it appears Marie Curie was far more humane:

It would be impossible, it would be against the scientific spirit ... Physicists always publish their results completely. If our discovery has a commercial future that is an accident from which we must not profit. And if radium is found to be used in the treatment of disease, it seems to me impossible to take advantage of that.

Bean-counters and politicians, please note!

MAKING LIQUID HELIUM

How we learned to make things cool, then cold, then very cold indeed

As we know, when you compress a gas quickly, it gets very hot. This is the basis of the fire piston (1) and the diesel engine.

On the other hand, if you let the hot compressed gas grow cool, then let it expand once more, it will get quite cold. This explains the workings of domestic refrigerators and freezers where the system acts as a heat pump, radiating heat from the compressed gas on the outside (the black grid on the back, in a refrigerator) and allowing it to expand on the inside.

Refrigerators are heat pumps that pump heat out of something, like a water pump taking water out of a well. A refrigerator running with its door open in a perfectly insulated room would make the room hotter! Work is needed to pump something from one place to another. If the two sides of a heat pump are in the same room, it has no more effect than a water pump moving water from one end of a pool to the other.

The beauty of even a simple refrigerator is that the compressed gas (sometimes compressed until it is liquid) is at room temperature. When the pressure is eased and it becomes a low pressure gas again, it is a great deal colder, certainly cold enough for the needs of commerce, trade, and normal home use.

Date: 1898.

Location: London, England.

Discovery: That hydrogen could be cooled and compressed until it became a liquid.

Discoverer: Sir James Dewar (1842–1923).

Impact: This led to liquid-fueled rockets, the production of liquid helium, and the discovery of superconductivity.

Up until the 1850s, ice ships sailed from Massachusetts, carrying cargoes of winter ice to the Caribbean, and even all the way to Australia. Back then, a "refrigerator" was just an insulated cupboard with a compartment for ice. But in 1851, John Gorrie of Florida patented a refrigerator which used compressed air, water, and brine as a refrigerant. This was not highly successful, but it showed that the principles were sound.

Soon, ice works were built to crank out blocks of ice, all the year round, all over the world. By 1880, a freezer ship could carry frozen meat from Argentina or Australia to Europe, where more and more people were cramming into the industrial cities. In the USA, milk from outlying farms was chilled in the 1860s before it was loaded onto trains, not to stop it souring, but to stop it being churned to butter during the rattling journey. Freezer cars came later.

By 1875, Lord Rayleigh could speak at the Royal Institution on "freezing machines," because physicists were getting the habit of freezing gases. It began when somebody wondered: If a refrigerant at room temperature could freeze water, what might be done if you chilled the refrigerant first?

They realized that the refrigerant has to be chosen carefully, so it can be compressed all the way to a liquid, after which it flows to the cooling system, where it can radiate heat outwards. After the refrigerant has cooled back to room temperature, it can be allowed to expand, cooling whatever is near where the expansion is happening.

This is the basic principle used in cryogenics, except that whatever is cooled in the first phase is then fed into the second phase, which is fed into the third phase, and so on. Then, as the temperature drops, a new problem emerges: the original refrigerant is no longer able to change back to a gas at that temperature. No matter what we do, the kitchen refrigerator will never provide us with liquid oxygen. It can take us a step on the way, but then we need to change refrigerants and run the steps again.

Michael Faraday (48) froze carbon dioxide in 1845, Raoul Pictet (1846–1929) and Louis Paul Cailletet (1832–1913) managed to liquefy oxygen and nitrogen in 1877. Each achievement resulted in a liquid that boiled constantly as heat energy seeped in and converted some of the liquid to a gas. Just like boiling water in a kettle, the boiling point temperature of a liquid gas is constant. As heat seeps in, a few molecules absorb it and carry off the extra energy, so the average energy per molecule in the container is reduced.

The problem was finding a storage system that would reduce the amount of heat seeping in, but in 1892, James Dewar invented the Dewar flask, which was a very effective tool for insulating the cold liquids. It uses two silver-coated glass walls separated by a vacuum to insulate the contents. Dewar did not patent the idea, but a smaller version of the flask was marketed under the trademarked name "Thermos," mostly to store hot drinks, where it stops heat seeping out instead of in.

Using his flask for storage, Dewar liquefied hydrogen in 1898 and studied its properties: the flask reduced the liquid's furious boiling, and made examination easier. Then soon after, in 1903, Konstantin Tsiolkovskii (1857–1935) had a bright idea, using liquid hydrogen as rocket fuel (16). Helium was the only gas which had not yet been liquefied, but Heike Kamerlingh Onnes (1853–1926) managed to reduce helium-4 to a liquid in 1908. Soon after, he observed superconductivity in metals held at very low temperatures, and physicists had a new problem to chew on.

Science is like that: Each discovery sets the scene for a whole range of new and interesting questions.

A 1950s advertisement gives a good indication of the transformation brought about in family homes with the advent of refrigeration.

DISCOVERING QUANTUM PHYSICS

How straightforward intuitive physics was stood on its head

Date: 1900.

Location: Berlin, Germany.

Discovery: That energy comes in small packets, with the energy and wavelength linked.

Discoverer: Max Planck (1858–1947).

Impact: It led to Einstein's 1905 explanation of the photoelectric effect, the transistor, and much more.

It was good to be a physicist in about 1894. Everything that needed to be known was known and understood. All that later generations had to do was to measure carefully, to more significant figures, many of the constants which had been identified and outlined by those who went before. It was an attitude that grew over the years, and before he died in 1879, James Clerk Maxwell mentioned the phenomenon and attacked it.

Niels Bohr (86) is often quoted as saying that prediction is very difficult, especially about the future. Bohr always said he got the quote from Robert Storm Petersen, who got it from somebody else. Whoever said it first was right: prediction is always a risky business. In 1895, physics was amazed by the discovery of X-rays; the next year, radioactivity came along. But by 1900, a far worse "unexpected" was looming. Physics found itself threatened by the Ultraviolet Catastrophe.

Gustav Kirchhoff (61) was the first to study the radiation from a black body—something which absorbed all wavelengths and so must emit them when heated. The problem was that if the black body emits all frequencies, and if there are more high frequencies (just as there are more numbers between a thousand and a million than there are between one and a thousand), then virtually all of the radiation would come out in the high frequency range, in the ultraviolet.

This was called the "ultraviolet catastrophe" (or sometimes the "violet catastrophe"), because it should have led to massive outpourings of energy at those frequencies. But the catastrophic picture was clearly wrong, because the catastrophe never happened! Either the logic was wrong (it wasn't) or the basic assumptions were wrong (they were). Something had to be done, and two people, Wilhelm Wien (1864–1928) and Lord Rayleigh (1842–1919), made valiant attempts.

Wien tackled the problem in 1896, proposing what we now call the Wien displacement law, which says that for a black body, the product of the wavelength corresponds to the maximum radiancy, and the thermodynamic temperature is a constant—the Wien displacement law constant. In mathematical terms, $\lambda_{max}T = b$ (or $\lambda_{max} = b/T$) where λ is the wavelength, T is the absolute temperature, and b is the Wien's displacement law constant, which has a value of 2.897756×10^{-3} m K. (The unit is meter kelvin, arising because we are multiplying a wavelength by a temperature T on the left-hand side of the equation.)

That equation may be hard to digest, but what it means is this: as the temperature rises, the maximum of the radiant energy shifts toward the shorter wavelength (higher frequency and energy) end of the spectrum. This is the "displacement" part of the displacement law. Wien's law worked well for high frequency (short wavelength) radiation, but it was less successful with low frequency radiation. This was not surprising, because Wien was engaging in data-snooping—trying to come up with a practical equation to relate a set of experimental results—but he was actually barking up the wrong tree.

In 1900, physicist Lord Rayleigh found another law for the lower frequencies which was later modified by Sir James Jeans (1877–1946). The Wien and Rayleigh-Jeans laws covered all frequencies between them, but neither completely filled the bill. Physicists are offended by any need to have two rules for two frequency ranges. At the very least, there has to be a missing law which sets the boundary between the two ranges: there has to be a reason why the cut-off is where it is.

Enter Max Planck, with a complex-looking but mathematically simple empirical formula, now called the Planck radiation law, which covers the whole range. Two months later, Planck showed that this law could be accounted for theoretically by making one simple assumption. It seemed radical at the time, but now it is a commonplace, and the basis for quantum theory.

A glowing red-hot ball of wire gauze provides a brilliant example of visible radiant heat.

He argued that the energy distributed among the molecular oscillators is not continuous, as people had assumed, but made up of a finite number of very small discrete amounts, each related to the frequency of the oscillation by the equation $e = h\nu$, where e is the energy, h is Planck's constant, and ν (the Greek letter nu) is the frequency of the radiation.

Strictly speaking, the h has a line through it. It is called "hbar" and represented by the italic letter h with a cross-bar through the ascender, but a plain h is commonly used, as most typefaces lack this character. Actually, Planck only said that the amounts of energy an oscillator could take up had to be multiples of $h\nu$, and the rest of the answer came from Einstein in 1905.

Still, however you write it or tell it, there was one clear issue that emerged from the first phase of the quantum revolution: light comes in small packets, each with a specific wavelength, which meant a fixed frequency and also a fixed energy. In a few years, when we got the idea of electrons jumping from one energy level to another, we had a straightforward explanation of why sodium emits that brilliant yellow light, and much more: that wavelength matches the energy change.

Einstein bought into it because ultraviolet light could "boil off" electrons from zinc—something called the photoelectric effect—but other wavelengths had no effect. If you assumed a minimum energy was needed to dislodge an electron from a zinc atom, that would explain how wavelength came into it. But any physicist hoping for calm after 1906 was as out of luck as that smug physicist back in 1894.

Planck and Einstein were just a beginning, not a conclusion.

DISCOVERING HORMONES

How an internal signaling system in animals was identified

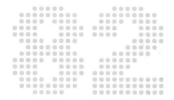

Date: 1905.

Location: London, England.

Discovery: Chemicals released into the blood can carry signals to distant parts of the body.

Discoverer: Ernest Henry Starling (1866–1927).

Impact: Starling's insight led us to understand the operation of shock, diabetes, human reproduction, and much more.

On June 20, 1905, the English physiologist Ernest Starling used the word "hormone" in public for the very first time. By then, scientists understood the nervous system, but hormones were a complete surprise to those unaware of the work Starling had been doing with his brother-in-law, William Bayliss (1860–1924), on pancreatic secretions.

Knowledge of the nervous system goes back at least to Galen (Claudius Galenus, 129–199 AD) who cut the nerve bundles of a pig, one at a time, showing that the pig only stopped squealing when the laryngeal nerve was cut, proving that this was the nerve which had control over the pig's "voice box."

Our model of the nervous system is a bit like a railway signal system, with committed "wires" fixed at both ends: a place where signals are generated, and a place where signals are reacted to. One signal results in one response in one place. Hormones work more like messages in bottles, cast into the sea and able to be read as they drift by. The analogy is a poor one, though, because hormones usually pass unnoticed until they reach their target.

Part of the hormone "picture" was already there in 1905, because a number of diseases were linked to disorders in particular glands: goiter and cretinism were associated with an enlarged thyroid gland, for example, but this was rightly regarded as a deficiency disease caused by a lack of iodine. Many folk remedies for these conditions used iodized salts or seafoods rich in iodine, even before we knew iodine existed (the element was detected in 1813). Its role in preventing goiter became more obvious after Eugen Baumann (1849–1896) showed in 1896 that iodine was only concentrated in the thyroid gland.

There were also cases where physicians gave patients extracts of animal glands such as the adrenal glands and the pancreas. So the world was ready for the hormone idea, but until Starling introduced the word, hormones were unknown.

Within a generation, many of the main hormones had been identified and purified, and work was under way on discovering their structures, which are as varied as their roles: insulin is made up of fifty-one amino acids, while epinephrine (adrenalin) and thyroxine are both modified versions of the single amino acid, tyrosine. The steroids are usually just several rings of carbon atoms with assorted add-ons that give them just the right charge and shape to be recognized by a receptor.

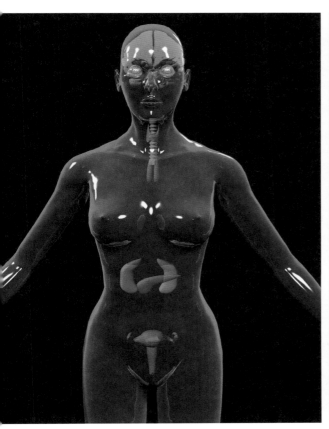 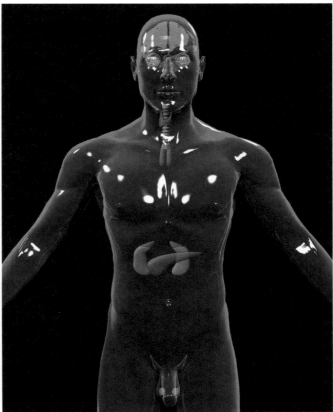

This brings us to one of the unusual features of chemical signals: sometimes an entirely different molecule can have an effect on a receptor, because one part of the molecule fits the receptor site like a key in a lock. There is a strong suspicion, for example, that some modern illnesses may arise from our bodies falsely recognizing organic solvents or compounds as hormones, and responding to them.

Some plants evolve poisons that drive away browsing animals, others have evolved arsenals of animal-harming hormone analogs. Red clover (*Trifolium pratense*), produces isoflavones and phytoestrogens which mimic female hormones. The clover is used in herbal remedies for menopause, but pregnant or breast-feeding women need to avoid it, and it also affects some animals. Rams, bulls, and boars which are exposed to subterranean clover (*Trifolium subterraneum*), have reduced sperm counts. Over time, grazing animals which avoided these clovers would have a reproductive advantage over those which ate them.

The second unusual feature of chemical signals is that some individuals may acquire a receptor in some place other than the norm, which makes the hormone develop a completely new function. Most of those mutants would die fairly quickly, but in a few cases there must have been an

In both females and males, glands (colored red) produce hormones that are necessary for bodily processes such as growth, metabolism, sexual development and function, and response to stress. The pituitary gland regulates the activities of the other glands, and the thymus is part of the body's immune response system.

advantage. This is the only way we can explain what happens when cattle thyroxine is added to a tank full of tadpoles, and the thyroxine makes the tadpoles change into frogs, even when they are far too small to survive as frogs. It is also the only way we can explain why prolactin has important but quite different actions in fish, amphibians, birds, and mammals.

The third unusual feature of hormones is the way they interact with each other in a complicated set of feedback systems, balances and cycles. The same hormone often acts in several places, like the hormones released at puberty which trigger a whole cascade of changes in the body and perhaps even in the mind. The surge of adrenalin (also called epinephrine), after a fright, sets off a whole range of responses that are collectively known as the "fight or flight" (or stress) response: blood is drained from the skin, making us go white, and the heart and lungs work faster, delivering more energy and oxygen to the muscles and organs of the body.

The best-known hormone is insulin, which controls blood sugar levels and so prevents Type I diabetes. This disease is caused when something makes a human's immune system attack a few key cells in a part of the pancreas curiously named the Islets of Langerhans. These are the cells which monitor blood sugar and, when there is too much, release insulin into the bloodstream. Once the cells are destroyed by a misguided immune reaction, blood sugar levels go out of control. Measured injections of insulin can maintain at least an imitation of blood sugar balance, but the long-term hope is that stem cell therapy will be able to restore the original natural function to the pancreas; gene therapy might also work.

Other common examples of hormone therapy include growth hormones for the dwarfed; use of the hormone erythropoietin to help crooked athletes produce more blood cells; the contraceptive pill for women, which uses estrogen and progesterone to adjust the menstrual cycle; and even RU-486, the so-called "morning-after pill," based on anti-progestin.

We think we understand hormones now. That probably just means we have not foreseen the next advance.

DISCOVERING RELATIVITY

How we learned that mass, energy, and time were not as simple as they once seemed

There are many examples of simultaneous discovery, and probably even more cases where it almost happened. When the time is ripe, the same discovery is often made in several places, almost at once. Three people rediscovered Mendel's work (66) at the one time; Leibniz and Newton were neck and neck with the calculus (33); Robert Stephenson and Humphry Davy (43) both claimed the miners' safety lamp as theirs; and Charles Wheatstone and Edward Davy were very close with their telegraphs (37). Alexander Graham Bell and Elisha Gray staked patent claims on the telephone on the very same day (70), and J. J. Thomson was barely the first in the race to discover the electron (85).

Physicists say that if Einstein had not proposed special relativity when he did, one of several other physicists would have done so within a year. If Hendrik Lorentz (1853–1928) missed out on working out the details, Jean Perrin (1870–1942) or somebody else would have cracked it. It was in the air. Special relativity's time had come, in 1905. It was only in 1908 that Max Planck dubbed Einstein's idea the "theory of relativity," because it applied the principle of relativity to explain how the universe is. The 1915 theory of general relativity has since been tucked in alongside special relativity, as though there was only one theory.

The principle of relativity says that natural laws should look the same to different observers in similar frames of reference, and in the late nineteenth century, Lorentz and Henri Poincaré (1854–1912) concluded that length and time needed to change when a speeding object was observed from another perspective.

The theory of special relativity relates mainly to light having a constant velocity in a vacuum; the time dilation effect which leads to the "twin paradox," where one twin remains on Earth while the other twin flies off at relativistic speeds; the FitzGerald contraction and other effects; and, in particular, the equation everybody knows and loves to quote when Einstein's name is mentioned, $e = mc^2$.

The theory of general relativity has more to do with the way gravity bends light as it passes close to massive objects. Really heavy bodies even form gravitational lenses, and people begin to talk about the "curvature of space-time." When you see a diagram with a large ball on a rubber sheet, this is general relativity, but that tends to be the realm of the heavy-grade physicist. But while relativity may look like something we could never test, it turns out that we can, and quite close by.

Date: 1905.

Location: Bern, Switzerland.

Discovery: A group of discoveries about mass, gravity, space, and time.

Discoverer: Albert Einstein (1879–1955).

Impact: This opened the way to understanding nuclear physics and the cosmos.

Particle tracks in a cloud chamber. What look like meaningless squiggles to us could reveal volumes about mass, velocity, and charge to physicists who knew about the fields in the chamber. This pattern shows a kaon decaying to three pions.

A lot of evidence about atoms has been derived from "atom smashers," but nature also smashes atoms, above our atmosphere, where energetic particles from the Sun and other stars hit the outer layers of thin air. Fragments are left, one of them being the muon, which behaves like a heavy electron (it has 206.7 times the mass of an electron, and the same charge)—but the muon rapidly breaks down into an electron and neutrinos.

The muon was discovered in 1937 by Carl Anderson (1905–1991) during cosmic ray experiments, but we should never be able to study them: the muon is unstable, and if you had a box full of them, just 2.2 microseconds later, half of them would have decayed, and after 4.4 microseconds you would have just a quarter of a box full. We say the muon has a half-life of 2.2 microseconds, but that is at rest, in its own frame of reference.

In fact they are traveling at close to the speed of light. When they go that fast, time dilation effects become important, and this extends their life considerably. Without time dilation, even at 0.9c (90 percent of the speed of light), muons would typically travel only about 700 meters in one half-life and fewer than 3 percent would travel 12 kilometers. In fact, large numbers reach the Earth's surface without decaying. Each minute, one muon strikes each square centimeter of the surface. In our frame of reference, the muons survive for many more seconds than they should, but if you were riding on one of a swarm of muons, half of them would be gone, just 2.2 microseconds— 2.2 millionths of a second—later.

You could argue that really huge numbers of muons are produced, so there are still lots of survivors at ground level. We have no reason to believe that, though, and the relativistic explanation fits the available data better. The muon is in a moving frame of reference, so time is slowed down for the muons relative to us, effectively extending their half-life as we see them, allowing some of them to reach the Earth's surface. (In their own time-frame, of course, the muons only last for a very short period of time indeed.)

At normal speeds, we need not worry too much about relativity, because Newton's laws and Newton's physics (32) work very well, and we can send spacecraft around the solar system without ever thinking about Einstein. If we want to understand what is out in space, though, Einstein becomes very important. But he wasn't infallible. When he was formulating his field equations for general relativity in 1915, Einstein found to his surprise that they implied an expanding universe. The redshifts which indicated an expanding universe to Edwin Hubble (90) had already been reported, but Einstein did not know this, so he inserted a "Cosmological Constant" or fudge factor into his equations, and missed out on predicting an expanding universe.

Nobody is perfect, but over time, science remains perfectible. At any given stage, scientists regard what they believe then as the best available way of understanding the world. They are always open to the possibility that a better idea may turn up. That is why science works so well.

DISCOVERING PLASTICS

How we learned to make our materials, rather than catching them

In the early nineteenth century, boxes were made of wood or tinplate; wires were insulated with gutta-percha (53); people wore clothes made of wool, silk, cotton, or linen, derived from plants or animals, with buttons of horn, bone, or tortoiseshell; false teeth were carved from hippopotamus or elephant ivory; books were bound with leather and stuck together with glue made from boiling down old bones; and fertilizer was animal dung or dead stuff. Just about everything was based on plant or animal materials.

At the end of the nineteenth century, we started using new and cleverer materials. The first "plastic" was celluloid, which was made from cotton. Say "celluloid" today, and most people will think of motion picture film. In fact, celluloid could also be molded under heat, but it was flammable. One of the few modern objects still made of celluloid is the table tennis ball, and it was the noise of the celluloid balls on early twentieth century bats that gave table tennis the "ping pong" name that serious table tennis players detest.

Celluloid is a thermoplastic, meaning it becomes soft when heated, just as gutta-percha does. This is why a squashed or dented table tennis ball can be restored more or less to shape by immersing it quickly in hot water, raising the air pressure inside while softening the celluloid. Watch out, though, because if you heat it too much, the part in contact with the water can develop interesting baroque outgrowths that add a disconcerting randomness to the game.

Date: 1907.

Location: Yonkers, New York, USA.

Discovery: The invention of the first synthetic plastic, Bakelite.

Discoverer: Leo Baekeland (1863–1944).

Impact: This material ushered in a new age in manufacturing and style because the material was firm under heat, but able to be molded before it set.

A collection of fabulous 1920s-style wireless sets (radios), all made from Bakelite.

In 1897, Adolph Spitteler (1846–1940) and Wilhelm Krische (often listed as Kirsche, but the original patent documents show his name as Krische) patented a casein plastic derived from milk, apparently after an accident involving a saucer of milk, a cat, and a bottle of formaldehyde. That may be a myth, but casein was discovered by them and marketed as Erinoid or Galalith.

The first modern plastic came in 1907. Bakelite was a true synthetic: it could be molded into complex shapes, it kept its shape after it had hardened, and it was comparatively cheap.

If you were in your thirties, and you had just invented a new sort of photographic paper, who would you take it to? Leo Baekeland thought he knew the answer in the 1890s. In those days, you took it to the experts in photography, Kodak, planning to ask $50,000 for the rights, and willing to settle for $25,000. In the end, he graciously accepted the million dollars that Kodak offered.

A super-scholar, Baekeland completed his doctorate in Belgium at the age of twenty-one, and had his professorial chair at twenty-four. He then won a three-year traveling scholarship to America, and while he was there he invented "Velox" photographic paper. Once he had his money,

Baekeland opened a laboratory and proceeded to fiddle, adding formaldehyde to phenol (carbolic acid, they called it in those days—the stuff that Joseph Lister (67) used as an antiseptic). The end result was a resinous material which stuck to the laboratory glassware, ruining it.

Nothing would clean the glassware, because no solvent would attack the resin. So Baekeland stood the whole problem on its head. Why not, he asked, make the resin even tougher and more resistant? This particular sow's ear was not going too well in the silk purse market, but it might possibly make do as a box! Where earlier chemists had treated the mixture gently, hoping to save their test-tubes and retorts, Baekeland did dreadful things, produced dreadful messes, and ruined glassware. It turned out to be several years' worth of dreadful messes and ruined glassware, so it was lucky he was rich!

Eventually, he found that heating the resin with an alkaline catalyst makes the stuff go soft at first, then irreversibly hard. If you did this while the resin was in a mold, it took a permanent shape. He had invented Bakelite, the first thermosetting "plastic." Unlike thermoplastics, thermoset plastics can be molded while they are hot, but then they set solid.

The world's manufacturers went bananas over Bakelite. You could make cheap cabinets for radios; you could even make cheap knobs to go on the radios and crystal sets of the day, and they could be styled in "modern" ways. You could make buttons, knife-handles, the cases of telephones— even cameras were made from Bakelite.

Up to the early twentieth century, many workers were paid to make containers from tinplate. Now we had Bakelite, and complex shapes could be made with a few chemicals and a simple mold. A few more skills had been lost, and a few more jobs, but the common people could have a little more elegance in their lives.

Today, we take plastics for granted, but it needed something like Bakelite, a material which lent itself to mass production, to get modern style quickly and cheaply into every home. It occurs to me to wonder, too, just what influence the molding methods and their needs had on the shapes which were adopted. Maybe the influence ran even deeper: just look at the Art Deco style!

Plastics have changed our lives in every way imaginable, some good, and some bad—think of the effects of plastic bags on wildlife. We cannot really blame Baekeland or any other inventor for the damage plastics have done, but we certainly can credit him with introducing us to the Age of Plastics.

What we then did with the plastics was our own silly fault.

MEASURING THE CHARGE ON THE ELECTRON

How we proved that electrons existed, then measured and weighed them

Date: 1910.

Location: Chicago, Illinois, USA.

Discovery: There is a fixed unit of electric charge; and the value of that charge.

Discoverer: Robert Andrews Millikan (1868–1954)

Impact: This proved beyond doubt that the electron existed as a particle.

The allocation of the terms "negative" and "positive" in electricity was an arbitrary decision by Benjamin Franklin (1706–1790), who imagined positively charged items as having a surplus of "electrical fluid" while negative items had a deficit. In those days, heat was a fluid, electricity was a fluid, anything which could not be explained was a fluid—the term was thrown around at will.

The word "electron" was around before anyone had worked out what an electron was. G. Johnstone Stoney (1826–1911) used it as early as 1874, when he even made an estimate of the value of the charge on the electron. The year before, James Clerk Maxwell had suggested that Faraday's law of electrolysis (69) supported the idea that electric charge might come in specific bits—in small electrical units. He reasoned that when you had electrolysis cells in series, with different metals, the deposits were proportional to the atomic weights of the metals, suggesting that each atom picked up an electron. That was a bit simpler than we see it now, but it was a start.

Maxwell even used the term "molecule of electricity," and Robert Millikan knew it. His 1917 edition of *The Electron* cites both Maxwell and Stoney as honorable predecessors, as well as J. J. Thomson (1856–1940), who showed that the electron had to be a particle. Millikan was careful to credit others, although he missed Sir Oliver Lodge's 1906 book, *Electrons or The Nature and Properties of Negative Electricity*. This title points up a problem in reading older accounts: a proton, before it was given that name, was also often referred to as an "electron." Lodge referred to negative electricity in his title so as to avoid any confusion. Millikan himself used the word "ion," as the oil drops he studied were charged by ionized particles, and he used the word loosely to describe any charged oil drop.

There was still some doubt about the nature of cathode rays, which were quite obviously a stream of electricity. The feeling in Germany was that electricity was a radiation, and infinitely divisible, just as light appeared to be. In 1897, J. J. Thomson established that he could measure the ratio of charge to mass for the electron, which meant it was a particle; for this work, he won the 1906 Nobel Prize. His son, G. P. Thomson (1892–1975), won the 1937 Nobel Prize for proving that it wasn't a particle after all!

Imagine a very small oil drop, pushed out into a chamber filled with air. The oil drop will slowly fall, pulled downwards by the force of gravity, and slowed by air resistance. Whatever happens, the drop will slowly fall. But suppose that the oil drop has gained a few extra electrons, or

lost a few electrons, and suppose there is an electric field in the air chamber, with charged plates at the top and the bottom.

A freely moveable charged particle in an electric field will move in response to the field. Positive oil drops will be pulled to the negative side of the chamber, and negatively charged oil drops will be pulled to the positive side. If you can vary the electric field, you can start to make some very interesting measurements. We now know that charge comes in bundles, so the charge of a body can only vary by whole numbers of electrons. And better still, if a real "ion" runs into the oil drop and changes the drop's charge, you can calculate the difference in the forces needed for the two charges.

The forces on the drop are the attractive force of the electrical field, and the force due to gravity acting on the drop. The gravitational force stays constant; if you can make a drop hover, first at one charge and then at another, using a change in a vertical electrical field, the calculations are easy, because you can eliminate the effect of gravity.

Then, when you do the sums, you find that the variation in the charge on the oil drop is always a multiple of a very small constant number, which just happens to be the charge on one electron, and which is just what Millikan expected. But before you can do these calculations, you need to squint through a microscope for very long periods of time, watching where the oil drop goes, and how fast. If the oil drop keeps going, you have to keep going as well, regardless of worldly things like dinner engagements, because you need as many measurements as possible on the one oil drop, so you can compare the drop with many different charges.

A computer model of electron flow in a 2-dimensional electrical landscape.

Years later, Millikan explained how he phoned his wife one night to ask her to go ahead to a dinner without him. He would follow, he said, and she should explain to the other guests that he had watched an ion for an hour and a half, and had to finish the job. Indeed, that was precisely what Mrs. Millikan reported to the assembled throng. They learned later that another lady at the table was shocked at the way young academics were paid.

"I think it's scandalous that they underpay these poor young professors so cruelly!" she exclaimed. "I always heard their salaries were small but I was really astonished when Mrs. Millikan told me that her husband had to miss his dinner because he had washed and ironed for an hour and a half, and had to finish the job."

Which raises the interesting question: Should modern scientists who need better funding think outside the box? It might even work for the defense forces!

DISCOVERING WHAT ATOMS ARE MADE OF

How we arrived at a modern view of the atom

Date: 1911.

Location: Cambridge, England.

Discovery: The model of an atom most of us still use, with electrons orbiting a nucleus.

Discoverer: Ernest Rutherford, 1st Baron Rutherford of Nelson (1871–1937).

Impact: For the first time, Rutherford's model identified the atom as having a nucleus, a discovery that would lead on to nuclear physics.

An atom is the smallest possible piece of matter that can take part in normal chemistry. No one has ever seen, nor probably ever will see, an atom, but that does not deter the physicist from trying to draw a plan of it, with the aid of such clues to its structure as he has.

Nobel Prize winner, Maria Goeppert-Mayer (1906–1972), writing in 1951.

Within a decade of Goeppert-Mayer's death, IBM physicists Gerd K. Binnig (1947–) and Heinrich Rohrer (1933–) produced scanning tunneling microscope pictures of individual atoms. They made their first pictures in 1981, and received the Nobel Prize for Physics in 1986. As Niels Bohr used to remind people, making predictions was problematical, especially about the future.

We had atoms-as-billiard-balls in the nineteenth century; then, in the twentieth century, most of the internal structure of atoms was worked out. We still visualize an atom as a piece of matter made up of a nucleus and some surrounding electrons, orbiting the nucleus in shells, rather like swarms of moonlets around a giant planet. It is a convenient example of a model used to explain a complex situation, but we know the atom is not really very much like that.

The best early evidence for atoms came from Joseph Louis Proust (1754–1826), who analyzed copper carbonate, and showed in 1799 that this

This composite colored scanning tunneling micrograph (STM) shows ferromagnetic interactions (red and yellow) between manganese atoms in a gallium arsenide semiconductor (white and yellow), shown as a molecular model.

chemical always had the same proportions of copper, carbon, and oxygen, no matter where it came from, or how it was prepared. Copper carbonate always had five parts of copper, one of carbon, and four of oxygen. Even if John Dalton (15) had not come to the idea of atoms from his studies on gases, somebody else would soon have done so, starting from the challenge of explaining Proust's law. It was an idea whose time had arrived.

Nobody asked what was inside an atom, though, because atoms were, by definition, unsplittable. It would have been a silly question. Then late in the nineteenth century, radioactivity suggested that there must be both positive and negative particles inside atoms. J. J. Thomson, who had shown that the electron was a particle, proposed an atomic model in 1904 that was a bit like a plum pudding. A large positively charged particle had smaller negative electrons scattered through it, and this was about as good a model as people could make until the proton was discovered.

In 1911, Ernest Rutherford (later to be Lord Rutherford) and Hans Geiger (1882–1945) tried firing alpha particles—charged helium nuclei—at a piece of very thin gold foil. Most of the alpha particles went straight through, but a very few of them bounced off. They used gold foil because it can be hammered into very thin sheets, just a few atoms thick, and because gold has very heavy atoms.

They were testing some aspects of the "plum pudding" model, and the bounce-backs were a complete surprise. Rutherford said later, "It was about as credible as if you had fired a 15-inch shell at a piece of tissue paper and it came back and hit you." The only explanation was that the bouncing particles were hitting something much denser than a plum pudding atom. They had to be hitting a concentrated nucleus instead. That was easy: in the Rutherford atom, you just assumed that the electrons were circling at a distance around the outside of the nucleus, and all would be fine.

Or would it? When particles move in a circle or an ellipse, this is what physicists call accelerated motion. The particles may be moving at the same speed, but they are continually changing direction, so they are accelerating. And when you accelerate a charged particle, it radiates energy, which means the electrons must fall in towards the nucleus, and merge with it. This does not happen, so that means the Rutherford atom cannot exist, and a better model was needed.

Enter Niels Bohr (1885–1962), who had studied with Rutherford, but was also familiar with the work of Max Planck (81). Bohr's solution was to propose that electrons could only orbit in certain stable orbits. This allowed the "orbital" model to live again.

The full answer came from Louis de Broglie (1892–1987): It all works perfectly well, so long as you consider that the well-known particles we call electrons are actually waves. When he proposed this in his thesis for a doctorate in physics, people laughed, and he was almost failed. Luckily, Albert Einstein was told about de Broglie's idea, thought briefly, and said that de Broglie might very well be correct. Einstein, you see, had toyed with a related idea some fifteen years earlier.

With the arrival of de Broglie's revolutionary brain wave (so to speak), quantum theory was away and running. The next stage in unraveling the atom came with the discovery of the neutron in 1932, then the discoveries of nuclear fission, nuclear fusion, and much more.

Then, just a few years later, de Broglie's revolutionary theory produced a whole new pay-off. If electrons had the properties of waves, then they could be focused, reflected, and refracted, just like any other sort of wave. But while microscopes cannot resolve anything smaller than a single wavelength, the wavelength of electrons is very small.

And so we got the electron microscope, the scanning tunneling electron microscope, and the images that contradicted the claims of Maria Goeppert-Mayer.

DISCOVERING X-RAY DIFFRACTION

How we acquired a new way of looking inside crystals

If seeing atoms was impossible in the early twentieth century, it was nevertheless possible to see the patterns that atoms made. Ever since Johann Kepler (23) in the early 1600s, people realized that the curiously regular shapes of crystals were an indication of the regular arrays of units that formed the crystals. People like Pierre Curie (79) had studied piezoelectricity: The way that crystals vibrate under an alternating current, or generate voltages when they are vibrated.

All types of waves show a curious property called diffraction. The name refers to the bending of a wave (change in direction), which occurs whenever a wave passes near an obstacle. Longer wavelength waves diffract through a greater angle than shorter wavelength waves.

In optics, a diffraction grating has a series of parallel lines, about the same distance apart as the wavelength of light. When light shines on a diffraction grating, an interference pattern sets up. You can see this by looking at the reflection of a bright light from the surface of a CD: The colored fringes are a result of many reflections interfering with each other, with the pattern determined by the form of the parallel lines—on a CD, they are parallel curves.

It is important not to confuse diffraction with refraction. Basically, diffraction involves a small-scale spreading of light beyond straight-line transmission, contrary to the "rule" that "light travels in straight lines." Diffraction is part of the reason radio waves travel around the planet, although the ionosphere is more important—but it was the observation of diffraction effects which established that light has wave-like properties.

Max von Laue learned in 1912 that the atoms of a crystal might be arranged in a space lattice. He suggested to Walter Friedrich that a large (and conveniently present) crystal of copper sulfate would diffract a beam of X-rays (78). Friedrich and Paul Knipping tried the experiment, but without success. Knipping then tried surrounding the crystal with photographic plates, and obtained the first picture of diffracted X-rays. As well as being a physicist, von Laue wrote a history of physics, in which he told of this experiment in discussing the space lattice theory of crystals. He saw the story beginning with Kepler, who first suggested that crystals are composed of packed spheres (an idea that was suggested also by Robert Hooke and Steno). The first to combine atoms with the space lattice theory was Ludwig Seeber (1793–1855) in 1824, when he suggested that solids might be made up of atoms holding each other in place by attraction and repulsion.

Date: 1912.

Location: Zürich, Switzerland.

Discovery: That X-rays could be diffracted from a crystal surface, revealing its structure.

Discoverer: Max von Laue (1879–1960).

Impact: Forty years later, this was the crucial tool in identifying the structure of DNA.

An X-ray diffraction image of lysozyme, an enzyme found in nasal mucosa.

According to von Laue, most of the physicists who were at all interested in crystallography had decided that atoms and molecules were scattered randomly in a crystal. Leonhard Sohncke (1842–1897) held true to the idea that crystals were regular arrays, but the idea was dying out. Paul von Groth (1843–1927) alone upheld the Sohncke tradition in his teaching in Munich. Reading between the lines, von Laue (also in Munich) agreed with von Groth, did some calculations, made a prediction, and set Friedrich and Knipping to test it with a zinc sulfide crystal and X-rays. Here is how von Laue described it later:

Because of their short wavelength, these waves are able to reveal optically the interatomic distances, whereas these elude radiations of longer wavelengths, such as light. These experiments also furnished the first decisive proof of the wave nature of X-rays, which up to then had been denied by some eminent scientists because of the particularly striking quanta phenomena shown by them ...

This immediately opened up two prospects: If the wavelength of the X-rays is known, the diffraction pattern reveals the structure and spacing of the crystal elements, while if the spacing is known, the wavelength can be determined.

In the long history of Nobel Prizes, several laureates were the children of earlier laureates, but only one pair, William Henry (Sir William) Bragg (1862–1942) and William Lawrence (Sir Lawrence) Bragg (1890–1971) shared the same prize, the 1915 prize in Physics, awarded for their application of X-ray diffraction. The older Bragg became director of the Royal Institution in 1923, which led to the RI becoming a world center for X-ray diffraction research. In a lecture delivered that year, the older Bragg explained why X-rays were important:

Yet ... the microscope can only go to a certain length: it stops far short of the point we must reach if we are to understand how the atoms are acting so as to give the various materials their specific properties. It can show the existence of separate crystals in the metal, but not the arrangement of the atoms in the crystals ... in the X-rays, we find a new hope ...

The younger Bragg became Professor of Physics at Manchester in 1919, and later succeeded Ernest Rutherford at Cambridge's Cavendish Laboratory in 1938. In an article in *Scientific American* in 1968, he wrote of the need to use short wavelengths:

Only X-rays have wavelengths short enough to satisfy this condition. For example, the distance between neighboring sodium and chlorine atoms in a crystal of sodium chloride (ordinary table salt) is 2.81 angstrom units ... whereas the most commonly used wavelength in X-ray analysis is 1.54 Angstroms.

The methods he pioneered allowed Wilkins and Franklin (94) to provide the key of DNA structure to Crick and Watson (94), who worked at the Cavendish Laboratory. Given time, everything in science connects up.

UNCOVERING HUMAN EVOLUTION

How Raymond Dart looked at a fossil cast of a brain and knew immediately that its owner walked on two legs

Charles Darwin had argued in 1869 that early humans would probably have evolved in Africa, based on the similarity of humans to the catarrhines (a group that includes the Old World monkeys and the great apes). In time, this turned out to be remarkably correct.

Australopithecus africanus is a probable ancestor (or else a very close relative) of ours. This species lived in South Africa about 3.0–2.5 million years ago. The first *Australopithecus* specimen discovered was the "Taung baby" or "Taung child," a partial skull of a juvenile which must have been buried in mud, some of which entered the skull and formed a cast of the brain.

Raymond Dart, an Australian anthropologist working in South Africa, was sent a box of rocks from the Taung quarry. Rummaging through, he found the brain cast first, and the skull portion soon after. The face was covered in a matrix of rock, and had to be carefully cleaned before it could be examined, but his first look at the brain cast told Dart this was a special find. He had worked with brain casts before and could see, just from the position of the brain stem, that this animal had a skull which attached to a vertical spine that lay directly below the skull, rather than behind it, as in chimpanzees and gorillas.

Date: 1924–25.

Location: Witwatersrand, South Africa.

Discovery: The "Taung child," the first example of *Australopithecus africanus*.

Discoverer: Raymond Dart (1893–1988).

Impact: For the first time, we had a fossil which showed an ancient hominid, a primate which walked upright, but had a small brain.

Interpreting fossils is an art. Experts need to know anatomy, how the parts work together, and what small differences mean, and they have to work with small clues. The position of the large hole in the skull where the spinal nerve leaves the brain, the foramen magnum, was immediately obvious in the shape of this brain. Any animal with a brain stem like that had to have walked upright.

We cannot be certain how the Taung child died, but we can deduce that the skull ended up on its side in a lime-rich deposit, where the brain case was slightly more than half-filled with the mud which would later harden to produce the cast.

Dart found most of the skull that went with the brain and called it *Australopithecus africanus*, meaning "southern ape from Africa." Today, we might argue that this is not the best name to give to an upright walking individual, even if it had a small brain, but Dart was trying not to draw too much fire upon himself from the Piltdown Man supporters. These were British scientists who said Dart's small-brained thing was wrong, attacking it and Dart because they were convinced that humans evolved a large brain first. They had no real basis for this claim, they just believed it—and they were wrong.

In the end, we learned that "Piltdown" was a concoction of a recent human skull and an orangutan jaw. Nobody knows for sure who the faker was, but I suspect priest and paleontologist Pierre Teilhard de Chardin (1881–1955), and I think his aim was to play a joke on the foolish English "big-brain-first" people. I handled and examined this "specimen" in 1993, and the evidence of fakery is very easy to see, once you know to look for it—so obvious that the faker must have wanted it to be seen. But the English scientists saw only what they wanted to see.

Australopithecus africanus flourished between (on present estimates) two and three million years ago, mainly in the East African Rift Valley, though it may have been more widely spread. The later finds confirmed Dart's original diagnosis, based on a single brain cast: whatever these things were, they walked on their hind legs, much like we do. Their limbs and their hands tell us this, their pelvises say the same thing, and so do the footprints left by their probable ancestors at Laetoli in Africa.

Dart was rather keen on the idea that these pre-humans may have used tools, and explained the absence of any stone remnants by suggesting that they were part of an osteodontokeratic culture—that they used bones, teeth, and horns as primitive tools, and that these later wore away or rotted.

But the question remained: Was this an ape-like human, or a human-like ape? The answer lay hidden inside the jaw, where it remained hidden until 1987. In both humans and the other apes, the "adult" teeth come into place in a specific way. There is one order of appearance in humans, and a different order in the other apes. Hidden inside the Taung baby's skull, teeth were erupting, and if we knew how they were developing, we would know what the Taung baby was—human or ape.

Sadly, there is only one Taung baby, and you cannot slice it up just to see what is inside. You can take X-rays, but there is too much other material in the way, and the things we are looking for are much too faint. It seemed for many years as though we would never know what was inside the jaw. Then in 1987, Glenn Conroy and Michael Vannier had a bright idea. Instead of cutting the skull into thin slices, they could make a series of "slices" with X-rays, and feed all of the results into a computer. A CAT scan would give the answer.

So the researchers took a series of X-ray "slices," just 2 mm apart, in three different dimensions: vertically, from front to back; vertically, from side to side; and horizontally. (They called it the sagittal, coronal, and transaxial planes, if you prefer the technicalities.) The method is less important, though, than what they found, because their answer was delightful: "the Taung 'child' is not a little human, but just as important, it is not a little ape."

The Taung baby is a betwixt-and-between, a half-and-half, a missing link—and we would never have known if the two researchers had not decided to give it a CAT scan!

We had to wait more than sixty years to find out about it, but it was worth waiting for, and Dart was still alive to know of his triumph!

A selection of hominid skulls from across the ages.

DISCOVERING ANTIBIOTICS

How we gained and wasted a natural resource to use against bacteria

Date: 1928.

Location: London, England.

Discovery: A fungus, *Penicillium notatum*, makes a chemical that can stop bacteria growing.

Discoverer: Alexander Fleming (1881–1955).

Impact: Once Fleming's chance discovery was made to work by Ernst Chain (1906–1979) and Howard Florey (1898–1968), many lives were saved.

Wallace Wilson was born in 1888 and died in 1966. President of the British Columbia Medical Association in 1928–29, he lived through the high and low points of antibiotics. At one point in his life, he penned a little verse, and medical tradition says it appeared first in a letter to Dr. E. P. Scarlett, probably in the 1920s. He called it "The Microbiologist's Prayer":

He prayeth best who loveth best
All creatures great and small.
The Streptococcus is the test
I love him least of all.

Whatever the origin of the verse, this describes the situation before antibiotics, and before sulfa drugs. Septicemia—"blood poisoning"—is a fearful experience, even with antibiotics. I suffered it while I was writing this book, and before I went to the hospital, I was shivering so hard from fever that I could neither type nor send a text message. Without antibiotics, I would have turned up my toes and died; with antibiotics, I just put my feet up for a couple of days.

After the development of anesthetics and antiseptic surgery, people in the late nineteenth century went to hospital to be cured, not to die. All too often, the operation was a success, but the patient still died, of a simple bacterial infection. Some way was needed to keep the inside of the patient free of infection.

As a class, antibiotics are "anti-life" in a targeted way. They are chemicals derived from micro-organisms which selectively destroy other microbes. We choose the ones which harm the bacteria while causing less harm to the patient. Antibiotics in some form have been used for about 2,500 years: Chinese physicians used moldy soybean curd on boils and other infections, while Louis Pasteur recorded in 1877 that anthrax bacilli grew well in sterile urine, but failed in non-sterile urine.

In 1928, Alexander Fleming was the first to record the antibiotic effect, after he found a fungus, *Penicillium*, contaminating a culture plate, and later saw that bacteria did not grow near the fungus. He named the active chemical "penicillin" but gave up too quickly on penicillin as a treatment for deep-seated infections. Instead of recommending it for systemic use, he suggested it be used as a dressing for surface wounds.

When Fleming noticed the operation of penicillin, there must have been a series of lucky mistakes. For starters, the plate on which it was found

Antibiotic fungus, *Penicillium*.

must have been left lying around. It could not have been placed in a warm incubator as normal. Having a plate contaminated with *Penicillium* happens sometimes when you culture bacteria, even if you are careful, but the myths say the spore must have drifted in through an open window. When plates are being poured or inoculated, microbiologists do all they can to reduce the number of stray spores, even down to filtering the air and flooding the sealed room with ultraviolet light. If he worked with a window open, Fleming's technique must have been very sloppy. And he was lucky: the *Penicillium* strain on the plate was a rare high-yielding strain which happened to be being cultured in a nearby laboratory—so it was not the result of a stray spore blowing in a window.

Still, he saw the effect, and published a brief account. Fleming listed the drug as a lytic agent, which it was not, but Ernst Chain was looking for lytic enzymes in 1938. Even though penicillin was no enzyme and no lysin either, it still killed bacteria, so Chain and Howard Florey undertook further studies. In the end, Fleming, Chain, and Florey shared the 1945 Nobel Prize for Physiology or Medicine, an award that left out Norman Heatley (1911–2004), whose solution to the challenge of extracting the penicillin from cultures was the key to their success.

When Chain and Florey's studies proved successful, production levels were increased, and in August 1942, Florey supplied some of the drug so Fleming could use it on a friend dying of meningitis. The patient recovered rapidly, and soon the myths started. In the depths of the war, the British needed some good news, and this did nicely. At about the same time, Florey moved to America to direct the mass production of penicillin, a task he carried out successfully. By 1943, penicillin was being used to treat war wounds, but the British press were left with Fleming as their accessible (and local) hero.

Penicillin was a wonder drug, and it was used with enthusiasm. Medical workers like Wallace Wilson must have cheered—though I think Wilson would soon have seen the dangers of overuse: he had that sort of mind.

By 1947, the first penicillin-resistant strains of *Staphylococcus* were being reported. By the time Wallace Wilson died in 1966, *Scientific American* was publishing articles on the transfer of resistance from one microbe species to another, and university lecturers were wondering why we had squandered such a marvelous resource. But the waste goes on today, with antibiotics being added routinely to animal and poultry feed, exposing bacteria to low doses that allow them to select for resistance.

The misuse of antibiotics has let the forces of evolution loose, shaping bacterial populations, selecting those with chemical defenses to the most common antibiotics, and in one or two cases, even to Vancomycin, the "antibiotic of last resort." For a while, science kept finding new classes of antibiotics, but that era has ended. We are fast returning to the situation in which Wallace Wilson penned his little prayer. Only this time, the ammunition locker is empty, and we don't have a prayer.

DISCOVERING HOW FAST THE UNIVERSE IS EXPANDING

How the red shifts of distant stars helped us to understand the universe better

Date: 1929.

Location: Mount Wilson, California, USA.

Discovery: The red shifts of distant stars revealed that the universe was expanding.

Discoverer: Edwin Powell Hubble (1889–1953).

Impact: This pointed to an extreme age for the universe, and led to the idea of the "Big Bang."

We call it Olbers' paradox, but we really ought to call it Halley's paradox or de Chéseaux' paradox, because Halley (in 1722) and de Chéseaux (in 1744) both asked the same question that Heinrich Olbers (1758–1840) published in 1826. Unless, of course, we know that Kepler (23) thought of it in 1610. The question they all asked was: "If the universe is infinite, why is it that the night sky is dark?"

During the day, our sky is bright because of scattered sunlight. On a moonless night, we only have the stars—but if the universe goes on forever, each time you double the distance, the volume increases eight-fold, so there are eight times as many stars in that next "shell," and twenty-seven times as many in the next, and so on. Stars get fainter with distance, so that stars twice as far away are only a quarter as bright, but if there are eight times as many, the outer shell should be twice as bright as the inner shell, and the further out you go, the more light there should be.

Now like every good paradox, this one tells us there is something wrong with our assumptions. It makes people think. Johann Mädler (1794–1874) pointed out in 1861 that if the universe had a finite age, that might explain the dark night sky. Some of the more distant stars might

be too far away for their light to have reached us yet, and the modern view is that this is a big part of the answer.

A top-down view of spiral galaxy NGC 1309 in the constellation Eridanus.

Depending on which school of thought you belong to, though, there is another possible answer, which at least partly explains our dark skies. It came from Edwin Hubble, an American Rhodes scholar who studied law at Oxford University before he turned to astronomy and found this possible answer, which definitely resolved another puzzle: Why all of those stars, comets, planets, meteors, and other bits had not all pulled on each other and come together under the force of gravity.

In 1929, after almost a decade of observations with the Mount Wilson 100-inch telescope, Hubble and Milton Humason revealed something unexpected: the stars were all receding, with the further ones traveling ever faster, so that those at some thirteen billion light years away (at the "Hubble radius") appear to be receding at the speed of light. On this basis, that limits the size of the universe we can ever know about, or see. In other words, the universe may indeed be infinite, but the part we can actually see is quite limited. That gives us that other possible answer to Olbers' paradox.

There were two parts to this discovery: The first was to calculate the speed of the receding stars, something that was easy enough to find by looking at the red shift—the Doppler shift of a receding light source—of distant stars or galaxies, looking at the standard lines on the spectrum (61), which seemed to be in the wrong places as we view them from Earth. The light still reaches us at the same speed when the source is moving away from us, but the frequencies are shifted.

The second challenge was to work out how far away the receding galaxies are. The answer was found in very special stars, the Cepheid variables. In the jargon of astronomers, these are "standard candles" which get their name from the first of their kind to be seen, Delta Cephei.

Henrietta Swan Leavitt (1868–1921) started as a human computer (a term which will be explained, two chapters on) at Harvard College Observatory, in 1908. She published her observation that brighter variable stars had longer cycles from bright to dark and back again, and confirmed this in more detail in 1912. This meant that if an observer measures the period of variation, then the real brightness—the absolute brightness—of the star is known. Distant stars will appear dimmer, but when the absolute brightness is compared with the star's relative brightness, its distance can be estimated quite reliably.

So the distance of any galaxy with Cepheid variables could be estimated. Cepheid variables are fairly rare, but a recent search of eighteen galaxies by the Hubble telescope (named after Edwin Hubble) revealed 800, more than enough to estimate the speed at which the universe is expanding. The rate is still a matter of argument, but it is probably between 50 and 100 kilometers per second per megaparsec. That is, stars 1 megaparsec away are receding at 50–100 km/s, while those at 2 megaparsecs are receding at 100–200 km/s. In spite of the significant variability in the estimates, this rate is still called "Hubble's Constant."

This finding set the scene for the Big Bang theory to be put forward. If quantum physics is hard to think about, and if evolution seems to make no sense on our time scale, cosmology is the double whammy, because it makes no sense on our time scale, and it is also hard to think about. But the Big Bang cosmology seems to stand up fairly well.

By an odd chance, "Big Bang" was a name cooked up by Fred Hoyle, one of the supporters of the competing Steady State model. His aim was to ridicule the opposing theory, but the name stuck. In fact, the Big Bang model stood up, unlike the Steady State model, which involved stars spreading out, and every so often, a new star springing up out of nothing to fill the gap.

Now that picture *really* hurts the brain!

DISCOVERING ATOMIC POWER

How we realized that unsplittable atoms really could split—and that when they did, they released energy

Albert Einstein called Lise Meitner "our Madame Curie," chemist Otto Hahn called her his colleague, and Otto Frisch called her his aunt. Her fellow students must have called her a rare event, for few young women studied physics in her day in Vienna. She completed her doctorate in 1905, then turned to the study of radioactivity.

In 1906, she went to Berlin to study with Max Planck (81) "for a year or two," and stayed there thirty years, teaming up with Hahn—in those days, work on radioactivity really needed the skills of the chemist and the physicist in combination. Meitner produced the accurate physical data, and Hahn produced the pure substances: It was a perfect team.

Of Jewish descent, Meitner fled from Germany to Vienna, Austria. When Germany invaded Austria in 1938, she escaped through the Netherlands to Denmark, and then to Sweden, but she kept up her old contacts. She had asked Hahn and Fritz Strassmann (1902–1980), to see if the neutron bombardment of uranium produced tiny amounts of radium.

If you are trying to find a millionth of a gram of radium in a sample, the chances are you will flush it down the plughole. Radium sulfate is insoluble, but not *that* insoluble. The trick is to precipitate it out, along with barium sulfate. You still lose a bit, but you keep most of it. Then you test to see if the precipitate is radioactive, which suggests radium is present. But the final test is to separate out the radioactive bit, and prove that it is radium. This time, the radioactive precipitate would not separate. Chemically, the radioactive thing was the same as barium, which was ridiculous. It just couldn't be—theory didn't allow it.

When the theories don't allow something that just is, you can deny the facts, or doubt the theory. The only proper scientific approach is to doubt the theory, and look for an amendment, or a better theory—anything else is fraud. Hahn wrote to Meitner to say there had to be radioactive barium in the mix, but where did it come from? We would say now that the atoms of uranium had "split" or fissioned under neutron bombardment. On Christmas Day 1938, fission was unknown—but that was about to change.

Otto Frisch was visiting his aunt and, after a good Swedish Christmas dinner, they tried to work out how radioactive barium could get into the precipitate. Hahn could not be mistaken, so they accepted that radioactive barium was there. Wandering through the snow, Frisch on

Date: Christmas Day, 1938.

Location: Near Göteborg (Gothenburg), Sweden.

Discovery: Radioactive nuclei decay.

Discoverer: Lise Meitner (1878–1968) and Otto Frisch (1904–1979), with data from Otto Hahn (1879–1968).

Impact: The realization led to the atom bomb and nuclear power.

Atomic explosion after the detonation of the world's first atomic bomb, at Alamogordo, New Mexico, on July 16, 1945. Three weeks later, atomic bombs were dropped on the Japanese cities of Hiroshima and Nagasaki.

skis, Meitner without skis, they sat for a while on a fallen tree trunk. On scraps of paper, they calculated a few values, and found the uranium nucleus was quite unstable. Given the right sort of shove, the nucleus might well split, and Meitner even explained where the energy came from, the energy which created the split. She noted a mass defect of about one-fifth of the mass of a proton: just about right, according to good old $e = mc^2$, to supply the energy needed.

Frisch told Niels Bohr, who knew at once that it must be correct, crying, "Oh, what idiots we all have been," and urging immediate publication. Soon after, Frisch left Denmark to visit Mark Oliphant in Britain. While he was there, World War II broke out and Frisch moved into Oliphant's laboratory, where most of the work focused on radar. But in the nine months between that Christmas Day and the start of war, Frisch and Meitner had published their findings and thoughts, meaning that the whole world had access to the idea of nuclear fission.

In Britain, Frisch worked on Bohr's belief that only one uranium isotope, U-235, would be fissile. Frisch looked at the Clusius tube as a means of enriching uranium, and worked out with a German refugee theoretical physicist called Rudolf Peierls (1907–1995) that about 100,000 Clusius tubes were needed to obtain the necessary amount of U-235, but that it was feasible.

Realizing that the atom bomb was possible, the Austrian and the German warned the British government, and the rest, as they say, is history. Frisch ended up in the United States working on the atomic bomb; Meitner refused to work on nuclear weapons, and remained in Sweden until 1960, when she retired and settled in Cambridge. Lise Meitner was never awarded the Nobel Prize, although she shared the 1965 Fermi Prize with Hahn and Strassmann.

In 1913, before World War I, H. G. Wells wrote a science fiction novel, *The World Set Free*, which involved the bombing of Berlin in 1956:

… with both hands the bomb-thrower lifted the big atomic bomb from the box and steadied it against the side. It was a black sphere two feet in diameter. Between its handles was a little celluloid stud, and to this he bent his head until his lips touched it. Then he had to bite in order to let the air in upon the inducive. Sure of its accessibility, he craned his neck over the side of the airplane and judged his pace and distance. Then very quickly he bent forward, bit the stud, and hoisted the bomb over the side.

We know what Bohr said about making predictions, but Wells did a fairly good job. In reality, the first atom bomb came eleven years sooner than he had expected, it was used against Japan, and no human could have picked the first bomb up and dropped it by hand. But it would get worse: warfare had discovered science, and it wasn't about to let go.

INVENTING THE DIGITAL COMPUTER

How the first computers were built to help win a war

The nineteenth century was full of machines and devices that were forerunners of the computer. Some of them had just one computer-like aspect, others had several. The Jacquard loom of Joseph Jacquard (1752–1834), for example, used digital storage on punched cards to determine which of the warp (lengthwise) threads should be raised and which should be lowered as the shuttle passed across. The result was a pattern in the cloth that could even look like an engraving.

Charles Babbage (1791–1871) was the inventor of a mechanical computer called the Analytical Engine, and he used to keep a woven portrait of Jacquard on his wall, generated by 24,000 cards—about 3 megabits of information. Babbage was impressed that when Prince Albert, Queen Victoria's husband, came to visit, the royal consort had immediately recognized the picture and its subject.

The telegraph (37) was a digital signaling device (it used "on" and "off"), but the telephone operated on the analog principle, where the current running along the wires was an analog of a voice signal that had to be decoded at the other end. Gramophones and phonographs used an analog—variable grooves in the record's surface—to produce sounds. Today, music is mostly digital, and so are most of the "photos" we take. At one time, even after World War II ended in 1945, people seriously

Date: 1943.

Location: Bletchley Park, England.

Discovery: The creation of the first digital computer.

Discoverer: Thomas (Tommy) Harold Flowers (1905–1998).

Impact: In the short term, the computer helped win the war against Nazi Germany, in the longer term, it revolutionized our society.

considered using analog computers rather than digital ones, but digital computers had a head start. It might help, though, to consider first what we mean by the word "computer."

When Australia's Sydney Observatory was built on top of a grassy harbourside hill in the 1850s, its sandstone buildings loomed over a busy port, and it was intended mainly as a source of accurate time in the Antipodes, so that ships' captains could set their chronometers. Every day, star sightings were taken, difficult calculations were made, and the master clock was set. The original plans included an office for the astronomer and a "room for the computer." This "computer" was not a machine, but one of those people who did all the calculating. In the early twentieth century, women like Henrietta Swan Leavitt (we met her two chapters back) got into astronomy by taking work as "computers."

Babbage's Difference Engine and Analytical Engine were both intended to be mechanical in their operation, and to print out tables of data (logarithms, sines, and other necessary values). As a demonstration, he proposed to output the values of $x^2 + x + 41$, which generates many prime numbers—failing only at $x = 40$, for reasons left to the reader to find! (As a hint, it fails also for $x = 41$.)

This gave Sir Robert Peel (whose smile was likened by Daniel O'Connell to the gleam of silver plate on a coffin lid) the opportunity to sneer and grandstand in the British Parliament:

I should like a little previous consideration before I move in a thin House of country gentlemen a large vote for the creation of a wooden man to calculate tables from the formula $x^2 + x + 41$.

In World War II there was no room for such vindictiveness. British democracy was somewhat bent by the needs of fighting a war, and technology was directed by imperatives like cracking the German Enigma code, which was generated by a pseudo-random machine, dependent on settings. Tommy Flowers had his chance because votes were not taken in wartime: orders were given instead.

Flowers was a telephone engineer who worked on electronic telephone exchanges after the war, but during the war he led work on the Colossus machines. Programming came from hard-wired function units and a switchboard, but the Colossi were in the same family as the first post-war computers. The coded text to be decrypted was stored on five-hole punched paper tape.

Flowers had started work with the British Post Office (which managed Britain's telephone services) in 1926, and by 1930 had the task of reducing the number of dialed calls that either failed or went to the wrong number. About 1935, he began looking at non-mechanical—that is, electronic—switches, to make the various connections. In essence, a digital computer is just a large number of switches, so the road to Colossus was open.

By 1942, he was at Bletchley Park, the secret British code-breaking establishment, but the Colossus began with a different problem—reading the paper tapes, which had to be done many times over, once for each pass of the program. In February 1943, Flowers proposed using electronic storage, arguing that the war would still be going a year later, when such a machine would be complete.

There were skeptics, of course, but the Post Office engineer knew the answers, because electronic storage used established technology and tested methods that he knew from his work on phone exchanges. He was told to go ahead, and succeeded. After the war, Flowers was given a low-level decoration (the MBE), and his work was hidden under the Official Secrets Act, until word about it began to leak out in the 1970s. It had gone unrecognized far longer than necessary, and his developments had to be made again, by a senior engineer who was able to suggest, without revealing any background, a solution that would work—wink, wink, nudge, nudge.

Many of the components remained the same for decades. Showing my age, I'll admit that I used five-channel punched teleprinter tape as computer input in 1963. As late as 1987, I was punching and submitting batch files, using the same kinds of punch cards that Herman Hollerith (1860–1929) invented a century earlier to process the results of the 1890 US Census.

And if you know where to look, you can find Vannevar Bush proposing hypertext—in 1945!

1940s IBM secretary / punch card operator using her office equipment.

DISCOVERING THE TRANSISTOR

How a replacement for the vacuum tube or thermionic valve was found, just in time

Date: 1947.

Location: Murray Hill, New Jersey, USA.

Discovery: Small, low-powered semiconductor devices could replace the vacuum tube.

Discoverer: William Shockley (1910–1989), John Bardeen (1908–1991), and Walter Brattain (1902–1987).

Impact: The whole modern electronic world depends on this single discovery.

If you were at all technically minded and born before 1940, you would probably have had some experience with the cat's whisker diode that was used in "crystal sets." This was a crystal of a semiconductor, usually galena (lead sulfide) mounted in Wood's metal, which was poked with a fine wire (the "cat's whisker") until a sensitive point was found which allowed the formation of something called a point contact rectifier. This allowed current to flow one way only through the junction.

A semiconductor is neither one thing nor the other: A substance which conducts electricity better than an insulator, but not so well as a conductor. Its resistance falls as temperature increases, and also when tiny amounts of impurities are added. Silicon is the most common commercial semiconductor, followed by germanium and gallium, and assorted alloys and compounds involving those elements. We know semiconductors best from transistors, now invisibly tiny elements in integrated circuits. But the first semiconductor device was the cat's whisker diode.

Ferdinand Braun (1850–1918) discovered the diode effect of the wire-galena type in 1874, and shared the 1909 Physics Nobel Prize with Guglielmo Marconi (1874–1937) for a variety of contributions to "wireless telegraphy." These included tuning circuits, but the cat's whisker was, for many years, the practical low-power alternative to a diode vacuum tube or valve (73).

Wherever venerable technologists gather, you can hear folk tales of engineers who (usually around 1927), encountered the transistor effect in one form or another. Some person, whose name is now forgotten, was messing around with a cat's whisker, and for some reason or other observed the transistor effect, but thought no more of it. Russell Shoemaker Ohl (1898–1987) certainly believed that Russians had done it in 1910, based on what he had read in the literature.

The transistor effect was based on quantum theory: think back to Louis de Broglie (86), and his way-out idea that electrons are waves. When people started to think about the way electron waves pass through a crystal, they saw that even tiny imperfections would change the way the electrons moved or did not move. Paul Wigner (1902–1995) started looking at metallic sodium, but the principles he developed had a wider application, as one of his students, John Bardeen (1908–1991), later realized.

A circuit board from a portable radio; notice all of the individual components. In time, these would all be incorporated in a single chip.

Russell Ohl was looking at the behavior of silicon at Bell Labs in 1940, working on crystal detectors for radar. He had Bell chemists prepare silicon which was largely purified, but the process concentrated one sort of impurity at one end, and another sort at the other end, producing ingots with p-silicon at one end and n-silicon at the other.

By chance, he cut a section which had p-silicon on one side and n-silicon on the other, and he began spotting some curious effects: light shining on it caused a voltage to develop, and there were other oddities. One of those who observed this was Walter Brattain, who quickly deduced that there had to be some internal and invisible barrier between the n- and p-doped silicon.

It was wartime, though, so such novelties had to be set aside. After the war, physicist William Shockley was freed from his wartime work on radar and given charge of a team of workers whose aim was to find a solid-state device that would replace the vacuum tube, but Brattain, in conjunction with Bardeen, made the first transistor. It was half an inch high, far larger than what we know today, but it worked. In simple terms, there were two contacts touching a germanium crystal that sat on a metal plate that was connected to a voltage source.

When a small current flowed into one of the contacts, it made a much larger current flow out of the other contact. This is the classical definition of amplification: A small difference produces a larger difference, whether it is Archimedes (12) using a lever to amplify a force, Lee de Forest (73) using an audion to amplify a signal, or a transistor doing the same thing. Keep in mind, though, that an amplifier can also act as a switch, allowing current or no current, and digital computers need lots of switches.

After the first successful operation of a transistor came the fury, because Brattain and Bardeen thought Shockley was stealing their thunder, hogging the credit. In fairness to an unpleasant man, Shockley had one idea they didn't, and that was to make the transistor as a sandwich—the so-called junction transistor, which was announced in July 1951.

By that time, the space race between the USA and the USSR was beginning to hot up, and solid-state electronics would be a great deal more effective in coping with the forces and vibrations of a rocket launch. So the transistor came just in time. Brattain and Bardeen remained close friends, but were always reserved about Shockley, who believed that most of the credit should be his, because the work was based on his idea of something he called the field effect.

The three shared the 1956 Nobel Prize for Physics. Brattain remained a tinkerer at Bell Labs, Bardeen won a second Nobel for work on superconductivity and, in 1955, Shockley formed a company to make his "Shockley diode." This was the first "Silicon Valley" company.

Even then, biotechnology was starting to make itself visible. It is a branch of science (though some might call it an industry) which relies on electronics, but reaches beyond it.

DEDUCING THE STRUCTURE OF DNA

Two scientists disobeyed instructions, and solved the basic riddle of life

Date: 1953.

Location: Cambridge, England.

Discovery: The structure and makeup of DNA.

Discoverers: James Watson (1928–) and Francis Crick (1916–2004).

Impact: Paved the way for genetic engineering, gene therapy, biotechnology, DNA fingerprinting, and much of modern medicine.

In 1944, Oswald Avery (1877–1955) and his colleagues showed that DNA—deoxyribonucleic acid (and not protein, as many had believed)—carried genetic information. This revelation fired the imaginations of scientists around the world. Clearly, this molecule with millions of atoms contained the instructions to control cells—the blueprint for life that was passed to each new living thing at the moment of reproduction.

This was what made every life form what it was—human, elephant, or petunia. If someone could work out the structure of this thread, they would understand the code of life: how genes are translated into living things. And then all sorts of possibilities that had only existed in the realm of science fiction might become feasible, like curing hereditary diseases or even creating new life forms.

After World War II, researchers could take up science again. Francis Crick was a physicist who had been doing research on naval mines, but he returned to Cambridge University in England to investigate proteins using X-ray diffraction (87). While he worked on that, Crick kept wondering about DNA. James Watson was a young American zoologist and geneticist who had just arrived at Cambridge to research viruses, but he shared Crick's interest in DNA. The two became obsessed with the problem and soon neglected what they were supposed to be doing as they hunted for the answers.

They knew that DNA forms huge molecules with many millions of atoms, and that different DNAs were put together differently, but they thought there had to be regular patterns. This meant DNA should form crystals that could be studied. Watson and Crick began examining X-ray diffraction photographs to understand DNA. Their work was as much physics and mathematics as biology, but it would reshape biology.

By 1953, the diffraction patterns revealed that the basic structure of DNA consisted of two helical, or long spiral strands—what we now call the double helix. There was still the question of how the bits were arranged, but the bits were already known. Over the years, biochemists had managed to pull DNA apart, so they knew there were sugar molecules (deoxyribose), phosphate groups, and four chemicals that are called bases: adenine, cytosine, guanine, and thymine.

Some people still doubted that DNA was the genetic material, so Erwin Chargaff (1905–2002) had started to analyze DNA from a variety of sources, to show that they were different in their proportions of the bases. They *were* different, and Chargaff reported in 1950 that the adenine and thymine levels were always similar to each other in a given sample, and so were the cytosine and guanine levels. Chargaff's measurements gave Watson and Crick the key to the problem. Realizing that the matching bases formed pairs, they began building paper models of the molecule, using X-ray diffraction data from Maurice Wilkins (1916–2004) and Rosalind Franklin (1920–1958).

Based on the X-ray diffraction data, they gave their model two backbone chains of sugar molecules and phosphate groups. Then, building on Chargaff's analysis, they worked out that adenine and thymine sat inside the double helix and made delicate links with each other, joining the two chains, and that cytosine and guanine did the same. It all made sense.

Of course, there were still many unanswered questions, but the structure offered a way for DNA to carry a code in the pattern of bases. More importantly, they could see a way for it to replicate, with each DNA strand pulling apart and acting as a template to form a new and complete second strand. In other words, one double strand becomes two single strands which become two double strands, each identical to the original DNA molecule.

They couldn't prove that DNA replicated like that, but they wanted the credit for saying it first. So they published their model in *Nature* in 1953, along with this statement:

It has not escaped our notice that the specific pairing we have postulated immediately suggests a possible copying mechanism for the genetic material.

This was probably the scientific understatement of the century.

DALI ON THE DIVINE

And now the announcement of Watson and Crick about DNA. This is for me the real proof of the existence of God.

Salvador Dali, on Crick and Watson's 1953 paper.

A stylized image of the double helix strands of DNA

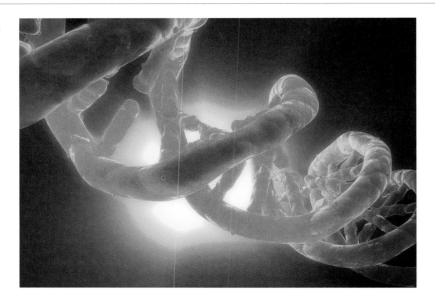

They must have had some idea that sets of bases coded for amino acids in proteins, but that was left out of their first paper. Soon after its publication, Crick deduced that the code would be a triplet of bases. Proving this took longer, but at his Nobel acceptance speech in 1962, Crick treated it as a proven fact. It took the work of many other scientists to establish how different sets of three bases code for a single unit—one amino acid in the chain that makes a particular protein.

Today, the entire sequence of bases in the genome of a new virus can be found in a day, allowing quick responses to outbreaks like SARS. With luck, future influenza epidemics will be stopped the same way. We can look at genomes and plot evolutionary trees, we can look at crime scenes, and use the DNA left behind to see who was there, we can modify plants to be healthier and we can use yeast cells to make important drugs. Without Watson and Crick's solution to the structure of DNA, none of this could happen.

Today we understand how DNA works and how it may be changed. What will the next half-century bring? With luck, we will find ways to treat the genes of sick people to prevent disease, and already, we are able to train our immune systems to seek out and kill some sorts of cancer.

For the rest, we will have to wait and see.

DEVELOPING THE INTEGRATED CIRCUIT

How we found a way to pack rooms of circuitry into a small box

It is hard to choose just one of Noyce and Kilby, the two thinkers who independently invented the integrated circuit. In the end, their companies, Fairchild Semiconductor and Texas Instruments, agreed to cross-license their technologies to each other. On the other hand, Kilby's patent was submitted first, and he was the one recognized by a share of the 2000 Nobel Prize for Physics.

To get an idea of the impact integrated circuits (usually referred to as ICs or chips) have, consider Intel's Core2Duo processors which helped write this book. It contains 291 million transistors in a space with an area of 143 mm². A square meter, about 10 square feet, would contain 7,000 chips, with enough transistors to provide more than 300 transistors for each person alive on the planet today.

Each of those transistors plays the same role as a vacuum tube or valve (73) in the oldest digital computers, but each tube required about 8 watts of power. Multiply that by 291 million, and you have a power need of around 2.3 gigawatts for a tube computer of the same power. That is the output of five coal-fired power stations. If we wired an equivalent circuit with individual transistors, the power needed would still be around 145 megawatts, so a coal-fired power station could run three of those and have a bit left over to make coffee, but not much more. The thermal design power (the amount of heat building up around the chip) is around 65 watts, which means about 40 million computers like mine can run on the output of those five power stations.

If you factor in your CD player, phone, TV, and MP3 player, you use a lot of transistors each day, and without chips we simply would not be able to keep up with the demand for power. This demand has increased over time, in part from the operation of a rule-of-thumb known as "Moore's Law."

This is generally stated in the form that the power of a computer, for a given number of dollars, doubles every eighteen months. The more technical formulation of the law is that the logic density of silicon integrated circuits has closely followed the curve $d = 2(t - 1962)$, where d is the density in bits per square inch and t is the year. In other words, the amount of information storable on a given amount of silicon has roughly doubled every year since the technology was invented.

The law, proposed by Gordon Moore, a co-founder of Intel in 1968, holds up well. Since the mid-1980s, the memory usage of evolving systems has doubled about once every eighteen months. The simple laws

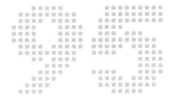

Date: 1958.

Location: Dallas, Texas, USA.

Discovery: A system of building a chip—a circuit with many components—all in one process.

Discoverer: Jack St. Clair Kilby (1923–2005) and Robert Noyce (1927–1990).

Impact: The modern consumer electronics industry, like the modern information technology industry, rests on the chip.

Silicon chips are a vital part of the Minuteman Missile's operating system.

of physics guarantee that Moore's law cannot continue to hold indefinitely, so eventually software and hardware makers will have to stop demanding ever more powerful computers with more RAM, faster access times and processing, and more storage.

In a sense, the first integrated circuit was the four-layered Shockley diode (93), which did the work of two transistors. Then, in September 1958, came Jack Kilby's first device, which was just a transistor and a few other components, all created on a germanium slice and able to generate a sine wave on an oscilloscope.

Kilby was a new employee of Texas Instruments in July that year, so when most of the TI staff went off for a summer break, he stayed behind and considered a problem. Transistors were tiny, they used less power than tubes, but they were fiddly and easy to damage if you soldered them clumsily—and each one had to be soldered in, where vacuum tubes just plugged into sockets that were already soldered in place. There was also a size problem, because while transistors could be made in tiny sizes, the tiniest were too small to be handled on assembly lines. Diodes, rectifiers, and capacitors also needed soldering, and any soldered joint could be "dry," a fault which stopped the circuit working.

Kilby began with the idea that passive devices like resistors and capacitors could be made from the same material as the transistors. In less than two months, he had his answer and a working model. He used masks to etch patterns onto a chip, and to build the components in layers. The first sample might have only generated a sine wave, but it proved that the concept worked, far more thoroughly than Cugnot's lumbering steam wagon (65) proved the value of locomotives. On February 6, 1959, Texas Instruments filed a patent application.

Robert Noyce had much the same idea at Fairchild Semiconductor in California, but he came up with a better way of connecting the parts. Fairchild knew that TI had already filed a patent application in the same area, so Fairchild went into more detail in their own patent, hoping to avoid infringement. In the end, the Fairchild patent, submitted later, was granted earlier, while TI's application was still being analyzed.

By 1962, the US Air Force's Minuteman Missile was using silicon chips, but the big winner was the calculator chip that Kilby designed as a demonstration product for TI. The cynicism and doubts evaporated as people realized they could replace their analog slide rules with something much smaller that delivered the digital accuracy of lumbering desktop calculators while sitting comfortably in their pocket. Some cautious diehards placed their slide rules in small glass cases with a sign reading, "Break glass in case of an emergency," but the emergency never came.

Chips are now found in pacemakers, bionic ears, diagnostic machines, watches and clocks, computers, telephones, dishwashers, washing machines, digital cameras, vehicles, and every consumer electronics item that you own.

This child born of of quantum physics, photography, and many other sciences controls our very lives.

DISCOVERING SEA FLOOR SPREADING

How the mysterious "drift" of the continents was explained, and went from science fiction to science

First came the idea of continental drift, a vague notion that somehow the planet had a changing surface. You only had to look at a map of the Atlantic Ocean to see how Africa would fit in neatly against South America. In 1596, a Dutch map maker called Abraham Ortelius (1527–1598) suggested that the two sides of the Atlantic had been torn apart, but he did not suggest what might have done it.

Once people started collecting plants and animals, some interesting parallels showed up, like the presence of monkeys. You could explain Asian monkeys by assuming they had wandered across from Africa (or vice versa), but the South American monkeys were a puzzle. A close inspection showed that the New World monkeys were quite different, suggesting that a great deal of evolution had happened since the groups separated. Other plant and animal distributions also made more sense if continents had originally been joined together.

In 1912, a German meteorologist named Alfred Lothar Wegener (1880–1930) published an account of how continental drift might have happened. He suggested that the supercontinent Pangaea began to split about 200 million years ago. Alexander Du Toit (1878–1948) in Johannesburg supported him and proposed that Pangaea first broke into two large pieces: Laurasia in the northern hemisphere, and Gondwanaland in the southern hemisphere; Laurasia and Gondwanaland later broke apart to make today's continents.

Date: 1960–1962.

Location: In the middle of the Atlantic.

Discovery: The floor of the Atlantic is spreading out from a central ridge.

Discoverer: Harry Hess (1906–1969).

Impact: The evidence of sea floor spreading showed that the Earth's surface is made up of plates that are moving, and all of a sudden, the planet's history made a lot more sense.

The key find was the distribution of a fossil fern named *Glossopteris*, found in South America, southern Africa, Australia—and Antarctica. But the snag was explaining the source of the huge force needed to move a continent around.

While we use the same terms today as Wegener and Du Toit, much of the explanatory background is different, and we regard some of today's land masses not as ancient continent-units, but rather as large pieces assembled from several different scraps.

Continental drift tried to account for the shapes of the world's large land pieces and the distribution of animals and plants. Plate tectonics works on the idea that the Earth's crust "floats" on the denser mantle beneath, and that parts are slowly moved around by convection effects. It explains the continent shapes, and plant and animal distributions, but it also explains the main mountain regions like the Himalayas and the Alps, the distribution of volcanoes and earthquakes, the location of island groups like Hawaii and the Aleutians—and the forces that drive the process.

It all began with the idea of sea floor spreading, and that came from mapping of the sea floor, at first carried out with long weighted lines lowered to the floor, and later with sonar, sending ultrasonic "pings" at the sea floor and timing their return. This revealed the shape of the seabed. The first published chart showing parts of the mid-Atlantic ridge appeared in 1855. Ships laying cables across the Atlantic also detected parts of the ridge, then in 1947, cores of the seabed showed that the sediment on the floor of the Atlantic was much thinner than it should have been under an ocean that had existed for four billion years. A rethink was needed.

Before long, other ships were mapping other sea floors and tracing the basically continuous global mid-ocean ridge, more than 30,000 miles long and sometimes more than 500 miles across. These were no mere hills, either; the mountains rose three miles above the sea floor.

Then there was an oddity that can be found in basalt: the magnetic fields sometimes go the "wrong" way—the reverse of today's magnetic field. We know now that every so often, there is a polar reversal, where the Earth's magnetic field "flips," reversing the magnetic north and south poles. As liquid basalt escapes from the Earth, the magnetic field of the moment is printed into the rocks.

If you map the zones of normal and reversed magnetic fields around the mid-Atlantic ridge, you see a pattern of "stripes" going across the sea floor. The way this is shown in school textbooks, most people think the sea floor is striped like a zebra. It isn't—the striping is just a way for a diagram to show the two polarities, and all the basalt is black. As mapping progressed, it became clear that the "stripes" were of different sizes, reflecting longer and shorter periods between reversals, but the amazing thing was that the two sides of the ridge showed a mirror pattern.

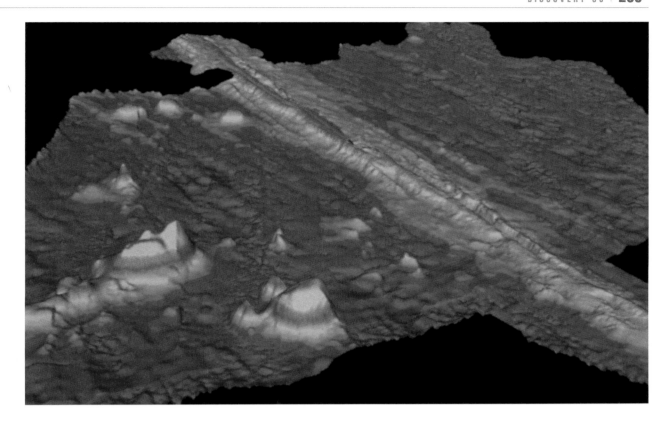

By 1961, people were beginning to hint, rather nervously, that maybe the basalt was oozing from the floor and spreading out to either side. During the 1960s, deep-sea drilling rigs began to bring up cores from the sea floor, and by 1968, fossil and isotope tests on the cores established a proof for the sea floor spreading hypothesis that Harry Hess proposed in 1962—young rocks near the ridge, old rocks further out.

This lets us explain the more peculiar earthquake areas. Spreading in one place means rocks being buried somewhere else. The subduction zones where one plate slides under another—the deep sea trenches, the position of Wallace's Line (51, 63), and even the origins of Africa's Rift Valley, where many of the earliest human and pre-human fossils are found today—were all explained.

The Himalayas, the Swiss Alps, and the Andes have all formed as the crust piles up where plates are colliding. The volcano-free earthquakes of Turkey and Greece are explained, for the movement between the plates there is not the sort that generates volcanoes. Around the Pacific, the Ring of Fire—the long chain of active volcanoes—is explained, while the Hawaiian islands are now seen as the result of a plate slipping over a "hot spot" that keeps generating volcanoes.

And that is probably enough for any single theory to have to explain.

The East Pacific Rise, a mid-ocean ridge on the floor of the Pacific Ocean.

MEASURING THE COSMIC BACKGROUND RADIATION

How we found the shadow of the Big Bang, and knew how the universe began

Date: 1964–65.

Location: Holmdel, New Jersey, USA.

Discovery: Detecting the cosmic microwave background radiation, an "echo" of the Big Bang.

Discoverer: Arno Allan Penzias (1933–) and Robert Woodrow Wilson (1936–)

Impact: This discovery established that the universe did, indeed, start with a Big Bang.

Discoveries can begin in the strangest of ways. When satellite communications were just beginning, the Telstar satellite was a wonder. Teenagers danced to "Telstar" as performed by The Ventures, but engineers worried about a slight hiss that could be detected in the microwave carrier that was used to take the telephone signals to and from the satellite.

There is always chatter, static, snow, or noise around: try listening to a radio that is tuned to no station, or tune to an unused TV channel, when you can hear the hiss and see the snow on the screen. Communication engineers spend a lot of time trying to improve the signal-to-noise ratio, and one easy trick is to identify the source and block it.

Two young Bell Labs researchers, Arno Penzias and Robert Wilson, took on the task of nailing the hiss, because they were working on microwave astronomy in any case. They pointed a huge horn antenna of the sort used to receive from Telstar at an empty patch of sky, just to check out their rig, and they heard a hiss. Clearly, they decided, the problem was on Earth, so they tested the horn. They climbed into the horn and cleaned up the "white dielectric material" left by pigeons that had been nesting there, in case the droppings were causing interference. They even eliminated the pigeons, but nothing changed.

The receiver itself was cooled with liquid helium to prevent any heat interference, but still the hiss remained. The signal had one odd characteristic: It was isotropic, meaning it appeared to be coming equally from all directions (*iso-* means "same," *-tropic* means "directions"). It had to be some form of space radiation, they decided.

At the same time, Robert Dicke (1916–1997) and his team were considering a way-out theory at Princeton, some 40 miles away. If the Big Bang had happened, they calculated, there should be a sort of echo of the time when all energy and all matter was created. By now, it would take the form of a faint signal in the microwave spectrum. Then Penzias and Wilson heard about a draft paper written by one of the Princeton group.

Sometimes, science is a courteous profession. Penzias and Wilson contacted Princeton, obtained a copy of the paper, invited the Princeton

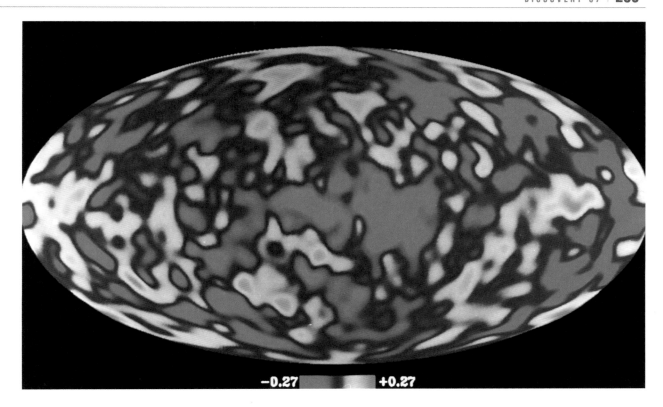

scientists to come and listen to their hiss, and the two groups arranged some very quick joint publication. Dicke's group wrote that radiation at 4,080 MHz could be a leftover of the Big Bang; Penzias and Wilson reported just such a radiation, pointing to the Princeton paper as an explanation of its origins.

There was still a major problem: the background definitely appeared to be coming equally from all parts of the sky. But if the radiation was isotropic—equally smeared—the earliest matter must have been equally smeared, and so the Big Bang could never have produced a universe with galaxies and stars and planets and us. Isotropic radiation said we weren't here.

Either the reasoning was wrong, or the measurements were wrong. Microwaves are influenced by water, which is why we can heat food in microwave ovens, so the likely culprit seemed to be the data, but for a quarter of a century, there was no test of it. In 1978, the world of science cheered Penzias and Wilson as they received the Nobel Prize for Physics, but still there was no test, and the radiation remained officially isotropic.

Then in 1989, the Cosmic Background Explorer, or COBE, was launched. Out in space, there is no water vapor to get in the way, so if the background radiation was lumpy, there was a better chance of seeing a

This 1990s microwave map of the whole sky is the product of one year's data from NASA's COBE (Cosmic Background Explorer) satellite.

few peaks and troughs that would affirm the possibility of our existence. After two years in near-Earth orbit, the measurements were analyzed and the news went out: the cosmic background radiation was lumpy, or in physicist-speak, it was anisotropic, not isotropic. The radiation was not equally smeared—and if the radiation had high and low points, that meant the matter in the universe after the Big Bang was unevenly distributed. It would have been possible for stars and galaxies to form.

The radiation picture was a snapshot of the universe some 380,000 years after the Big Bang, although they could still only make foggy images of it. We could see no further back than that time, because it took 380,000 years for the strange swamp of primordial particles to solidify into the sort of matter that we understand—the sort of matter that we are made of. It was at that moment, 380,000 years after the universe began, that we had our beginnings, so physicists were disappointed that it was such a fuzzy view.

A decade later, clearer pictures came from two sources. One was in the Atacama Desert in northern Chile, high up—so high and so dry that there is almost no water vapor left between the ground and space; so high that workers need to have supplementary oxygen supplies. An array of thirteen linked microwave antennas pulled together an image of a small part of the sky.

Out in space, at L2, the second Lagrangean Point where a satellite can hover between the gravity of the Sun and the gravity of the Earth, WMAP—the Wilkinson Microwave Anisotropy Probe—produced the same sort of image, but this was a larger budget item, and WMAP gave us the whole of the sky.

Each set of images told the same story: there was fine detail out there. One day, perhaps, we will see it even finer, and learn from the universe's baby photos.

By the way, the "snow" you can see on an untuned TV receiver is more than noise: about 1 percent of the dancing dots on the screen are cosmic background signals.

Don't waste your time looking for the anisotropy that excited the physicists, though. The signal will be buried in the noise, but more importantly, the equipment you are using is about as useful for looking at the cosmic background radiation as a stethoscope is for counting craters on the Moon. You will just have to take the scientists' word for it that the radiation is lumpy.

FINDING THE TRUE CAUSE OF ULCERS

How we found that bacteria, not stress, causes duodenal ulcers

It was a stupid idea, of course. Everybody knew that nothing can live in the stomach, so how could bacteria be lurking there and causing a terrible illness. Anybody who thought so was mad!

Before Barry Marshall and Robin Warren shared the 2005 Nobel Prize for Physiology or Medicine for their mad idea, Barry Marshall published a collection of papers written by people who had proposed the same mad idea, and been ignored, either because they did not argue hard enough, or simply because the time was not right.

This sort of thing is not unusual: Charles Darwin's list of people (63) who beat him to proposing evolution by natural selection is a good example, but so is the way Gregor Mendel's research was ignored (66). Darwin got attention because he presented his readers with an overwhelming body of evidence in the form of examples. Mendel's work just had to wait until the time was right, when three researchers unearthed his results in a single year after making similar observations.

Marshall and Warren simply would not take "no" for an answer, would not accept that their idea was mad. It was simple, it was radical, and it *was* mad. They asserted that duodenal ulcers—nasty sores in the lining of the gut—were caused by bacteria, and not by stress.

Everybody *knew* stress was the cause. Doctors had treated ulcers by controlling stress and diet, and had even achieved cures that way, so when the two argued that bacteria caused ulcers, they were abused and ridiculed. This professional reaction did not escape those who wrote the citation for their Nobel Prize, which notes that they "with tenacity and a prepared mind challenged prevailing dogmas."

The history is fairly straightforward. Warren was a pathologist who kept finding the same curved bacteria in the lower stomach—the antrum—of patients with ulcers. Either the bacteria were nurtured by the ulcer in some way, or they caused it; or maybe the conditions that led to ulcers made a suitable environment for the bacteria. Since patients showed signs of inflammation in the gastric mucosa close to where the bacteria were seen, it looked like a very close link. The bacteria seemed worth examining, and Marshall joined him in the work.

They succeeded in cultivating a previously unknown bacterium (now named *Helicobacter pylori*) from biopsies of patients with ulcers, and they showed that the ulcers could be cured completely by killing these new bacteria with antibiotics. If you cast your mind back to Koch's postulates

Date: 1983–84.

Location: Perth, Western Australia.

Discovery: That duodenal ulcers are caused by a bacterium, *Helicobacter pylori*.

Discoverer: Barry J. Marshall (1951–) and J. Robin Warren (1937–).

Impact: The discovery made ulcers much easier to cure.

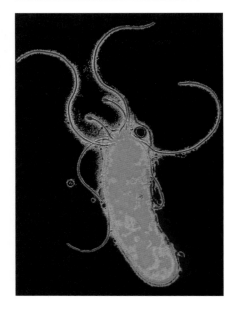

Helicobacter pylori, the rigid helical bacillus that causes duodenal ulcers.

(71), there was one step remaining: they needed to show that the organism they had cultured could cause the original disease.

This is where ethics comes into the picture. It is not a new problem, but Marshall took a radical step that others had taken before him. Joseph Goldberger (74) had done it, and so had J. B. S. Haldane, who wrote in an essay entitled *On Being One's own Rabbit*:

One might, of course, have tried experiments on a rabbit first, and some work had been done along those lines; but it is difficult to be sure how a rabbit feels at any time ... most rabbits get frightened, and to do the sort of things to a dog that one does to the average medical student requires a licence signed in triplicate by two archbishops, as far as I can remember.

To dodge this, Warren, like Haldane, made himself the test animal. He ingested *Helicobacter pylori*, and promptly developed ulcers. Of course, a cynic might argue that the stress of the test played a part, but the cynic would then have to offer to take the same test.

Warren was lucky. While we now accept that *H. pylori* causes more than 90 percent of duodenal ulcers and 80 percent of gastric ulcers, there is evidence to suggest that some individuals develop stomach cancers as a result of *H. pylori* infections. Interestingly, one kind of stomach cancer is likely to regress when the bacterium is eliminated with antibiotics.

He was probably also lucky to get a positive result. Half of all humans carry the bacterium, but only 10 to 15 percent progress to inflammation or ulcers. In the end, though, his experiment worked, and peptic ulcer disease can now be cured by a short course of antibiotics and acid secretion inhibitors.

One of the lessons of science is that any dogma can be taken to extremes. For a long while, disease was thought to be the result of miasmas, smells, and invisible poisons, and germ theories were sniffily dismissed. Malaria was the result of bad air, cholera was said to be caused either by bad smells, being red-headed, or as a result of hysteria brought on by listening to non-conformist preachers, and tuberculosis was deemed to be caused by too much sugar or something else in the diet.

Then the pendulum swung back, and diet-related diseases like pellagra were said to be caused by microbes that were yet to be discovered.

Another lesson of science is that mad ideas can be worth pursuing. Before AIDS was known, an increase in the incidence of a cancer called Kaposi's sarcoma sounded an early warning bell. This cancer is usually dealt with by the immune system, but HIV attacks the immune system and the rare cancer thrives. Then, because of the way HIV is spread, medical workers assumed initially that it was a lifestyle-related condition, because the first signs were seen in homosexuals and drug users.

Chance, said Pasteur (62), favors the prepared mind. Unprepared minds have no chance at all of making great discoveries.

FINDING PLANETS OUTSIDE THE SOLAR SYSTEM

How we proved that there is more than one solar system

The dream of finding unheard-of people goes back 2,000 years or more, with stories from China of people visiting the moon in the first century AD, and from Rome in the second century AD. Then there was a sudden surge of fiction about going to the moon in the 1630s and 1640s, soon after the first telescopes revealed Jupiter's moons and hidden features on the lunar surface.

Galileo (24) looked at the moons of Jupiter and wrote about how Jovians would see their moons; Johann Kepler (23) wrote a story about traveling to the moon; and others had similar ideas. Even Isaac Newton (32) attached a somewhat rambling essay to the third edition of his *Principia*, in which he said at one stage:

And if the fixed Stars are the centers of other like systems, these, being form'd by the like wise counsel, must be all subject to the dominion of One.

Kepler's *Somnium* describes lunar exploration. The hero, Duracotus, was pulled along the track of the Earth's shadow during a lunar eclipse, reaching a neutral point where the gravitational effects are equal and opposite. This was before Newton, and shows us that gravity was a well-understood effect, long before Newton explained how it operated. From that neutral point, Duracotus fell to the Moon under the influence of its gravity. Kepler also discussed the problems of being above the atmosphere, and outlined ways to keep the human alive against the huge g forces:

His limbs must be arranged in such a way that his torso will not be torn away from his buttocks nor his head from his body, but the shock will be distributed among his individual limbs. Then a new difficulty follows: extreme cold and impeded breathing. The cold is relieved by a power which we are born with; the breathing, by applying damp sponges to the nostrils.

The dream of finding life on other planets attracted scientists in the seventeenth century. It was a dream shared by John Wilkins, the Anglican Bishop of Chester during England's Civil War; by Francis Godwin, Bishop of Hereford; and even by Cyrano de Bergerac, the French wit most famous today for his nose. In 1777, Joseph Haydn's farcical opera *Il Mondo Della Luna* was also about travel to the moon.

Even in the 1800s, at a time when astronomers had measured the extreme temperatures of the lunar surface, stories were written about

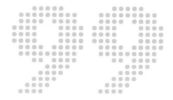

Date: 1992.

Location: A star far, far away, called PSR B1257+12.

Discovery: That we could detect a massive planet orbiting PSR B1257+12.

Discoverer: Aleksander Wolszczan (1946–) and Dale Frail(1961–).

Impact: We suddenly knew that our solar system is not alone.

The Very Large Array radio telescope sits on the plains of San Agustin, 50 miles west of Socorro, New Mexico, USA. Each antenna dish is as big as a house, and is mounted on railroad tracks.

travel to the Moon and meeting Moon creatures. We all know now the Moon is useless for life as we know it, so our search for ETs has had to reach out to other planets.

Many planets are unsuitable for Earth-type life: they need to be in the "Goldilocks zone"—not too hot and not too cold. They also need to be in the right size range, but the easiest ones to detect are big. In our solar system, only Earth falls in the Goldilocks zone, though some scientists think Mars may have supported life when the Sun was younger. For now, we must turn to planets around other stars, but how do we see them?

Imagine two skaters linking hands and spinning around on the ice. If they are the same weight, they rotate around a central point, where their hands are—their center of gravity. If one of them is heavy, and the other is light, the center of gravity will be closer to the large skater. If a sumo wrestler skates with a child, it will appear as though the child is just swinging around the wrestler.

If you look very closely, you will see that the wrestler is wobbling—not because he is fat, but because the other skater moves the wrestler's center of gravity. Stand on one side, and the wrestler will sometimes seem to be coming towards you, and at other times, will be moving away. When a star is moving towards us in its wobble, it shows a blue shift; when it is receding, it shows a red shift. The frequency of that changeover shows us how fast a heavy body orbits around it, and with clever mathematics, the approximate size of the body can be worked out as well.

The first extrasolar planet was found around the pulsar PSR B1257+12 in 1989 (though it was not confirmed until 1996). The hunt began in earnest in 1992, and astronomers had developed a list of almost 300 extrasolar planets when this book was written. The total will almost certainly pass that number before this book is printed. Most of these are too large for life, too close to their star, or too far away, but there are extra (and smaller) planets now being found around some stars where the first find was a giant.

The next step may be to concentrate on those stars where the planets cross in front of the star from time to time. If they do that, then planets like Earth—too small to be detected—might show up by their spectra when light from the star reaches us after passing through the atmosphere of those planets. It may be too much to expect that life there would have chlorophyll like that made by Earth plants, but we might be able to detect oxygen in the atmosphere, for example.

One day, we might shake tentacles with ET, or at least share information with ET. Now that would be a Great Discovery! And if you are nodding your head, you share the Dream.

DISCOVERING THE POLYMERASE CHAIN REACTION

How we learned to take traces of DNA, increase the amounts, and test the new DNA

Now finally, a discovery which is still expanding into new areas. At a rough guess, it will become known as *the* Great Discovery of the twentieth century—which is why I have saved it up for last.

In carbon chemistry, the end of a name often tells us a great deal. A name like butanoic acid identifies a compound which any chemist can draw, with 8 hydrogens, 4 carbons, and 2 oxygens all in their right places. Even a single letter (propanol or propanal) can make a difference in a structure, and new chemists need to learn a new language.

When Albert Szent-Gyorgyi proposed the name "ignose" for what we now call vitamin C, the name told chemists that he thought it was a sugar (from the –ose) and of unknown structure (from the ign-). Arthur Harden, the editor of the *Biochemical Journal*, objected to jokes, so Szent-Gyorgyi (who did not) proposed calling it "godnose." Fussy and boring Harden suggested "hexuronic acid," and that was used, for the time being. Today, scientists can be slightly more amusing, especially in naming enzymes, which all end in -ase. Sometimes, the name applies to a group or class of enzymes, so care is needed.

Any enzyme that breaks down proteins, for example, is called a protease, deoxyribonuclease (or DNase for short) is an enzyme that breaks down

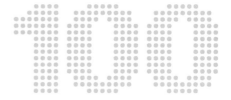

Date: 1986.

Location: California.

Discovery: The use of enzymes that would cause DNA to duplicate itself, with the new DNA then duplicating itself, and so on.

Discoverer: Kary Mullis (1944–).

Impact: DNA fingerprinting, solving crimes, using genetics to detect species and sub-species, genomics.

Grand Prismatic Spring in Yellowstone National Park, Wyoming, USA.

DNA, and so on. A reverse transcriptase is an enzyme that transcribes single-strand RNA to single-strand DNA, while a transcriptase reads off DNA and generates complementary (matching) RNA.

A DNA polymerase is an enzyme which assists in DNA replication. There can be lots of them, so this is a class name, but one of them turned out to be particularly interesting. Taq DNA polymerase was discovered in a bacterium called *Thermus aquaticus* that was found in 1966 by Thomas Brock in hot springs at Yellowstone National Park. These were not just ordinary hot springs, though: they were boiling!

Under hot conditions, proteins and DNA are denatured, which means they are ripped apart, and the cells containing them die. This is why we use heat to pasteurize food and sterilize surgical instruments. Any bacterium that swims around in boiling water is interesting because it is alive. What is really interesting is how the bacterium keeps its proteins and nucleic acids together, or how it patches the damage in them.

The new bacterium turned out to be one of the oldest—one of the Archaea—but it sat for years in the American Type Culture Collection, a repository in Washington DC. In 1986, Kary Mullis bought the sample that would net him a Nobel Prize in 1993, thinking that the polymerase in such a bacterium would be tough enough to keep functioning throughout repeated generations of duplication, allowing the process to be automated. He paid just $35 for his sample. So we got the marvelous enzyme most commonly referred to as "Taq polymerase," and in 1991, Mullis sold the rights for his process to Hoffmann-La Roche for $300 million.

The polymerase chain reaction or PCR is now standard fare for people watching police procedurals on television. A tiny sample of DNA left at a crime scene is multiplied until there is a large enough sample to allow comparisons to be made. The amazingly tough Taq polymerase survives, making each DNA strand replicate many times, where other polymerases are only good for one "pass"—one round of replication.

In the early days, the only way to increase the size of a gene was to plant it in a single-celled organism like a bacterium or a yeast, let the cells breed, and then harvest them. Now Taq polymerase drives the polymerase chain reaction, a process which lets researchers replicate stretches of DNA, without needing any cloning techniques.

This, the last of the hundred great discoveries in this book, was made late last century, but science is not at an end: Mullis got his Nobel Prize after a tiny wait of seven years; even Watson and Crick had to wait nine. So most of the Nobel laureates of the next decade will be rewarded for work that has already been done—great discoveries that have already been made, but which most of us have not even noticed!

Parts of science have moved on, though, from the friendly and collaborative form that it took in the days of Galileo and Fahrenheit. Now science is often about money. Large profits have been made from Taq polymerase and a number of law suits have been fought over who "owns" the enzyme. Still, when *Time* magazine contacted Thomas Brock in November 2007, he was philosophical:

Yellowstone didn't get any money from it [the discovery]. I didn't get any money, either, and I'm not complaining. The Taq culture was provided for public research use, and it has given great benefit to mankind.

Like Brock's sample of *Thermus aquaticus*, discoveries sit waiting for somebody to ask the right question, and when money is not involved, scientists collaborate and share.

The Archaea were only identified as a separate domain by Carl Woese at the University of Illinois in 1990. In 2003, Rick Cavicchioli at the University of New South Wales asked an interesting question: Why do the Archaea not cause any diseases in humans? They have the potential to infect humans and, given the number of known Archaea, Cavicchioli estimated that there should be about thirty of them attacking us, yet there seem to be none.

So far, there has been no answer to this apparently simple question. Perhaps they do attack us, and we just don't know, or maybe there is some switching mechanism that stops them. When it comes, the answer to that question may indeed be a great discovery, but until we find the answers and learn to use them, who can say how great any discovery it will be, or what it will mean?

DISCOVERY 101

What will be the next great discovery, and who is most likely to make it?

Out there, somewhere, there is a discovery, an observation, a measurement that does not quite fit the present model for something. There is an idea, a notion, a hunch that will some day become a great discovery of science. I have no idea how long it will take for us to realize that it is both a discovery and a *great* discovery, but it will occur to us one day that we ought to have seen it coming.

I have no intention of trying to predict what it might be, because as Niels Bohr used to say, making predictions is problematical, especially about the future.

We can say that some people out there will already have predicted it—in 1906, rocket scientist Robert Goddard was thinking of the energy in a gram of radium and wondering if it could be used to power a rocket. In 1913, H. G. Wells described the dropping of an atom bomb (91). Nobody paid attention.

Most predictions miss the mark. For the past hundred years, every depiction of the future has offered us food pills, flying cars, and easy access to space, and none of those has happened. Then again, remember Arthur C. Clarke's First Law:

When a distinguished but elderly scientist states that something is possible, he is almost certainly right. When he states that something is impossible, he is very probably wrong.

We can, though, speculate on what would be nice to discover. The great discoveries of the twentieth century include general relativity and quantum theory, but these operate on vastly different scales, and they don't mesh. The situation is a bit like the one Max Planck (81) found in 1905 when he tried to reconcile Rayleigh and Wien: Each had a partial explanation, but they did not mesh. Some people think string theory will provide the meshing, and it would be nice if it did, but we don't seem to be there yet.

It would also be nice to find more efficient ways of generating energy but those are unlikely. It is essential, then, that we develop better ways of using energy. All my life, fusion reactors have been about fifteen years off, and they still are. Far too many humans and whole species and ecosystems will die if we do not find an energy source that is clean, but far too many other humans are too busy taking profits to care. Many of the ills of our society can only be cured by the equivalent of putting the genie back in the bottle, and I doubt that we will ever discover a way of doing that. It would be nice if we could, though.

It would be nice if we found some way of getting through to the disbelievers—the habitual opponents of science who insist, without knowing any science, that they are right and the scientists are wrong. The Web is full of cranks and conspiracy theorists, eager to tell you that scientists are lying about the shape of the Earth, the effectiveness of vaccines (or the diseases caused by vaccines), the availability of unlimited power from water (or crystals), evolution, plate tectonics, or anything else the crank never quite understood at school. These people have a standard approach of selecting one or two key items, taking them out of context or misrepresenting them, and when corrected, just continuing to trot out the same nonsense. This sort of problem is curable through good science education, but even when the correct information is taught, it isn't always caught.

It would be nice if we could have agreement that, yes, scientists are human, and some of them will lie sometimes, but they can't lie about science, because other scientists are watching, and will catch them out. Small lies may take longer (Dulong and Petit's fraud (69) lasted 166 years before I found it, and other people found it at about the same time), but they are all flushed out in time. Big lies don't take long at all!

It would be nice if we had a scientific proof of just how stupid it is to treat the superiority of any human race as valid. Being proud of your race makes as much scientific sense as being proud of having an ear lobe. It would be nice if we found a way of mending faulty genes that detract from the enjoyment of life. Like John Dalton (15), I have deficient color vision: I can live with that, and I can live with my short legs, but the pain and suffering caused by some other random mutations strike me as unjust.

Ignorance of science is the big problem. We need to be concerned about GM crops, but the public concerns we hear about GM are foolish, based on ignorance and superstition. GM will not eat our babies, though it could endanger biodiversity, as all GM researchers realize. We need to avoid squandering the benefits of GM the way we wasted all those antibiotics, and GM researchers know that. We need to have people understand that all foods "have genes in them." It would be nice if people understood that there are genes jumping species barriers all over the place in nature.

Out there, somewhere, there is a discovery, an observation, a measurement that does not quite fit the present model. It would be good if people took a deep breath, looked at Ingo Potrykus' Golden Rice with an open mind, and saw the huge benefit it could bring to humanity. At the moment, it is blocked from being a Great Discovery by those who claim that any GM which does good must be evil because, by their impenetrable logic, GM *has* to be evil, and a GM crop that does good has been created by Evil Scientists striving to dominate

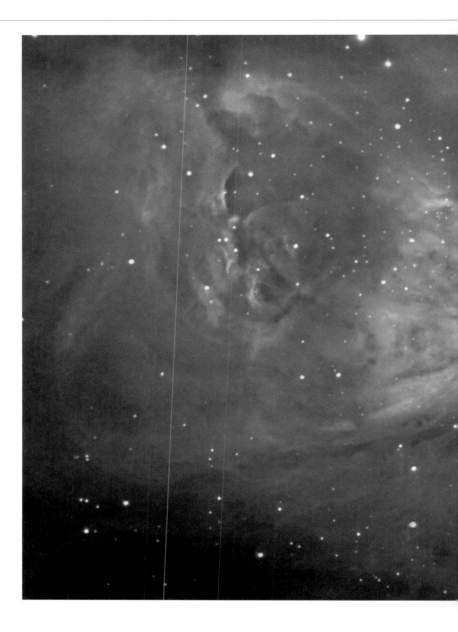

the world. It would be nice if policy were determined by something deeper than comic-book scenarios. It would be nice if so many things could happen, if so many things were understood.

But why should I do all the work? Write out your own wish list, then wait ten years, to see whether any of your wishes are any closer to becoming known facts.

The Orion Nebula is 1,500 light years from Earth and measures several light years across. It is visible to the human eye as a fuzzy patch in the constellation of Orion.

The first thing to do when you set out to make predictions is to consider what is likely: filter your ideas and thoughts through the basic laws of science. A new energy source or a new type of energy is possible but unlikely, but generating a greater supply of energy by extracting it from the wind or the sun is more likely, and so on.

Think like a scientist!

THE CUTTING ROOM FLOOR

Discoveries that almost made it into the list

Here are another 100 developments in science and technology that I considered, and then left out. They are all important, but these were either not quite important enough to make my first 100, or they did not enable other discoveries, or the discoverers are unknown or open to dispute.

The discoveries below were still pretty neat!

Inventing the loom

Inventing spinning

Inventing the spinning wheel

Inventing cement

Discovering brick making

Discovering charcoal making

Inventing electroplating

Inventing alloys

Inventing steel making

Discovering aluminum

Inventing two-phase materials

Inventing zone refining

Discovering how to measure the strength of materials

Inventing the tanning of leather

Discovering surfactants

Discovering distillation

Discovering Brownian motion

Discovering osmosis

Discovering how materials move in plants

Discovering the pathways of photosynthesis

Discovering the pathways of respiration

Discovering homeostasis

Inventing the bow and arrow

Inventing gunpowder

Inventing the cannon

Inventing the woomera and the aerofoil

Inventing the stirrup and bit

Inventing balloon flight

Inventing heavier-than-air flight

Inventing jet propulsion

Discovering thermodynamics

Inventing the heat pump

Discovering prion diseases

Developing organ transplant methods

Discovering friction and lubrication

Discovering the arch

Inventing the wheel

Inventing the bicycle

Inventing the lathe

Inventing the screw

Inventing the wheelbarrow

Inventing the clock escapement

Inventing the drill bit

Inventing the seismograph

Inventing the art of grinding and milling

Inventing the steam hammer

Inventing the circular saw

Inventing the sewing machine

Inventing Röbling's marvelous wire cables

Inventing the pneumatic tire

Inventing the railway locomotive

Inventing barbed wire

Developing speech

Inventing paper

Inventing the pencil

Inventing motion pictures

Inventing the phonograph

Inventing television

Inventing hypertext

Inventing digital storage

Discovering isotopes

Discovering organic chemistry

Discovering pesticides

Inventing radar

Inventing the art of scanning

Developing the rudder

Developing the lateen sail

Discovering atomic fusion

Inventing the turbine

Inventing the achromatic lens

Inventing the oil immersion lens

Inventing the astrolabe and sextant

Discovering the Cape of Good Hope and Cape Horn

Predicting global warming

Inventing geometry

Inventing logarithms

Inventing probability

Inventing formal logic

Discovering optical diffraction

Discovering piezoelectricity

Discovering the planets Uranus, Neptune and Pluto

Discovering the electromagnet

Inventing archeology

Inventing the Leyden jar

Inventing the induction coil

Inventing the cathode ray tube

Discovering the Neandertals

Inventing pigments

Discovering viruses and antivirals

Developing in vitro fertilization

Discovering genomics

Cloning Dolly the sheep

Discovering stem cells

Discovering animal behavior

Developing the uniformitarian principle of geology

Inventing the geological map

Discovering the soil cycle

Inventing the plow

Inventing the yoke and horse collar

Inventing the combine harvester

References

The following works and sources helped or inspired me while I was writing this book, and may be of value to the reader. The numbers in brackets after each entry indicate the discovery or discoveries for which a work is relevant. The material from journals is often more technical; the books are usually easier reading.

Ada, Gordon and David Isaacs, *Vaccination*. Sydney: Allen & Unwin, 2000. (40)

Amato, Ivan, *Stuff: the materials the world is made of*. New York: BasicBooks, 1997. (84)

Beaumont, Anthony, *Ransome's Steam Engines: an illustrated history*. Newton Abbot: David & Charles, 1972. (36)

Bell, E. T., *The Development of Mathematics*. New York: McGraw-Hill Book Company, 1945. (10)

Bellamy, W. Dexter and John W. Klimek, "Some properties of penicillin-resistant staphylococci," *Journal of Bacteriology* 55(2): 153–160, February 1948. Available through PubMed Central. (89)

Bender, Barbara, *Farming in Prehistory: from hunter-gatherer to food-producer*. New York: St. Martin's Press, 1975. (2)

Berlin, Leslie, *The Man Behind the Microchip: Robert Noyce and the invention of Silicon Valley*. New York: Oxford University Press, 2005. (95)

Booth, Martin, *Opium: a history*. London: Simon & Schuster, 1997. (5)

Bown, Stephen R., *Scurvy*. Harmondsworth: Penguin Books, 2004. (74)

Boyer, Carl B., *The rainbow*. Princeton: Princeton University Press, 1987. (34)

Boyer, Carl B. (revised Uta C. Merzbach), *A History of Mathematics*, 2nd edn. New York: John Wiley & Sons, 1991. (10)

Bragg, Sir Lawrence, "X-ray crystallography," *Scientific American*, July 1968. (87)

Brannt, William T., *Petroleum: its history, origin occurrence, production, physical and chemical constitution, technology, examination and uses*. Philadelphia: Henry Carey Baird & Co, 1895. (64)

Brannt, William T., *India Rubber, Gutta-percha and Balata*. Philadelphia: Henry Carey Baird & Co, 1900. (53)

Briggs, Asa, *A Social History of the Media: from Gutenberg to the Internet*, 2nd edn. Cambridge: Polity, 2005. (20)

Brinkman, William F., Douglas E. Haggan and William W. Troutman, "A history of the invention of the transistor and where it will lead us." *IEEE Journal of Solid State Circuits* **32**, 1858–1865, 1997. http://www.sscs.org/AdCom/transistorhistory.pdf (93)

Bronowski, Jacob, *The Ascent of Man*. London: British Broadcasting Corporation. (1, 7)

Buck, W. Roger et al (eds), *Faulting and Magmatism at Mid-ocean Ridges*. Washington: American Geophysical Union, 1998. (96)

Bulloch, William, *The History of Bacteriology*. London; New York: Oxford University Press, 1938. (62)

Bullough, William Sydney, *The History of Hormones*: an inaugural lecture delivered at Birbeck College, London, 27 October 1953. London: Birbeck College, 1954. (82)

Bylebyl, Jerome J. (ed.) *William Harvey and His Age: the professional and social context of the discovery of the circulation*. Baltimore: Johns Hopkins University Press, 1979. (26)

Carpenter, Kenneth J., *The History of Scurvy and Vitamin C*. Cambridge: Cambridge University Press, 1986. (74)

Cavicchioli, R., Curmi, P.M.G., Saunders, N. and Thomas, T. 2003. "Pathogenic Archaea: do they exist?" *BioEssays* **25**:1119–1128. (100)

Clarke, Gary N., "A.R.T. and history, 1678–1978," *Human Reproduction* **21**(7), 1645–1650, 2006. (30)

Cooper, Emmanuel, *A History of World Pottery*, 3rd edn. London: Batsford, 1988. (6)

Crease, Robert P., *The Prism and the Pendulum: the ten most beautiful experiments in science*. New York: Random House, 2003. (11, 41)

Crick, Francis, *What Mad Pursuit*, New York: Basic Books, 1988. (94)

Crosby, Alfred W., *Throwing Fire*. Cambridge: Cambridge University Press, 2002. (16)

Crowther, J. G., *British Scientists of the Nineteenth Century*. London: K. Paul, Trench, Trubner & Co., Ltd., 1935. (43, 45, 48, 54)

Cutler, Alan, *The Seashell on the Mountaintop: a story of science, sainthood, and the humble genius who discovered a new history of the Earth*. New York: Dutton, 2003. (35)

Darwin, Charles, *On The Origin of Species*, 6th edn. New York: New American Library, 1958. (63)

Darwin, Charles, *The Voyage of the Beagle*. New York: Natural History Library/Doubleday, 1962. (63)

Dawson, Pat, "The gold in Yellowstone's microbes," *Time*, November 21, 2007. (100)

de Kruif, Paul, *The Microbe Hunters*. London: Jonathan Cape, 1943. (71, 89)

Defalque R. J. and A.J. Wright, "Quistorp and "Anaesthesia" in 1718." *Bulletin of Anesthesia History* 24(1): 5–8, January 2006. Available at http://www.anes.uab.edu/aneshist/quistorpmain.doc (55)

Defoe, Daniel, *A Journal of the Plague Year*. London: J. M. Dent & Sons (Everyman's Library 289), 1908, reprinted 1961. (31)

Desowitz, Robert S., *The Malaria Capers*. New York: W. W. Norton, 1993. (5)

Diamond, Jared, *Guns, Germs and Steel*. New York: Vintage Books, 1998. (2, 68)

Dunham, William, *The Mathematical Universe*. New York: John Wiley & Sons, 1994. (10)

Einstein, Albert and Leopold Infeld, *The Evolution of Physics*. New York: Simon & Schuster, 1967. (15)

Einstein, Albert, *Einstein's Miraculous Year: five papers that changed the face of physics*, edited and introduced by John Stachel et al. Princeton: Princeton University Press, 1998. (15, 83)

Fara, Patricia, *Sex, Botany & Empire: the story of Carl Linnaeus and Joseph Banks*. New York: Columbia University Press, 2004. (39)

Faraday, Michael, *The Philosopher's Tree: a selection of Michael Faraday's writings*, compiled by Peter Day. Bristol; Philadelphia: Institute of Physics Pub., 1999. (48)

Fauvel, John, Raymond Flood, Michael Shortland and Robin Wilson (eds), *Let Newton Be!* Oxford: Oxford University Press, 1988.

Fenichell, Stephen, *Plastic: the making of a synthetic century*. New York: HarperBusiness, 1996. (84)

Flannery, Tim, *The Future Eaters*. Sydney: Reed Books, 1994. (2, 68)

Franklin, Benjamin, *The Benjamin Franklin Sampler*. New York: Premier Books, 1956. (38)

Freed, Les, *The History of Computers*. Emeryville: Ziff-Davis Press, 1995. (73, 92, 95)

Fuller, Dorian Q., Emma Harvey and Ling Qin, "Presumed domestication? Evidence for wild rice cultivation and domestication in the fifth millennium BC of the Lower Yangtze region." *Antiquity* 81 (312), 316–331, 2007. (2)

Galilei, Galileo, *Dialogues Concerning Two New Sciences, First Day*. New York: Dover Publications, 1954. (28)

Garfield, Simon, *Mauve*. London: Faber & Faber, 2000. (59)

Garratt, G. R. M., *The Early History of Radio: from Faraday to Marconi*. London: Institution of Electrical Engineers, in association with the Science Museum, 1994. (76)

Geison, Gerald L., *The Private Science of Louis Pasteur*. Princeton: Princeton University Press, 1995. (62)

Gernsheim, Helmut, *History of Photography*. London: Thames and Hudson, 1988. (57)

Gest, Howard, "A 'misplaced chapter' in the history of photosynthesis research; the second publication (1796) on plant processes by Dr Jan Ingen-Housz, MD, discoverer of photosynthesis." *Photosynthesis Research* 53: 65–72, 1997. (27)

Gies, Frances, *Cathedral, Forge, and Waterwheel: technology and invention in the Middle Ages*. New York: HarperCollins Publishers, 1994. (14)

Gimpel, Jean, *The Medieval Machine*. London: Futura Publications, 1979. (14)

Girifalco, Louis A., *The Universal Force*. New York: Oxford University Press, 2007. (41)

Gleick, James, *Isaac Newton*. London: Fourth Estate, 2003. (31, 32, 33)

Gondhalekar, Prabhakar, *The Grip of Gravity: the quest to understand the laws of motion and gravitation*. Cambridge: Cambridge University Press, 2001. (41)

Gould, Laura L., *Cats Are Not Peas: a calico history of genetics*. New York: Copernicus, 1996.

Gray, Stephen, *Philosophical Transactions*, 6 (1731), published 1733. (37)

Gurney, Alan, *Compass*. New York: W. W. Norton, 2004. (17)

Haldane, J. B. S., *Possible Worlds and Other Essays*. London: Harper & Brothers, 1927. (98)

Hall, Nina (ed.) *The Age of the Molecule*. London: Royal Society of Chemistry, 1999. (84)

Hardenberg, Horst O., *The Middle Ages of the Internal-combustion Engine, 1794–1886*. Warrendale: Society of Automotive Engineers, 1999. (65)

Harré, R. (ed.), *Some Nineteenth Century British Scientists*. London: Pergamon Press, 1969. (61, 80)

Herodotus, *The Histories*, Harmondsworth: Penguin Classics, revised edn, 1972. (9)

Hetzel, Basil S., *The Story of Iodine Deficiency*. Oxford: Oxford University Press, 1989. (74)

Hoffmann, Banesh, *The Strange Story of the Quantum*. Harmondsworth, Pelican Books, 1963. (81)

Hoffmann, Roald, "Döbereiner's lighter," *American Scientist*, **86** (4), 326, July–August, 1998. Accessed online at http://www.americanscientist.org/template/AssetDetail/assetid/27722, December 28, 2007. (50)

Hong, Sungook, *Wireless: from Marconi's black-box to the audion*. Cambridge: MIT Press, 2001. (73, 76)

Hutchings, Donald, *Late Seventeenth Century Scientists*. London: Pergamon Press, 1969. (29, 31-4)

Jiang, Leping and Li Liu, "New evidence for the origins of sedentism and rice domestication in the Lower Yangzi River, China." *Antiquity*, **80** (308) 355–361, 2006. (2)

Johanson, Donald C. and Maitland A. Edey, *Lucy: the Beginnings of Humankind*. Harmondsworth: Penguin Books, 1990. (88)

Johnson, Norman A., *Darwinian Detectives: revealing the natural history of genes and genomes*. Oxford; New York: Oxford University Press, 2007. (66)

King, Henry C., *The History of the Telescope*. New York: Dover Publications, 1979. (18, 24)

Kurlansky, Mark, *Cod*. London: Vintage Books, 1997. (21)

Lahanas, Michael, *The Antikythera Computing Device, the most complex instrument of antiquity.* http://www.mlahanas.de/Greeks/Kythera.htm, last accessed February 2008. (13)

Landels, J. G., *Engineering in the Ancient World.* London: Constable & Co., 1998. (14, 36)

Laue, Max von, *History of Physics*, trans. Ralph Oesper. New York: Academic Press, 1950. (87)

Leigh, G. J., *The World's Greatest Fix: a history of nitrogen and agriculture.* New York: Oxford University Press, 2004. (4)

Levi, Primo, *The Periodic Table.* London: Abacus, 1986. (69)

Lilienfeld, Abraham M. (ed.), *Times, Places, and Persons: aspects of the history of epidemiology.* Baltimore: Johns Hopkins University Press, 1980. (58)

Lister, Lord Joseph, "On the antiseptic principle in the practice of surgery," *British Medical Journal*, **2**, 246, 1867. (67)

Liu, Li, Gyoung-Ah Lee, Leping Jiang and Juzhong Zhang, "The earliest rice domestication in China." *Antiquity* **81** (313) September 2007, http://www.antiquity.ac.uk/ProjGall/liu1/index.html, accessed November 5, 2007. (2)

Loomis, Elisha Scott, *The Pythagorean Proposition.* Washington DC: National Council of Teachers of Mathematics (reprint of 1940 edition). (10)

Lyell, Sir Charles, *Principles of Geology.* Harmondsworth: Penguin Classics, 1997. (44)

Macinnis, Peter, *Rockets: Sulfur, Sputnik and Scramjets.* Sydney, Allen & Unwin, 2003. (16, 99)

Macinnis, Peter, *The Killer Bean of Calabar and Other Stories.* Sydney, Allen & Unwin, 2004 (published in the US as *Poisons.* New York: Arcade Books, 2005). (5)

Margulis, Lynn and Dorion Sagan, *Microcosmos: four billion years of evolution from our microbial ancestors.* London: Allen & Unwin, 1987. (49)

Margulis, Lynn and Dorion Sagan, *What is Sex?* New York: Simon & Schuster Editions, 1997. (30)

Margulis, Lynn, *Symbiotic Planet: a new look at evolution*, 1st edn. New York: Basic Books, 1998. (30, 63)

Marshall, Barry, *Helicobacter Pioneers.* Carlton: Blackwell Science Asia, 2002. (98)

Mason, Peter, *Cauchu: the weeping wood.* Sydney: Australian Broadcasting Commission, 1979. (53)

Mason, Peter, *The Light Fantastic.* Sydney: Australian Broadcasting Commission, 1981. (43)

Mason, Peter, *Blood and Iron.* Ringwood: Penguin Books Australia, 1984. (7)

McNichol, Tom, *AC/DC: the savage tale of the first standards war.* San Francisco: Jossey-Bass, 2006. (72)

Medawar, Sir Peter, *The Strange Case of the Spotted Mice.* Oxford: Oxford University Press, 1996. (52)

Meharg, Andrew A., *Venomous Earth: how arsenic caused the world's worst mass poisoning.* Hampshire: Macmillan, 2005. (7)

Merricks, Linda, *The World Made New: Frederick Soddy, science, politics, and environment.* Oxford; New York: Oxford University Press, 1996. (79)

Michette, Alan and Sławka Pfauntsch (eds), *X-rays: the first hundred years.* Chichester; New York: John Wiley & Sons, 1996. (78)

Millar, Ronald, *The Piltdown Men.* St. Albans: Paladin, 1974. (88)

Millikan, Robert Andrews, *The Electron.* Chicago: University of Chicago Press, 1917 (Phoenix Science Press facsimile, 1963). (85)

Mossman, Susan (ed.), *Early Plastics: perspectives, 1850–1950.* London: Leicester University Press/ Science Museum, 1997. (84)

Nicholson, William, "Account of the new Electrical or Galvanic Apparatus of Sig. Alex. Volta, and Experiments performed with the same," *A Journal of Natural Philosophy, Chemistry, and the Arts* **4**, 179–187 (July 1800). To be found at http://www. ucl.ac.uk/sts/chang/nicholson_v3/Nicholson.pdf, accessed December 26, 2007. (45)

Ohl, Russel S., *An Interview Conducted by Frank Polkinghorn*, Center for the History of Electrical Engineering, January 6, 1975. http://www.ieee.org/ portal/cms_docs_iportals/iportals/aboutus/history_ center/oral_history/pdfs/Ohl020.pdf (93)

Osborne, Roger, *The Floating Egg: episodes in the making of geology*. London: Jonathan Cape, 1998. (44)

Pancaldi, Giuliano, *Volta: science and culture in the Age of Enlightenment*. Princeton: Princeton University Press: 2003. (42)

Parker, Andrew, *In the Blink of an Eye*. London: The Free Press, 2003. (44)

Parker, Barry R., *Quantum Legacy: the discovery that changed our universe*. Amherst: Prometheus Books, 2002. (81, 86)

Parkinson, R. B. et al., *Cracking Codes: the Rosetta Stone and decipherment*. Berkeley: University of California Press, 1999. (8)

Passmore, John A. (ed.), *Priestley's Writings on Philosophy, Science and Politics*. New York: Collier Books, 1965. (27)

Pauling, Linus, *The Meaning of Life* (edited by David Friend and the editors of *Life*). New York: Little Brown, 1990. (94)

Peierls, Rudolf, *Atomic Histories*. Woodbury: AIP Press, 1997. (86)

Pimentel, D., R. Zuniga and D. Morrison, "Update on the environmental and economic costs associated with alien-invasive species in the United States." *Ecological Economics* **52**: 273–288, 2005. (68)

Pliny (Gaius Plinius Secundus), *The History of the World*, translated by Philemon Holland. New York: McGraw-Hill, 1964. (9, 19)

Pollan, Michael, *The Botany of Desire*. London: Bloomsbury, 2002. (2, 5)

Postgate, John, *Microbes and Man*. Harmondsworth: Pelican Books, 1969. (71)

Power, D'Arcy, *William Harvey*. London: T. Fisher Unwin, 1897. (26)

Rayner-Canham, Marelene F. and Geoffrey W. Rayner-Canham, *A Devotion to Their Science: pioneer women of radioactivity*. Philadelphia: Chemical Heritage Foundation; Montreal: McGill-Queen's University Press, 1997. (79)

Reeves, Richard, *A Force of Nature: the frontier genius of Ernest Rutherford*. New York: Atlas Books: W. W. Norton & Co., 2008. (79)

Reingold, Nathan (ed.), *Science in Nineteenth Century America*. London: Macmillan, 1966. (46, 75, 77 and others)

Reynolds, Terry S., *Stronger Than a Hundred Men: a history of the vertical water wheel*. Baltimore: Johns Hopkins University Press, 1983. (14)

Richet, Pascal, *A natural history of time; translated by John Venerella*. Chicago; London: University of Chicago Press, 2007. (47)

Roberts, Russell (ed.), *Specimens and Marvels: William Henry Fox Talbot and the invention of photography*. London: Aperture in association with the National Museum of Photography, Film and Television , 2000. (57)

Rorres, Chris, *A Formidable War Machine: construction and operation of Archimedes' iron hand*. Symposium on Extraordinary Machines and Structures in Antiquity August 19–24, 2001, Olympia, Greece. http://www.math.nyu. edu/~crorres/Archimedes/Claw/harris/rorres_harris. pdf. (12)

Rosen, William, *Justinian's Flea: plague, empire, and the birth of Europe*. New York: Viking, 2007. (58)

Sacks, Oliver, *Uncle Tungsten*. London: Picador, 2002. (69)

Schrödinger, Erwin, *What is Life?* Cambridge: Canto Books 1992. (94)

Seifer, Marc J., *Wizard: the life and times of Nikola Tesla: biography of a genius.* Secaucus: Carol Pub., 1996. (72)

Seitz, Frederick, *Electronic Genie: the tangled history of silicon.* Urbana: University of Illinois Press, 1998. (95)

Singer, Charles, *A Short History of Anatomy from the Greeks to Harvey.* New York: Dover Publications, 1957. (19)

Singh, Simon, *The Code Book.* London: Fourth Estate, 2000. (92)

Sleeswyk, André Wegener, "Vitruvius' odometer," *Scientific American* **245** (4) October, 1981, 188–200. (13)

Smil, Vaclav, *Creating the Twentieth Century: technical innovations of 1867–1914 and their lasting impact.* New York: Oxford University Press, 2005. (65)

Smoot, George and Keay Davidson, *Wrinkles in Time.* London: Abacus, 1995. (90, 97)

Spielman, Andrew and Michael d'Antonio, *Mosquito.* London: Faber & Faber, 2002. (5)

Spindler, Konrad, *The Man in the Ice.* London: Weidenfeld & Nicolson, 1994. (7, 88)

Standage, Tom, *The Victorian Internet.* New York: Walker & Company, 1998. (37)

Stern, Ellen Stock and Emily Gwathmey, *Once Upon a Telephone: an illustrated social history.* New York: Harcourt Brace, 1994. (70)

Struik, Dirk J., *Yankee Science in the Making.* New York: Collier Books, 1962. (51)

Tait, Hugh (ed.), *Five Thousand Years of Glass.* London: Published for the Trustees of the British Museum by British Museum Press, 1991. (9)

Thomas, J. M., *Michael Faraday and the Royal Institution: the genius of man and place.* Bristol; Philadelphia: A. Hilger, 1991. (48)

Thorne, Kip S., *Black Holes and Time Warps.* London: Papermac, 1995. (83, 97)

Thorne, Stuart, *The History of Food Preservation.* Casterton Hall, UK: Parthenon Publishing, 1986. (3)

Tiley, Nancy, *Discovering DNA: meditations on genetics and a history of the science.* New York: Van Nostrand Reinhold, 1983. (66)

Trinkaus, Erik and Pat Shipman, *The Neandertals.* New York: Vintage Books, 1994. (88)

Walker, C. B. F. et al., *Reading the Past: ancient writing from cuneiform to the alphabet.* Berkeley: University of California Press/British Museum, 1990. (8)

Wallace, Alfred Russel, *The Geographical Distribution of Animals.* New York: Harper & Brothers, 1876. This edition is available online as page images from the University of Michigan, http://quod.lib.umich.edu/m/moagrp/ (51, 63)

Wallace, Alfred Russel, *The Malay Archipelago.* New York: Dover Publications, 1962. (51, 63, 68)

Watson, J. D. and F. H. Crick, "A structure for deoxyribose nucleic acid," *Nature,* **171**, 737, 1953. (94)

wWatson, James, *The Double Helix.* Harmondsworth: Penguin Books, 1968. (94)

Wells, H. G., *The World Set Free,* first published 1914. http://www.gutenberg.org/etext/1059. (91)

White, Gilbert, *Gilbert White's Journals,* edited by Walter Johnson. Cambridge: MIT Press, reprinted 1970. (40)

White, Gilbert, *The Natural History of Selborne.* London: The Cresset Press, 1947 (there is also a Penguin edition which may be easier to locate). (40)

White, Michael, *Acid Tongues and Tranquil Dreamers: tales of bitter rivalry that fueled the advancement of science and technology*. New York: Morrow, 2001. (33, 72)

Woodbury, Robert S, *History of the Gear-cutting Machine: a historical study in geometry and machines*. Cambridge: MIT Press, 1958. (13)

Wyse Jackson, Patrick, *The Chronologers' Quest: episodes in the search for the age of the Eearth*. Cambridge: Cambridge University Press, 2006. (47)

Zinsser, Hans, *Rats, Lice and History*. London: George Routledge & Sons, 1937. (71)

Zirker, Jack B., *An Acre of Glass: a history and forecast of the telescope*. Baltimore: Johns Hopkins University Press, 2005. (18)

A general reading list

These are works that I keep on my shelves and draw frequent inspiration from, and which almost certainly formed the foundations of some of my thoughts. These are mostly older books, as classics often are, but they can probably be found in libraries. Try a few of them!

Boorstin, Daniel J., *The Discoverers*. London: J. M. Dent, 1984.

Bronowski, Jacob, *Science and Human Values*. New York: Julian Messner, 1956.

Bronowski, Jacob and Brice Mazlish, *The Western Intellectual Tradition*. London: Hutchinson, 1960.

Hofstadter, Douglas, *Gödel, Escher, Bach: an eternal golden braid*. Stanford Terrace: The Harvester Press, 1979.

Merton, Robert K., *On the Shoulders of Giants*. New York: Harbinger Books, 1965.

Perutz, Max, *Is Science Necessary?* Oxford: Oxford University Press, 1991.

Petroski, Henry, *Invention by Design*. Cambridge Massachusetts: Harvard University Press, 1996.

Silver, Brian L., *The Ascent of Science*. Oxford: Oxford University Press, 1998.

Singer, Charles, *A Short History of Scientific Ideas*. Oxford: Oxford University Press, 1959.

Snow, C. P., *The Two Cultures*. Cambridge: Cambridge University Press, 1992.

Thomas, Lewis, *The Lives of a Cell: notes of a biology watcher*. New York: Viking Press, 1974.

Uglow, Jenny, *The Lunar Men*. London: Faber & Faber, 2002.

Wolpert, Lewis, *The Unnatural Nature of Science*. London: Faber & Faber, 1992.

Index

A

accelerated motion 228
Achilles and the tortoise 94
agar 191
Agassiz, Louis 139–141
Agricola, Georgius 121
agriculture 16–18, 21, 137, 265
AIDS 189–190
air pressure 81–83
air pump 83–86
alphabets 33
alternating current 191–193
altitudinal zonation 182
Altmann, Richard 136
America 64–66
ammonia 137
Ampère, André Marie 128, 131
amplification 245
amplifying variable current
    194–195
analog principle 241–242
analogy 78
anaphylactic shock 142
anatomy 59–60, 63, 76–78, 99
Andersen, Hans Christian 128
Anderson, Carl 220
anesthetics 149–151, 234
Ångström, Anders 165, 199, 200
aniline 159–160
animals: cells 134–136;
    classification 109–111; diseases
    196–197; distributions 251–252;
    electricity 116–118; embryology
    142; evolution 129–131, 166–
    168; fossils 121–123; migration
    140–141
anode 132
anthrax bacillus 189–191, 234
antibiotics 24, 234–236
antibodies 142
Antikythera 44–45
antisepsis 179–181, 234
Arabian oil fields 172
Arago, François Jean Dominique
    204
arc lights 119–120

Archaea domain 262, 263
archeology 141
Archer, Frederick Scott 154–156
Archimedes 39, 41–43
Aristophanes 56
Aristotle 39, 44, 59, 86, 87
Armati (inventor of spectacles) 58
Arrhenius, Svante 182
aspirin 25
astronomy 156, 236–238,
    259–261
Atlantic ocean: mid-Atlantic ridge
    251–252; trade route 64–66
atmospheric pressure 81–83
atom 49–51, 184, 220; model of
    226–228
atom bomb 240–241
atomic power 239–241
atomic theory 124
atomic weight 184–185
Australia 108, 183, 196
Australopithecus africanus 231–233
automobiles 42, 138, 176
autoradiogram 178
Avery, Oswald 246
Avicenna 59–60, 121

B

Babbage, Charles 241, 242
Bacon, Roger 58
bacteriology 160, 257–258
Baekeland, Leo (Bakelite) 137,
    221–223
Baliani, Giovanni Batista 81
Ball, Sir Robert 130
Balmer, Johann Jakob 199–201
bank notes 155
Banks, Joseph 108, 124
"Barcoo rot" 196
Bardeen, John 244–246
Barnard, Edward Emerson 156
barometer 81–83
batteries 108, 127–128, 133, 174
Baudelaire, Charles 154–155,
    156
Bauer, Franz 134
Baumann, Eugen 216
Bayliss, William 216

Becquerel, (Antoine) Henri
    209–211
Beddoes, Thomas 125, 149–150
Bell, Alexander Graham
    186–188
Bell, Melville 187
beriberi 196–197
Bernoulli, Daniel 49
Berti, Gasparo 81
Berzelius, Jöns Jacob 50, 136, 137
Big Bang theory 238, 254–256
binary system 96
Binnig, Gerd K. 226
Biochemical Journal 261
biology 170
black bodies 214
black holes 153
Black, Joseph 75, 147
Bletchley Park (UK) 243
blood circulation 76–78
blood poisoning 234
blood transfusion 78
blood typing 142
Bode, Johann 199
Bohr, Niels 214, 228, 240, 264
Bonpland, Aimé 182
books 61–63
botany 88
Boulton, Matthew 102–103, 146
Boyle, Robert 49, 81, 84–86,
    154
Bradley, James 152
Bragg, Sir Lawrence 230–231
Bragg, Sir William 230–231
Brahe, Tycho 69
Brattain, Walter 244–246
Braun, Ferdinand 245
Broad Street pump 157
Brock, Thomas 262, 263
Bronze Age 29
Brown, Robert (Brownian motion)
    50–51, 134–136
Buffon, Comte de 129, 168, 169
Bunsen, Robert 119, 164–166
Burdon-Sanderson, John 181
Burke, William 60
Burnet, Macfarlane 143
Bush, Vannevar 243

C

Cailletet, Louis Paul 212
calculus 94–96
caloric/calorie 146–147
caloric engine 174–175
calotype process 154
Camerarius, Rudolf 88
canal building 122
cane toads 183
cannon casting 146
Canterbury Tales (Chaucer) 19–20
capillaries 77–78
carbolic acid 179–181
carbon chemistry 173, 261
carbon dioxide 79, 80, 176, 182
Carlisle, Anthony 124
Carlson, John 54
Carnot, Sadi 147
carriers 189
Carroll, Lewis 155
Carthusian monks 104
casein 222
catalysis 136–138
catalytic converters 138, 176
cathode 132
cathode rays 206, 224
cattle plague 179, 180
cattle thyroxine 218
Cavendish, Henry 114–115, 152, 231
Cavicchioli, Rick 263
cell theory 134–136, 142
celluloid 221
Cepheid variables 238
ceramics 26–28
Cerenkov radiation 153
Chain, Ernst 235
chalcolithic site 29–30
Chappé, Claude 105
Chargaff, Erwin 247
charged particles (ions) 194
Charlemagne 25
Chaucer, Geoffrey 19–20, 62
chemistry 49–51, 159, 184–186, 261; chemical reactions 136–138; chemical signals 217
Cherokee script 31–32
chimpanzees 24

Chinese Commercial Code 106
Chinese physicians 234
chips *see* integrated circuits (ICs)
chloroform 149, 150, 151
cholera 157
chromatic aberration 98
chromosomes 135, 177–178
chronometers 242
circle and ellipse 69–70, 72, 94, 228
Clarke, Arthur C. 264
classification 109–111
clay pottery 26–28
climate change 139–141
clock-making 45
cloud formations 108
Clusius tubes 240
coal gas 174–175
coal gas lighting 159
coal tar 159–161
collodion process 154–156
Colombo, Realdo 76
color spectrum 96–98, 164–166
Columbia fly room 177
Columbus, Christopher 64–66
combustion engine 174–176
communication 8, 104–106, 186–188, 201–203
compass 54–56
compound splitting 124–125
computers: Analytical Engine 241, 242; Colossus 195, 242–243; digital 241–243; integrated circuits (ICs) 249–251
conductors 118
Congreve, William 52
Conroy, Glenn 233
continental drift 251–253
contraceptive pill 218
Cook, James 108, 196
Copernicus, Nicolaus 63, 66–68, 69
copper carbonate 226–227
corpse preservation 118
Correns, Carl 177
Cosmic Background Explorer (COBE) 255–256

cosmic background radiation 254–256
Couper, Archibald 159
cowpox 111–113
cretinism 216
Crick, Francis 231, 246–248
Crimean War 161–162
Crookes, William 165, 207
cross-cutting relationships, principle of 101
crude oil 171
cryogenics 212
crystal radio sets 195, 202, 244
crystals 49, 71, 209–210, 229–231
Cugnot, Nicolas Joseph 174
cuneiform 32
Curie, Marie 208, 209–211
Curie, Pierre 209–210, 229
curvature of space–time 219
Cuvier, Georges 122

D

da Gama, Vasco 196
da Vinci, Leonardo 60
Daguerre, Louis 154
Dali, Salvador 247
Dalibard, Thomas-François 106–107
Dalton, John 50, 147
dams 48
Dart, Professor Raymond 11, 231–233
Darwin, Charles Robert 11, 88, 131, 149, 231, 257; evolution by natural selection 169–171; influence of von Humboldt 182
Darwin, Erasmus 169
data 161–163, 242
data-snooping 199
Davy, Edward 105
Davy, Sir Humphry 119–120, 124–125, 131
de Bergerac, Cyrano 259
de Broglie, Louis 228
de Chardin, Pierre Teilhard 232
de Charpentier, Jean 139
de Chéseaux 236
de Forest, Lee 195, 245

de Graaf, Regnier 87
de Rivaz, Isaac 118, 174
de Saussure, Nicholas 80
de Vries, Hugo 177
decibel 188
deep-sea drilling 253
Defoe, Daniel 90
Demisiani, Johann 72
Desaga, Peter 165–166
Dewar, Sir James 211–213
diabetes, Type I 218
Dicke, Robert 254–255
diesel fuel 176
diffraction 229
digital computers *see* computers
dinosaur fossil 123
Dioscorides 149
discoveries, effects of 9
disease 111–113, 157, 179; causes
    of 156–158; contagious
    141–143; deficiency 196–198;
    germ theory 189–191; statistics
    on 161–162; "Woolclasser's
    Disease" 189
disinfection 179
dissection 59–60
distance estimation 64
DNA structure 178, 231, 246–248;
    polymerase chain reaction
    261–263
Döbereiner: Lamp 136–137; laws
    of elements 184–185
Domagk, Gerhard 161
Domesday Book 47
Donkin, Bryan 19
Doppler shift 238
double helix 247, 248
Drake, Edwin 171–172, 175
Draper, J. W. 156
drugs, addictive 26
drying food 19
Du Toit, Alexander 251–252
Dulong, Pierre-Louis 185, 199
duodenal ulcers 257–258
duplication 154–156
Durban Declaration 190
Dürer, Albrecht 60
Dutrochet, René 134–136

dyes 135–136, 137, 159–161

E
Earth: age 99, 129–131;
    atmosphere 81–82; magnetic
    field 55; rotation 66–68; shape
    and size 39–41, 64
earthquakes 253
East Pacific Rise 253
ecology 181–183
Edison, Thomas Alva 11, 118,
    120, 193; telephony 187–188;
    thermionic effect 194–195
Edison-Swan Electric Company
    120
egg cells 86–88
Egyptian mummification 19
Ehrlich, Paul 161
Eijkman, Dr. Christiaan 196
Einstein, Albert 215, 219–221,
    228, 239
electric cell 116–118
electric chair 193
electric eels 116–118
electric light 119–120
electric light bulb 120
electric motors 128, 131–133
electric transformers 127–128,
    192
electrical attraction 126
electrical currents 131–133
electrical distribution 128
electrical engineering 193
electrical generators 128, 133
electrical relay 105
electricity 106–108, 116–118;
    generation 191–193;
    transmission 192
electrobulb 125
electrode 132
electroforming 118
electrolysis 124–125, 132
electrolyte 132
electrolyze 132
electromagnetism 126–128, 187;
    electromagnetic induction
    132–133, 191–193;
    electromagnetic spectrum 98;

electromagnetic waves 201–203
electron microscope 136, 228
electrons 224–226
elements, periodic table of
    184–186, 210
embryology 142
emission spectrum of hydrogen
    200
energy 146–148
environment 181–183
enzymes 137, 261–262
epidemics 90, 157, 179, 180, 248
epidemiology 156–158
Eratosthenes 39–41, 64
ethanol 175
ether 149–150, 204–206
ethics 258
Euclid 38
European Union 95
evolution 129–131, 166–168,
    169–171; human 231–233

F
Faber 187
Fabricius 76
Fahrenheit, Gabriel 74–75
Fairchild Semiconductor 249, 250
famine 198
Faraday, Michael 125, 165–166,
    185, 192, 212; first electric
    motor 131–133
Farmer, Professor Moses 120
feedback, from a governor 103
feedback systems in hormones
    218
Fermi Prize 240
fertilizers 21–23
"fight or flight" response 218
fire, discovery of 14–16
fire pistons 15–16, 175
firestick farming 15
fireworks 51
Fisher, Sir Ronald 170
FitzGerald, George 201
Fizeau, Armand Hippolyte 151,
    152, 204–205
flasks 167, 168
Fleming, Alexander 234–235

Fleming, John Ambrose 195
Florey, Howard 235
Flowers, Tommy 242–243
fluorescence 206, 208, 209
flying 51–53
food preservation 19–21
force of attraction 114–115
fossil fuels 182
fossils 63, 99, 100, 101, 121–123;
    Glossopteris (fossil fern) 252;
    "Taung child" 231–233
Foucalt, Léon 151, 152
Frail, Dale 259
Franklin, Benjamin 106–108, 116,
    224
Franklin, Rosalind 231, 247
Fraunhofer lines 164–165
freezer ships 212
Fresnel, Augustin 204
friction 147
Friedrich, Walter 229–230
Frisch, Otto 239–240
Frith, William 154
fruit flies 177–178
Fuchs, Leonhard 63
fungi 198, 234–236
Funk, Casimir 197

G
Galapagos finches 170
Galenus, Claudius 59, 216
Galileo, Galilei 68, 81, 82, 151,
    259; telescope 71–73;
    thermometer 74
Galvani, Luigi 116–118
galvanic currents 126–127
garlic 55–56
gas compression 211–213
gas lighting 120, 159, 174
gas measurement 124
gas shroud 205
gases 49
gasoline 175–176
gastric ulcers 257–258
gears 44–46
Geiger, Hans 228
general relativity, theory of 219
genetically-modified crops 265

genetics 134–136, 176–178
    see also DNA structure
genome mapping 177–178
genomics 178, 248
geography 63
geology 99–101, 121–122,
    139–141
geometry 36–38
germ theory 181, 189–191
German Enigma code 242
Gilbert, William 55–56, 106, 126
glacial movement 139–141
glass, heating 164
glass making 34–36, 58
global warming 176, 182
glossopetrae 99
Gmelin, Leopold 184
Goddard, Robert H. 51–52, 264
Goeppert-Mayer, Maria 199, 226,
    228
goiter 216
Gold, Thomas 172–173
Goldberger, Joseph 198, 258
"Goldilocks zone" 260
Gondwanaland 251
Goodyear, Charles 145
Gorrie, John 212
governor, centrifugal 103
gramophones 241
Grand Prismatic Spring 262
Graunt, John 162
grave robbers 60
gravity 91–93, 219–221;
gravitational constant 114–115
Gray, Asa 170
Gray, Elisha 186–187
Gray, Stephen 104–106
guano 23
gunpowder 51
Gutenber, Johannes 61–63
Guthrie, Frederick 194–195
gutta-percha 144–146

H
Haber, Fritz 23, 137
Haeckel, Ernst 181
Hagenbach, Professor 201
Hahn, Otto 239, 240

Haldane, J. B. S. 258
Hales, Stephen 80
Halley, Edmond 129, 236
hammers, law of 11–13
Harden, Arthur 261
Hardy-Weinberg Law 177
Hare, William 60
Harvey, William 76–78, 86–88,
    142, 182
Haüy, René 49
Haydn, Joseph 259
Hayes, Sir Henry 139
heat and mechanical energy
    146–148
heat capacity of elements
    185–186
Heatley, Norman 235
Helicobacter pylori 257–258
Henle, Jakob 141–143
Henry, Jospeh 105, 187
Herodotus 39
Herschel, Sir William 98
Hertz, Heinrich 98, 201–203
Hess, Harry 251
Hiawatha 155
hieroglyphs 32
Hippocrates of Cos 25
histology 160
HIV (human immunodeficiency
    virus) 189–190
Hobbes, Thomas 38
Hoffmann-La Roche 263
Hofmann, August Wilhelm von
    159
Hollerith, Herman 243
Homer 166
hominid skulls 233
Homo erectus 14
Homo habilis 14
Homo sapiens 14, 111, 170
Hooke, Robert 84, 96, 100, 134,
    229; microscope 89–90
Hooker, John 170
horizontality, law of original 100
hormones 216–218
horsepower 146
hot springs 262
Hoyle, Fred 172, 238

Hubble, Edwin Powell 221,
236–238
Huggins 201
human computers 238, 242
human evolution 231–233
human glands 217
human test animal 258
humans, early 11–12, 14–16,
16–18
Humason, Milton 237
Hutton, James 122
Huygens, Christiaan 151, 152,
204
hydrogen cooling *see* liquid
helium
hydrogen lines in visible
spectrum 199–201
hypertext 243

I
IBM 243
ice ages 139–141, 182
ice works 212
ideograms/logograms 32, 106
Iliad (Homer) 166
illustration 154–156
immunity 112
immunology 141–143
incunabula 61, 63
India rubber 145
indigo 137
Indonesia 196
Industrial Revolution 45
inflection 75
information organization
161–163
Ingen-Housz, Jan 80
inheritance, laws of 176–178
inoculation 111–112
insulin 218
Intel 249
internal combustion engine
174–176
ion 132
Ireland 139, 140
Iron Age 29, 30
"iron hand" 42–43
irrigation 18

island ecologies 183
isomorphology 184
isotropic signal 254–255

J
Jackson, Charles 150–151
Jacquard, Joseph (Jacquard loom)
241
Janssen, Zacharias 89
Japan, atom bombing of 241
Japanese Jomon 26–27
Japanese navy 196
Jeans, Sir James 215
Jefferson, Thomas 121
Jenner, Edward 111–113
Joly, John 129
Joseph, Jean-Baptiste 129
Joseph, Lord Lister 179–181
Joule, James Prescott 146, 147,
192
Julian calendar 66
junction transistor 246
Jupiter's moons 151–152

K
Kaposi's sarcoma 258
Kekulé, August 159
Kelvin, Lord 127, 130–131, 205
Kepler, Johann 49, 69–71, 72,
229, 259
Kilby, Jack St. Clair 249–251
kilns 29
kinetoscope filmstrip 155
Kirchhoff, Gustav 164–166, 214
Kirsche *see* Krische, Wilhelm
Knipping, Paul 229–230
Koch, Robert 189–190, 257–258
Kodak camera 156
Koelreuter, Joseph 88
Krische, Wilhelm 222
kwashiorkor 198

L
laboratory glassware 35
Lagrangean Point 256
Lamarck, Jean Baptiste 169
Lamb, Horace 161
Landsteiner, Karl 142

lateral continuity, principle of
100–101
Latin names 75, 110
Laurasia 251
Le Chatelier's Principle 137
lead in petrol 176
Leavitt, Henrietta Swan 238
Leclerc, Georges Louis 129, 168
Leibniz, Gottfried Wilhelm 94–96
Lenoir, Jean Joseph 174–175
lens 56–58, 72–73, 89, 90
lever 41–43
Liebig, Justus von 23, 159
life insurance tables 162
light: speed of 151–153; wave
model of 204–206
light bulbs 120
light refraction 98
light spectrum 96–98
light wavelengths 164, 215
light waves 90, 153
lighting 58, 119–120, 136–137,
171
lightning 106–108, 116
limiting factor principle 23
Lind, James 196
lines of force 191–192
Linnaeus, Carolus 109–111
Linnaean Society of London
170–171
Lippershey, Hans 71, 89
liquefied gas storage 212
liquid-fueled rockets 52
liquid helium 211–213
liquid hydrogen 52
Lister, Joseph 223
Llewellyn, Martin 86, 87
Lockyer, Norman 165
locomotive 174, 175
Lodge, Sir Oliver 224
logic156 156
Long, Dr. Crawford 150
Lorentz, Hendrik 219
Lower, Richard 78
Lucretius 49–51
lunar eclipse 151–153
lunar exploration 259–260
Lyell, Charles 131, 170

M

McDougall, Alexander 180
Mädler, Johann 236–237
Magdeburg hemispheres 84–85
magnetic fields 126–128, 252–253
magnetism 54–56, 132
Magnus, Albertus 121
Malthus 170
manure 21
Marconi, Guglielmo 195, 203, 245
Margulis, Lynn 136
marine navigation 54–56, 64–66, 242
Marshall, Barry J. 11, 257–258
mass 219–221
mathematics 94–96
mauve 159–160
Maxwell, James Clerk 114–115, 155, 201, 205, 214, 224
Mayer, Julius Robert 80, 148
mean free path 194
measurement and statistics 8
mechanical energy and heat 146–148
Medawar, Peter 143
medical science 59–60
medicinal plants 24–26
Medicis 72
medieval mills 48
Meitner, Lisa 239–241
Mendel, Gregor 176–178, 257
Mendeleev, Dmitri 184–186
mercury 74, 137
mercury pumps 85–86
metals 29–31, 121–122, 124, 138, 185
metaphysics 126
Metchnikoff, Ilya 141, 142
Michelangelo 60
Michell, John 114–115, 152–153
Michelson, Albert Abraham 204–206
microbiology 189–191, 234–236
microscope 89–90, 158
microwave astronomy 254–255
microwave map of the sky 255, 256

middens 16
Millikan, Robert Andrews 224–226
mills 46–48
mining technology 102
mitochondria 136
Mitscherlich 184
Montgomerie, William 144
moon 91–93
Moore, Gordon ("Moore's Law") 249–250
moral statistics 162–163
Morgan, Thomas Hunt 177
Morley, Edward Williams 204–206
Morse system 105–106
Morton, William T. G. 149, 150
Moseley, Henry Gwyn Jeffreys 186
motion, laws of 91–93
Mount Wilson telescope 237
Mullis, Kary 261–263
mummification 19
muon 220
music, science of 36
mutants 176–177

N

National Electric Light Association 119
Native Americans 22
natrum 34
natural history 182
natural philosophy 126
natural selection see evolution
Needham, John 168
nervous system 216
Newcomen, Thomas 101–102
Newton, Isaac 49, 72, 164; calculus 94–96; color spectrum 96–98; law of gravitation 91–93; laws of motion 221; Principia 259
Nicholson, William 124
Niepce, Joseph 154
Nightingale, Florence 161–162
nitrogen compounds 23

nitrous oxide 149–150
Noyce, Robert 249–251
nuclear fission 228, 239–240
nuclear fusion 228
nucleus 134–136
nucleus of the atom 209–211
numerology 97–98
nutrition 196–198

O

obsidian 34
odometer 44
Øersted, Hans Christian 126–128, 131
Ohl, Russell Shoemaker 244–245
oil exploration 171–173
oil geology 172
oil making 159
oils as lubricants 171
Olbers, Heinrich (Olbers' paradox) 236
Oliphant, Mark 240
On The Origin of Species (Darwin) 170–171
Onnes, Heike Kamerlingh 213
opiates 149
optics 229
ores 29–31
organic dyes see dyes
organic fertilizer 21, 23
Orion Nebula 266–268
Ortelius, Abraham 251
Ostwald, Wilhelm (Ostwald process) 50
Otto, Nikolaus August (Otto Cycle Engine) 175
oxygen 80

P

paleontology 232
pancreas 218
paparazzi 155
paper mills 48
Paracelsus 63
Pascal, Blaise 82–83
Pasteur, Louis 142, 180–181, 189, 191, 258; disproving spontaneous generation 166–168

pasteurization 262
patents: lawsuits 263; scientific
    spirit and 211; silicon chips
    250; mentioned 154, 186, 193,
    194, 195, 222, 249
pathology 257
peak oil 172–173
Peel, Sir Robert 242
Peierls, Rudolf 240
pellagra 197–198
pendulum 114–115
Penicillium notatum 26, 234–236
Pennsylvania Rock Oil Company
    172
Penzias, Arno Allan 254–256
periodic table of elements
    184–186
Perkin, William Henry 159, 160
perpetual motion machine 148
Perrin, Jean 51, 219
Peter the Pilgrim 55
Petersen, Robert Storm 214
Petit, Alexis-Therese 185, 199
Petrarch 62
Petri, Richard Julius (Petri dish)
    190–191
phagocytes 142
Phoenicians 33
phonographs 241
photographic paper 222
photography 154–156
photomicrography 135
photosynthesis 79–80, 134
physiology 76–78, 134–136
pickling food 21
Pictet, Raoul 212
pictograms 32
pictorial charts 161–162
piezoelectricity 209–210, 229
Pilgrim fathers 22
Piltdown Man 232
pipe organs 203
Planck, Max 214–215, 219, 228,
    239, 264; Planck radiation law
    215
plants 63; associations 182;
    chemical signals 217;
    classification 109–111;

distributions 251–252; genes
    176–177; medicines 24–26;
    photosynthesis 79–80;
    physiology 134–135;
    reproduction 88, 111;
    peciation 141
plastic materials 144–146
plastics 145, 221–223
Playfair, John (Playfair's Law)
    121–122
Poincaré, Henri 219
Poisson, Siméon-Denis 204
polio vaccine 190
pollution from copper smelting
    30
polonium 210
polymerase chain reaction *see*
    DNA structure
polyneuritis 196–197
Pope, Alexander 166
porcelain insulators 27
positive and negative electricity
    116, 224
positive and negative numbers 75
potassium hydroxide 125
pottery 26–28
pottery glazes 34
predictions 264–267
Priestley, Joseph 80
printing 58, 61–63
prism 97
probability 162–163
prolactin 218
protons 224, 227
Proust, Joseph Louis 226–227
Ptolemy, Claudius 39, 68
pumps 82, 85–86, 157
punch cards 243
Pygmalion (Shaw) 187
pyramids 37–38
Pythagoras 36–38, 39

Q

quantum physics 214–215, 228,
    244
Quetelet, Adolphe 162–163
quinine 25, 159
Quistorp, Johann Bernhard 149

R

rabbits, released in Australia 183
radiant heat 215
radiation 98, 132, 206–208;
    radiation laws 214–215
radio waves 201–203, 229
radioactive nuclei decay 239–241
radioactivity 131, 209–211
radios 222
radium 210–211, 239
Ramesses II 35
Raphael 60
rare and endangered species 183
Ray, John 100
Rayleigh, Lord 214, 215
record-keeping 31–33
rectifier 128, 194
Redi, Francesco 166–168
refraction 229
refrigeration 211–213
relativity 219–221
respiration 80
restoring force 114–115
Richet, Charles 142
river siltation 22
RNA 262
rock formation 99–101, 139, 253
rock oil 171–172, 173
rocket propulsion 51–53, 213
Rohrer, Heinrich 226
Roman ships 41–42, 44
Rømer, Ole 152
Röntgen, Wilhelm Conrad
    206–208, 209
root canal therapy 145
Royal Institution (London) 125,
    130, 131, 210, 230
rubber 144–146
"rules of thumb" 8, 39, 249
Rumford, Count (Benjamin
    Thompson) 146
Rutherford, Ernest 130–131, 161,
    226, 228, 231

S

salt lakes 129
salt splitting 124–125
salting food 19

Santorio, Santorio 74
Sapper, Eugen 137
SARS (Severe Acute Respiratory Syndrome) 156, 158, 248
Savery, Thomas 101–103
scanning tunneling micrograph (STM) 226, 227, 228
Schleiden, Matthias Jakob 134–135
Schwann, Theodor 134–135
science: beginnings of 11–13; mythology of 9
sciptorium 61
scurvy 196
sea floor spreading 251–253
sea salinity 129
Seeber, Ludwig 229
semaphores 104–105
semen 88
semiconductor 244
Semmelweis, Ignaz 180
Senebier, Jean 80
septicemia 234
sexual reproduction 86–88
Shaw, George Bernard 187
Shelley, Mary 125
shipbuilding 65–66
Shockley, William 244–246; Shockley diode 246, 250
Siegesbeck, Johann 111
Siemens, Werner 144
signalling 104–105
silicon 244, 245
silicon chips see computers
Silicon Valley 246
Sizi, Francesco 72
skin grafts 143
slide rules 251
smallpox 111–113
smelting 29–30
Smith, William 122
Snow, John 151, 156–158
social physics 162–163
sodium hydroxide 125
sodium ions 164–165
Sohncke, Leonhard 230
solar energy 80
solar hydrogen 165

solar system 39–41, 63, 66–68; extrasolar planets 259–261; planetary movement 69–71
solenoids 128
space 53, 219–221, 246
Spallanzani, Lazzaro 88, 168
spark gaps 201–202
spark plugs 175
special relativity, theory of 219
species interdependence 181–183
spectacles 56–58, 108
spectral lines 164–166, 199–201
spectroscope 164–166, 199
speech symbols (notation) 187
speed of light 151–153
sperm cells 86–88
Spina (inventor of spectacles) 58
Spitteler, Adolph 222
splitting by electricity 124–125
spontaneous generation 166–168
Sprengel, Konrad 88
springs 84
stadium 64
starfish (seastars) 142
Starling, Ernest Henry 216–218
static electricity 116–118, 133
statistics 161–163
Steady State model of the universe 172, 238
steam engines 46, 48, 101–102, 146, 174–175
steam power 101–103
Stensen, Niels 99–101
sterilization 262
Stifel, Michel 75
stone tools 11–13, 14, 16
Strassmann, Fritz 239, 240
stress 257
Stukeley, William 91
substations 128
sulfa drugs 161, 234
Sumerians 31–33
superconductivity 246
superposition, law of 99–101
surgery 59, 134, 149–151, 179–181, 234
Swan, Sir Joseph Wilson 120
switchboard operators 188

switches 242, 245
Sydney Observatory 242
syllabary 31
syphilis 161
Syracuse 41–43
Szent-Gyorgyi, Albert 261

T
table of elements 184–186
Takaki, Kanehiro 196–198
Talbot, William Henry Fox 154
Tasq DNA polymerase 262–263
"Taung child" 231–233
taxonomy 110
technology, beginnings of 11–13
tectonic plates 253
telegraph 104–106, 144, 186–187, 241
telephone 186–188, 241, 242
telescope 69, 71–73, 93
Telstar satellite 254
temperature measurement 74–75
temperature vs heat 147
Tennyson, Alfred Lord 155
Tesla, Nikola 191–193
Texas Instruments 249, 250
Thales 79, 184
thermionic effect 194–195
thermodynamics, laws of 147
thermometer 74–75
thermos flask 212
Thermus aquaticus 262–263
Thirty Years' War 70, 84
Thomson, G. P. 224
Thomson, J. J. 224, 227
time 219–221
Torricelli, Evangelista 81–82
totalizator 95
trace elements 23
transistor 244–246, 249–250
Tschermak-Seysenegg, Erich von 177
Tsiolkovskii, Konstantin 52, 213
tuberculosis 191
Twain, Mark 162
"twin paradox" 219
typography 61–63
Tyson, Edward 170

U

ulcers 257–258
ultraviolet 98, 214, 215
Uluburun wreck 34
uniformitarian view 139
universe: Big Bang theory 238,
    254–256; expanding universe
    221, 236–238; extrasolar
    planets 259–261
US Air Force 250, 251

V

V2 52
vaccination 111–113, 141–142
vacuum 81–82, 153, 194,
    204–206
vacuum tubes 194, 195, 208, 244,
    249, 250
valves 194, 195, 249
van Helmont, Johann Baptista
    79–80, 166
van Leeuwenhoek, Anton 87,
    89–90
Vancomycin 236
Vannier, Michael 233
variolation 112–113
Venus of Dolní 26
Vermilion Cliffs (Arizona) 100
Very Large Array radio telescope
    4, 260
Vesalius 63
Victoria, Queen of England 151,
    157
viruses 113
vitamins 21, 197, 198, 261
Viviani, Vincenzo 81
vivisection 59
Vogel 201
volcanoes 130, 253
Volta, Alessandro 116–118, 124,
    174
voltage 119–120, 192
Voltair 91
von Groth, Paul 230
von Guericke, Otto 83–85
von Humboldt, Alexander 23,
    182
von Laue, Max 229–230

W

Wallace, Alfred Russel 140, 170;
    Wallace's Line 140–141, 183,
    253
Warming, Eugenius 182
Warren, J. Robin 257–258
water wheels 46–48
Watson, James 231, 246–248
Watson, Thomas 187, 188
Watt, James 101–103, 146
wavelength diffraction 229
weapons manufacture 31, 52
Wegener, Alfred Lothar 251–252
Wells, H. G. 240
Wells, Horace 150
Westinghouse, George 193
whale oil 171
Wheatstone and Cooke 105
Wheatstone, Sir Charles 187
Wickramasinghe, Chandra 172
Wien, Wilhelm 214–215
Wigner, Paul 244
Wilkins, John 259
Wilkins, Maurice 231, 247
Wilkinson, John 103
Wilkinson Microwave Anisotropy
    Probe (WMAP) 256
willow tree experiment 79
Wilson, Robert Woodrow
    254–256
Wilson, Wallace 234, 235–236
windmills 48
wine souring 168
wireless sets 222
wireless telegraphy 245
Wistar, Caspar 121–122
Wittgenstein, Ludwig 69
Woese, Carl 263
Wollaston, William Hyde 164
Wolszczan, Aleksander 259
World Health Organization 158
World War I 186, 209
World War II 195, 239–241, 242
writing 31–33, 56

X

X-ray 13, 35, 186, 206–208; CAT
    scans 233

X-ray diffraction 208, 229–231,
    246–247

Y

Young, James 159
Young, Thomas 204
Younger Dryas period 17

Image Credits

Australpress: p.213
Corbis: p.9, p.10, p.15, p.22,
p.25, p.27, p.33, p.37, p.40, p.45,
p.50, p.55, p.57, p.65, p.67, p.73,
p.77, p.97, p.105, p.107, p.117,
p.130, p.150, p.155, p.158, p.188,
p.205, p.210, p.222, p.243.
Getty Images: p.12, p.17, p.30,
p.62, p.123, p.125, p.133, p.145,
p.148, p.237, p.248.
Photolibrary.com: p.13, p.20,
p.35, p.43, p.47, p.53, p.60, p.70,
p.75, p.80, p.82, p.85, p.87, p.90,
p.92, p.95, p.100, p.103, p.112,
p.115, p.120, p.127, p.135, p.138,
p.140, p.143, p.153, p.160, p.163,
p.165, p.167, p.170, p.173, p.175,
p.178, p.180, p.183, p.185, p.190,
p.193, p.195, p.197, p.200, p.202,
p.207, p.215, p.217A, p.217B,
p.220, p.230, p.233, p.235, p.245,
p.250, p.253, p.255, p.258, p.260,
p.262, p.266-267, p.225, p.227,
p.240.

Acknowledgements

A lot of people played their part in the shaping of this book. It had its genesis in a book that Rex Meyer, Jim Hawes, Peter Stanbury and I started writing in about 1972. Part of my contribution was to write brief biographical sketches, with quotes, of famous biologists. I later expanded those, and moved into other branches of science.

Robyn Williams at the ABC Science Unit got me writing more focused historical vignettes in about 1985. I began pursuing the people who gave their names to the units of science and to things like Avogadro's hypothesis, the Bunsen burner, Boyle's law, Chargaff's rules, the Curie point, the Faraday cage, the Kelvin scale, Le Chatelier's principle, the Pauli effect and even the hardest of them all to track down, the Wimshurst machine.

In all, I wrote about 150 pieces and I got into the habit of chasing down how discoveries were made, what people were doing when they had that vital "aha!" moment. With no real plans for publication, I began gathering the data, the quotes, the comments and the background for about 600 short articles, some of which I have drawn on here.

For the most part, I uncovered the original material I needed in branches of Fisher Library at the University of Sydney, which generously allows alumni to use its resources, so my thanks to them. I also relied in the later stages of this book on the State Library of NSW and their indefatigable staff. And I found a number of original papers placed on the Web by Hasok Chang, Roald Hoffmann and Li Liu. This is what the Web ought to be about!

Somewhere along the way, I fell among the company of editors, and during the 1990s, quite a few freelance jobs came my way from a number of them who seem to chat among themselves. Because I am a complaisant chap who understands editing and listens to advice, my name was passed on, and somewhere along the way, I came across Scott Forbes when we worked together on a project for *Reader's Digest*.

Then Scott passed my name on to Will Kiester at Pier 9, who asked me if I would be interested in taking on a couple of books. I agreed with an enthusiasm that left him a little shaken, and so we began work on *100 Great Discoveries*. We refined the format on two sample articles, with Scott chipping in as the editor and patient shaper of the author, and then things went quiet.

Will Kiester moved on, returning to the USA, and Diana Hill became my encourager and commissioning editor at Pier 9. Then, out of the blue, she advised me that this project had the nod, and the hard work started. First, we went through a reappraisal of the best hundred, then the writing began.

Most of my manuscripts are read by a number of friends, people I have come to know and trust over the Internet. In this case, David Allen spent some time reading and advising, and he also introduced me to TextAloud. David's sight is failing, but TextAloud lets him convert text to mp3 files, and while my sight is holding up, I did the same. Reading a large manuscript is onerous, especially when you know what to expect, because you always see what you expect to see. Listening to a machine reading the same text, the errors jump out at you, so after Desney Shoemark, my trustworthy editor, had been over the text, I listened to it, and my wife Christine read it. Thanks TextAloud, thanks Chris!

Because I set out for Europe at a crucial time, Desney and Emma Hutchinson arranged for me to get a set of page proofs to read on my travels. While I responded to these, more of the load than usual has fallen on Desney's shoulders, and I praise her for devotion above and beyond the call of duty. She also put up with all sorts of oddness with aplomb and equanimity.

Nobody likes errors, especially not writers, which is why we have proofreaders like the eagle-eyed Anne Savage. Proofreaders are lateral thinkers who learn to question everything. Any surviving errors must be because I muddied the waters too effectively—but thanks to Anne, they will be lonely!

This is the fourth book I have done with Pier 9, and there are more in the pipeline, which says a great deal about my satisfaction with the whole company. Thanks, guys and guyesses!